Student's Resource Book

WITHDRAWN

John Murray
in association with
Inner London Education Authority

APPIL First Edition Project Team
John Bausor
Leslie Beckett
Allan Covell
David Davies
Martin Hollins

APPIL Revised Edition
Co-ordinated by Martin Hollins
This resource book has been compiled by Martin Hollins and edited by Allan Covell

Design, typesetting and page layout by Tony Langham
Diagrams by Technical Art Services and John Sangwin

Acknowledgements

Thanks are due to the following, who have permitted the use of copyright material: Transport & Road Research Laboratory (Fig. 4.1); Central Electricity Generating Board (Fig. 4.10); BBC publications; The Institute of Physics; W.H. Freeman and Company Ltd; New Scientist; Longman Group UK Ltd; Nuffield-Chelsea Curriculum Trust; The Royal Institution.

The following examination boards have permitted reproduction of questions: Oxford and Cambridge Schools Examining Board; Joint Matriculation Board; Nuffield Foundation; University of London Examination Board; The Associated Examination Board.
(*Note.* The answers in this book have not been provided or approved by the examination boards, who accept no responsibility for their accuracy or the method of working given.)

The following photographs are by Tony Langham : Fig 2.4, Fig 2.5

Thanks are due to Peter Warren for the cartoons in this publication.

Every effort has been made to contact copyright holders of other material used who kindly gave their permission for the first edition. The authors and publishers regret any omissions and will be pleased to rectify them in future printings.

Published by John Murray (Publishers) Ltd,
50 Albemarle Street, London W1X 4BD

APPIL first edition 1979–80
Revised edition 1989–90
This edition 1989–90
Reprinted 1991, 1994

Printed in Great Britain by St Edmundsbury Press

British Library Cataloguing in Publication Data

Advanced Physics Project for Independent Learning (APPIL):
  student's resource book
  1. Physics
  I. ILEA Physics Project Team   II. Advanced Physics Project
  for Independent Learning
  530
  ISBN 0–7195–4581–1

Contents

continued

Part 1
Learning with APPIL

What is APPIL?

This course is called **APPIL**.

The name stands for Advanced
                Physics
                Project for
                Independent
                Learning

Words like APPIL are called **acronyms**. They play a useful part in helping us to remember things.

Who is it for ?

APPIL can be used by anyone studying physics at this level. It is highly desirable that before starting the course you should have GCSE at grade A, B or C in Physics or Science (double award), Mathematics and English. There is nothing to prevent you using APPIL if you do *not* have these grades, but you must realise from the start that it will obviously mean additional hard work.

What is different?

The physics is the same, the Advanced Level syllabus is the same, but the learning process is different. Not totally different, but very likely different in important ways from what you have done before.

Up to the present you have probably had a teacher allocated to your class for every period of the week. If you have been lucky enough to have 'private study' periods you may or may not have used them effectively - only you can tell! And only you can tell whether you have made good use of your teachers!

Probably you have done quite a lot of work at home, but most people do only what is set, if that. Your work has been very much teacher-directed: you have been **teacher-dependent** in your learning.

In contrast, in this course you are expected to develop the skill of working on your own. We do *not* expect you to learn in a *totally* independent way: but for *part of your timetabled physics time* you will not actually be taught.

Independent learning is nothing new: in a sense all learning is independent, since no one can learn something for you. A teacher, lecturer, television programme or book may put certain ideas before you, but only you can learn them, understand them, and use them. Alternatively, you might ignore them, misunderstand them, or just fail to grasp them at all.

Why independent study?

Studying independently has several important advantages over learning only from a teacher:

(a) Independent study allows you to learn at your own pace as opposed to learning in a group from a teacher where everyone has to work at the same speed, which is probably too fast for some and too slow for others.

(b) Different people learn best in different ways. Independent learning lets you choose the way that suits you best.

(c) Some parts of the subject will interest you more than others. With an independent learning approach you can go deeper into the areas which you find most interesting.

(d) If you go on to study at a university, polytechnic or some other place of higher education, you are likely to be left very much to your own devices: you will have lecturers rather than teachers. Independent learning at A-level will be a good preparation for that situation and, in fact, for many others.

(e) Some schools have small groups of students at Advanced Level, and it may be difficult to spare a teacher for about five hours per week for so few. Independent learning may make it possible to run A-level courses in these situations by giving you a teacher for just part of the time. You can then have personal help for this part of the time, and work from the course material for the rest.

(f) If the more straightforward aspects of your course are done by independent study, your teacher or lecturer has more time to help you with tricky points or specific problems, so you can expect to learn more effectively.

What are the limitations?

We are *not* suggesting a 100% independent learning approach because:

(a) There will be parts of the subject, or particular problems, where you will need the help of a teacher.

(b) It is difficult for students to know how much to attempt in a given time, and help is essential, at least in the early stages, in setting yourself sensible goals and in 'pacing' your work.

(c) It takes time to get used to independent learning, and most people have little experience of working in this way.

> 'The problem is that we have been taught by teachers for five years.' (This is one of several comments included in this resource book from students in the trials schools.)

(d) Discussion with other students is a very useful way of clarifying your ideas, and learning some of the tricky aspects of the subject.

> 'We work alone, but if we have a problem we first ask each other and if we can't solve it, we ask the teacher.' (Student)

(e) Experiments are sometimes done more easily in a group of two or three than on your own.

(f) Physics is usually carried out by groups of people: almost all physicists in industry, university and other places work as part of a team.

(g) For some purposes, such as demonstrations using very complex or expensive equipment, or special lectures, it is sensible to collaborate with other schools or colleges.

(h) Apart from the actual subject matter of the course there are other points which can best be dealt with by your own teacher (e.g. new application of physics, careers advice, last night's TV programme, where to read up a particular topic, etc.). By the end of the course, however, we expect that you will be more confident and experienced, so you will need to call on help much less than at the beginning.

What is the course plan?

There are eight units, three starter units and five second-level units. The way they relate to each other is shown in the diagram on the next page.

There are three possible starter units, and all three should be completed before the second-level units. Otherwise, the starter units and the second level-units can be studied in any order, although it is preferable to study FF before EM and EN.

The decision about which sequence to follow will probably be made by your teacher.

The starter units do not, in all cases, take you to a full A-level standard. This is quite deliberate, so don't let it worry you: you will get there by the end of the course!

Theme	Materials	Fields	Waves
Starter Units	Behaviour of Matter **UNIT BM**	Force and Motion **UNIT FM**	Waves and Vibrations **UNIT WV**
Second-level Units	Thermal Properties **UNIT TP**	Forces and Fields **UNIT FF**	
	Electronic systems **UNIT ES**	Electromagnetism **UNIT EM**	Electrons and the Nucleus **UNIT EN**

Course plan

What is needed?

For each unit you will need:

(a) This Resource Book (for reference).
(b) The Student's Unit.
(c) Textbooks (at least one, possibly two or three).
(d) Library (for reference and background reading).
(e) Apparatus for the experiments.
(f) Equipment for other activities (depending on the unit).
(g) Time! You should spend at least ten hours each week (roughly five hours of timetabled time and five hours at home) on APPIL work. For some of the timetabled time (possibly all) your teacher will be available. Ideally, all these sessions should be in a physics laboratory.

There is also a Teacher's Resource Book for use by teachers and technicians.

What is the Student's Unit ?

The function of the Student's Unit is to provide a programme for independent learning. It is not a textbook: it is a guide to using texts, experiments and other resources to help you learn and study physics.

Each unit starts with pre-requisites: what you should know, understand or be able to do before starting. In the starter units this takes the form of a test to check your previous work. The later units refer back to work you should already have done during this course.

Each unit is divided into topics which include the following:

(a) A summary of the topic including detailed statements of objectives.
(b) Text which introduces the basic ideas and explains points which might be difficult.
(c) References to books.
(d) Full details of experiments.
(e) Details of other activities.
(f) Five different types of questions.

(g) Extensions: extra material which is included to develop your understanding or introduce interesting applications.

What are objectives?

These are statements of what you should be able to do when you have completed a piece of work. The importance of objectives is that it is much easier to know whether you have attained them than it is with the syllabus alone. For example, the syllabus may say 'law of gravitation', but the objectives would say something like:

When you have completed this topic you should be able to:

1 Define, use and derive the dimensions of the gravitational constant G.

2 State how the force of gravitation between two particles depends upon the mass of the particles and their distance apart.

3 Describe a laboratory experiment to determine the gravitational constant.

4 Solve problems involving gravitational forces.

While objectives are placed at the beginning of the section of work, to make full use of them you need to come back to them when you have completed that section, or while you are working on it. You can then check how far you have achieved what is intended. The questions on objectives also help here. One useful idea is to base your note-taking on the list of objectives (see Section 1.3 'A good way to make notes').

Why so many types of questions?

By considering each type in turn, you will understand the different purposes they serve.

Study questions

To answer these you should refer to material outside the Student's Unit such as textbooks, reference books, experimental results or other material.

The answers to these questions will be a useful part of your own notes.

Discussion questions

These are in some ways like study questions, but there is no 'right answer', so they are best dealt with by discussing ideas with other people.

Development questions

These involve you in the development of a proof or an idea. By working through the steps of a development question you will learn more effectively than by just reading the steps in the book, because you are actively involved.

Self-assessment questions

These are included so that you can assess your own progress. If you cannot answer one, or get it wrong, you should go back over the work or seek help from a colleague or your teacher. If you get it correct, you can be reassured you are making good progress.

Questions on objectives

At the end of each topic there is a set of questions which relate closely to the objectives at the beginning. In some ways they are like self-assessment questions because they allow you to check that you have actually achieved what the objectives state. Your teacher has the answers, and may mark this exercise, or may give you the answers so that you can mark your own.

Two further kinds of questions are used in parts of this course:

Comprehension and data analysis questions

These types of questions are increasingly being used in A-level Physics papers, because understanding scientific printed material, and drawing conclusions from data, are important activities in physics.

Examination questions

Particularly towards the end of the course you will want to be sure you can do the sort of question which will come up in the exam. So questions, or part questions, taken from past examination papers will be given to you at the appropriate time. You may also be given an 'End-of-Unit Test'.

Taking all the question types together, you will get plenty of practice at the various forms in which questions can be set in the examination.

Q 1.1 Self-assessment question

(a) Is the following statement TRUE or FALSE? 'To use APPIL you need to have grade A, B or C in Physics at GCSE'.
(b) How long each week should you spend on APPIL? ∎

Q 1.2 Self-assessment question

(a) What advantages does independent study have?
(b) When is independent study *not* the appropriate method? ∎

Q 1.3 Self-assessment question

(a) Which features of APPIL are designed to enable you to check your progress and make sure you understand the work?
(b) Which two features of APPIL are particularly relevant to making your own notes?
(c) Which types of question require you to use external sources of information?

How is an APPIL unit used?

There are a number of ways in which you can use the units:

(a) One way is to work steadily through from beginning to end, doing the various questions, experiments and activities as you come to them. But experiments and activities can only be done when apparatus or equipment is available, so a bit of advance planning will be needed. Progress monitors are provided to help with this.

(b) A different approach, which might suit some people better, would be to glance through the whole unit, and then work on whatever aspects interest you first. You would then have to fill in the gaps to develop an overall grasp of that topic. If you decide to work in this way, the objectives and questions on objectives are specially important. You may also find that one part depends on an earlier part, so that you have to 'back-track' in order to understand it.

(c) A third approach is to start from the objectives. Look through these and see which of them you can do already. Check this by trying the questions on objectives (*before* going through the topic). If you can do all the questions on objectives, you might as well leave out that topic, unless there is something of special interest. This is the most economical way to use APPIL in terms of your own time, but be careful to pay attention to any topics about which you are uncertain. If you think you need not study a particular section, make sure you can do the test questions which relate to it.

> '*If you do the questions, you learn the things that the rest of the unit says, so there is not much point in having the rest of the unit, just a list of books and questions*'.
> (Student) (An extreme view!)

Whichever method you use, extensions are available if you want to go further into a topic. This is usually valuable for examination purposes, as well as for general interest. Often these link to option topics required for the A-level syllabus of a particular examination board. Your teacher will let you know which you need to cover. Study guides for each are given in part 5.

How long does it take?

You have eight units to get through in rather less than two years (say 60 effective weeks). This means that each unit should take on average about seven weeks, leaving time for optional topics and for some revision at the end. The units vary in length, and the suggested time for each is clearly indicated. You may take a bit longer on the first one that you do, but avoid doing this regularly. The progress monitors will help you to keep up-to-date.

> '*Without the teacher you may tend to slack... you get lazy*'. (Student)

What does the teacher do?

This will depend on you, your teacher, and how APPIL is used. He or she will probably teach some sections directly, perhaps introducing a topic or unit, and then be available for consultation during physics periods or at other times.

In general, you should seek help when you cannot make progress on your own or with your colleagues. This may mean you cannot understand something, or you cannot do a question, or it may be you need help with an experiment or equipment. Don't forget that technicians may also be available to help you directly with practical problems.

It is quite likely that your teacher may wish to have regular 'problem sessions', or to treat certain parts of the subject in a different way. APPIL is a flexible system, and can be used in a variety of effective ways.

> '*If you are on your own, if you get stuck yopu give up*'. (Student)

Q 1.4 Self-assessment question

How should you avoid taking too long over a unit? ∎

1.2

Learning

Not a great deal is known about how people learn, but the following points certainly hold true.

Active learning

Active learning is much more effective than passive learning. This means you should in some way be involved in making a response to do what is presented, rather than just sitting dreamily reading. For this reason in APPIL you will find plenty of varied activities. This may seem like hard work compared to just listening to a teacher, but that is one reason why it is more effective.

Span of concentration

A student's span of concentration is limited. You have probably had the experience of reading a page in a book and then realising you had no idea what you had just read! The best plan is to take a break and do something different, coming back to your study later. You could break off for a brief chat, have a cup of coffee, or take some exercise. But do not forget to return to your study afterwards!

Varying the activity

Varying your activity leads to more effective learning. APPIL includes quite a wide variety of activities: reading, answering questions, using computers, doing experiments, watching videos, listening to audio-tapes, making notes, drawing diagrams, solving problems, etc. You will not do all of these in every unit, but we have tried to make sure you have a good mixture of activities.

The right age for learning

People reach a peak of intelligence around the age of 16 to 17. At least, whatever is measured by 'intelligence tests' does not increase after that age. You are probably as good at learning now as you will ever be. Make the most of your opportunities.

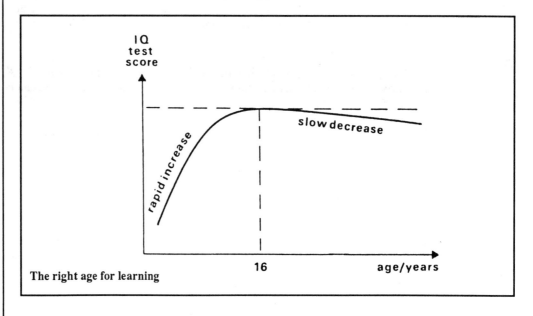

Figure 1.1

The right age for learning

Different kinds of learning

Some things are remembered more easily than others. This is very important in learning science subjects.

Facts

Facts are easily forgotten, particularly isolated facts. In physics, many facts are important, but only a few are worth remembering. Those which *need* to be remembered must be very thoroughly learned if you are to retain them, that is, you must come back to them again and again until they are firmly fixed in your mind. Years ago you probably learned in this way the answer to 7 x 9 (a mathematical fact). If so, you will still remember it now.

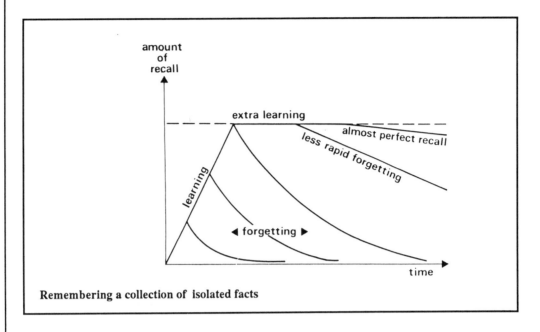

Remembering a collection of isolated facts

Figure. 1.2

Many people find that remembering isolated facts is greatly helped by mnemonics, that is, ways of forming an easily remembered pattern (for example, Richard Of York Gave Battle In Vain for remembering **ROYGBIV**, the initial letters of the rainbow colours).

Concepts

'You have got the impression that contemporary physics is based on concepts somewhat analogous to the smile of the absent cat.' (Albert Einstein)

Concepts or ideas are not so much learned as *understood*. Once you have grasped a concept (for example, the meaning of electrical resistance) you will not forget it easily. Most of the work involved in A-level physics is of this sort. It is important to make sure you *understand* each new idea before you go on to the next.

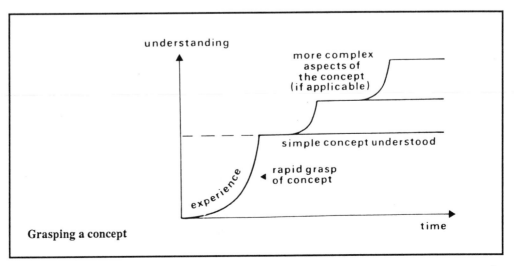

Grasping a concept

Figure. 1.3

Often concepts are grasped quite suddenly: you 'see the point' of something, and after that it seems easy. For other, more complex, concepts you may find your understanding gradually getting deeper.

While a mnemonic is an artificial or arbitrary pattern imposed on the facts, concepts can be seen as a natural way to organise a variety of facts.

Skills

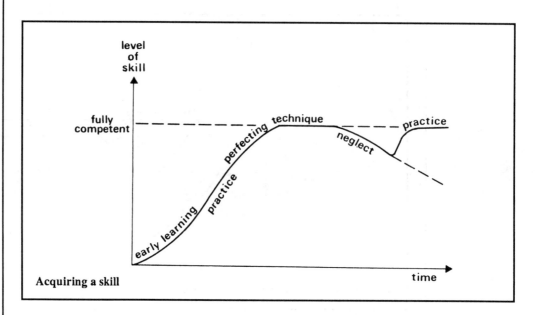

Figure. 1.4

Acquiring a skill

Skills are important in many fields, and once acquired probably last almost as well as concepts. (It is said you cannot forget how to ride a bicycle.) In A-level Physics there are several important skills you need to develop. Examples would be interpreting graphs, solving mathematical problems, connecting electrical circuits.

Skills can only be developed with practice: unlike concepts they *do not* come quickly, so you must spend time on them. If you neglect a skill you have developed to a high level, you will need to practise again to get back to that level, but this will probably not take very long.

Attitudes

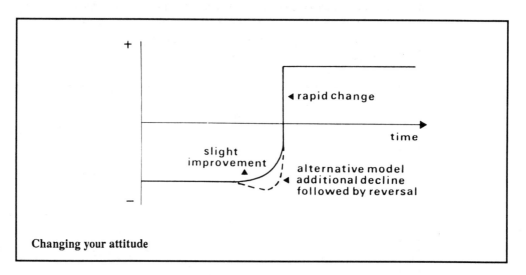

Figure. 1.5

Changing your attitude

Attitudes are crucial because your attitudes to the subjects you study have a strong influence on how well you do. In general, people's attitudes remain unchanged for long periods, but they can change rapidly on occasions.

Consider your own attitude to physics: if it is positive ('I think physics is interesting/important/ useful') you will probably do quite well. If your attitude is negative, it is worth trying to change it: this is not as difficult as it sounds, and could make a big difference. Note that your attitude towards the subject is *not* the same as your opinion about its difficulty: most people think physics is fairly difficult, but many of them also consider it interesting, important and useful.

Q 1.5 Self-assessment question

(a) What are the four different categories of things you can learn?
(b) Which one of these is rather easy to forget?
(c) Which one of the four is particularly common and important in physics?
(d) When do most people reach their maximum ability to learn? ■

Attitudes and learning

Adults learning by correspondence can learn as well as younger students in a classroom. This is a surprising fact. As was mentioned previously, sixth form students are at their 'learning peak', and are used to studying. Older people have passed their peak and are usually out of practice at studying; and correspondence courses have many snags, such as no one for the student to ask when they get stuck, no colleagues to discuss work with, no one (except a correspondence tutor) to let the student know how they are doing.

To understand why adults learning in a rather difficult way can do so quite well, and the implications this has for APPIL, answer the following question.

Q 1.6 Development question

(a) Are there any advantages of correspondence courses used at home compared to class work in a school or college? If so, make a list.
(b) What can you say about the attitudes of someone who starts a correspondence course and persists with it to the end?
(c) Since APPIL has the advantages of correspondence courses without the snags, and the students are younger, what would you expect in terms of the effectiveness of learning? ■

Learning styles

> '*I prefer to use a textbook which gives you all the information in one area and then the questions at the end of the chapter.*' (Student)

People have different learning styles. Some people learn best by making progress in a definite sequence, as if in a logical straight line. They are called 'serialists'. Others like to survey a whole area of knowledge, collect all the relevant ideas, and then make sense out of them themselves. People like this are called 'holists'. Presumably some people fall between the two extremes. Physics is usually taught in a 'serialist' way. But if that does not suit you, APPIL materials can also be used in a 'holist' way: you must find the method that suits you best.

Self-assessment

Students succeed best when they can assess their own progress accurately. You may have had the experience of not knowing how you were getting on in some subject. This is always disconcerting - you wonder if you have done too much or not enough. A good teacher keeps you informed by marking work, giving tests, and in other ways. In APPIL there are regular checks by which you can make sure you are working to the right level. There is a built-in 'feedback system' to help you monitor your progress.

Learning by discussion

In talking about a subject you discover your weak points, and reinforce your knowledge.

Discussion is encouraged in APPIL. You should discuss work with your friends, particularly the 'Discussion questions' which are open-ended and have no single right answer. You may find you have to agree to differ on some things.

'Clusters' of schools are sometimes formed so that groups from different schools can meet together regularly. If this sounds a good idea to you, ask if it would be possible.

Using knowledge

Using knowledge helps you to retain it. This applies to all levels: facts, concepts and skills. In APPIL there are numerous problems to enable you to apply what you are learning, and thus to help you to retain it.

Do not skip these questions, or you will not learn so well. All the previous points have been taken into account in producing APPIL materials. You will see how in other parts of this book.

Using all of your brain

You may have read statements to the effect that all of us use only a small fraction of the brain-power which we have available: estimates vary between 4% and 10%. If this has any truth in it at all there is much scope for improvement.

Another finding which you may have met is the idea that the two, largely separate, sides of the brain have largely different emphases: the left hemisphere (at least in right-handed people) is responsible for language, logical thinking and mathematics whereas the right hemisphere is responsible for spatial awareness, artistic appreciation, music and the like. It has been suggested that by organising learning so that both sides of the brain are involved a great increase in effectiveness can be achieved.

These ideas have been developed in a number of books, for example 'Accelerated Learning' by Colin Rose and 'Use Your Head' by Tony Buzan. However, you might like to reflect on the fact that people have been learning things, using ' trial and error' methods, for a very long time, so it is perhaps a little implausible that a totally new approach could have very dramatic effects. As a scientist, though, you might think the area worth investigating by personal experiment.

1.3 How to study

Studying is a very individual thing. It is possible to give suggestions about how to do it, but in the end you must find out the ways that suit you. Most important is to *think* about how you should study, rather than just starting in an unthinking way and probably forming bad habits that lead to inefficient learning.

The book by Tony Buzan called '*Use Your Head*' will be found very useful in helping you to develop good ways to study and learn. It has a most unusual approach, it is extremely easy to read, and it uses the techniques it describes. The book includes sections on Your Mind Is Better Than You Think, Reading, Memory, Key Words and Notes, Brain Patterns, and a particular method of study.

In addition, the following are helpful and relevant:
Barrass, R. *Study - A guide to effective study, revision and examination techniques*
Freeman, R. *Mastering Study Skills*
Harman, C. and Freeman, R. *How to Study Effectively*
Maddox, H. *How to Study*

There are many similar books which you may find worth looking at.

Planning

Decide how many hours a week you should spend. For an A-level subject, this probably means at least five hours *in addition* to timetabled time. Then plan when to do it - an hour each day Monday to Friday, 1 hour 15 minutes on Monday, Tuesday, Wednesday and Thursday, two long sessions on Wednesday and Saturday, or whatever suits you best. Also plan ahead, so that you can tell how your work will fit into the time available.

Environment

You won't learn much if all the time you are thinking about food, or listening to someone else's phone call. You need a quiet, warm place (not too hot or you will get dozy) with room for all the books and papers you require. If this is difficult at home, a public library can be useful, or you could find somewhere at school or college. Make sure you have enough light, and are not likely to be interrupted.

> '*They find it difficult to concentrate on the book in the lab with all their friends around. In this school there is no other place where they can go.*' (Teacher)

Habits

Develop habits which help your study rather than hinder it. For example, plan to study at times which fit in well with your usual mealtimes. Some people find they can study well early in the morning - others don't! Keep everything you need in a convenient place, so you don't have to spend ten minutes searching for things whenever you want to study. Develop a system of making notes which suits you (see later).

Q 1.7 Study question

Use your own timetable and knowledge of your own circumstances to produce a plan of how you will study at home (or elsewhere). Include the place you will study, timing in a typical week, and a list of things you will need. ■

Objectives

Many people study, but don't really know in detail what they are trying to achieve. This is where objectives come in: they tell you exactly what you should be able to do at the end. (If you can do it already, don't spend long on that part.) So when you start a study session, look at the relevant objectives to make sure you know the point of your study. Objectives help you to sort out what is most important from other material so you can give more attention to where it is needed.

Concentration

It is obvious that you are not likely to learn well if you do not concentrate on what you are studying. However, it is surprising how often people think they can study and do something else at the same time. You would do better to give all your attention to physics for half an hour and *then* watch your favourite TV programme, rather than try to do both at once! Physics contains a good deal of concentrated material. To read this effectively does need effort. So determine to study seriously when you are studying.

Memory

You might like at this point to refer back to the section about how people learn. An important aspect of effective remembering is understanding. Avoid trying to remember concepts before understanding them. You will then be able to remember them both more easily and more accurately. Another important point is to link what you want to remember to what you already know: build up an existing pattern rather than start a new one. For factual knowledge, learn the material as thoroughly as possible, and use it as frequently as possible (see also 'Application page 17).

Reading

This could be a whole topic in its own right. Most people could read much better than they do, and few realise that there are several different sorts of reading.

> *'Some books are to be tasted, others to be swallowed, and some few to be chewed and digested.'* (Francis Bacon)

Scanning means searching rapidly through a book or chapter for one particular point - a word, a symbol, a description.

Skimming means quickly going through a book to get an overall idea of what it contains. You would probably use the list of contents in doing so.

Light reading is appropriate for popular newspapers, or some novels. The story carries you along, and you don't need to spend long thinking about it. This sort of reading is rarely appropriate in science subjects, although it plays a (small) part in some arts subjects.

Mastery reading indicates that you need a thorough and detailed understanding of what you are reading. You have to spend time over this sort of reading, making sure you have grasped one point before going on to the next.

Often it is useful to skim a chapter first, and then read it more thoroughly (see SQR^3, page 17). In science subjects, with many technical terms and mathematical symbols, the rate of reading needed to absorb the ideas may seem very slow, but that is just a reflection of the very concentrated nature of the material.

Reading more effectively

There are many books and courses which will help you to improve both your comprehension and speed of reading. Try your school library or local public library: a good one to start with is 'Read better, read faster' by Manya and Eric de Leeun (Penguin).

Using an index

It is surprising how few people can use an index really well - but it is a very valuable technique of study. In particular, if there is an area in which you feel unsure, you can decide on the key words, look them up in the index of a suitable book, and then read (selectively) the appropriate sections. In APPIL, study questions commonly give your key words or ideas to study, and using the index can be important.

Q 1.8 Study question

Make notes on how to improve your reading from whatever sources are available to you. ■

A good way to make notes

There is no 'best way' to make notes! Any notes you make are for your benefit, not someone else's, so you should do what suits you. Some people (very few) find they need to make hardly any notes. They are fortunate! On the other hand, most people make too many notes, at least to begin with. Do not write more than you need, consider the reasons for making notes:

- to assist the learning process;

- to identify the most important areas;

- to give structure to the subject matter;

- to provide a basis for revision.

Avoid wasting your time making notes which do not contribute to these ends, or which are in an unsuitable form. People sometimes copy sections out of a textbook. This has very little value - you can work out why by thinking about the reasons above.

Q 1.9 Self-assessment question

For each of the four reasons above, give a better technique than copying from a book. ■

If you understand a topic thoroughly, you will need less detailed notes than for ones you find difficult.

It is useful to devise a system of headings and sub-headings, bearing in mind that it should be flexible enough to deal with a variety of topics.

Do not begin to write your notes until you have surveyed a whole section, and have the whole picture. Think carefully before you write. Turning ideas into diagrams is often helpful.

By the time you have worked through a topic you should have some or all of the following:
(a) Headings to organise your notes.
(b) Statements of laws, definitions, symbols, etc. which must be remembered.
(c) Accounts of experiments (either brief notes or full descriptions, together with results and conclusions).
(d) Notes from videos, audio tapes and similar resources.
(e) Answers to *all* the study questions.
(f) Your own notes on discussion questions.
(g) Answers to development questions and self-assessment questions. (You may not think it worth keeping all of these.)
(h) Diagrams and brief notes based on the text of the Student's unit (so far as you think any are needed).

At this stage you should look back to the objectives and make sure you have covered them all. You might like to reorganise your notes in relation to the objectives, and add anything necessary to clarify them. Some people make a list of the objectives for reference later. You could also construct an ideas diagram, to show how the ideas in the chapter (or whole unit) relate together.

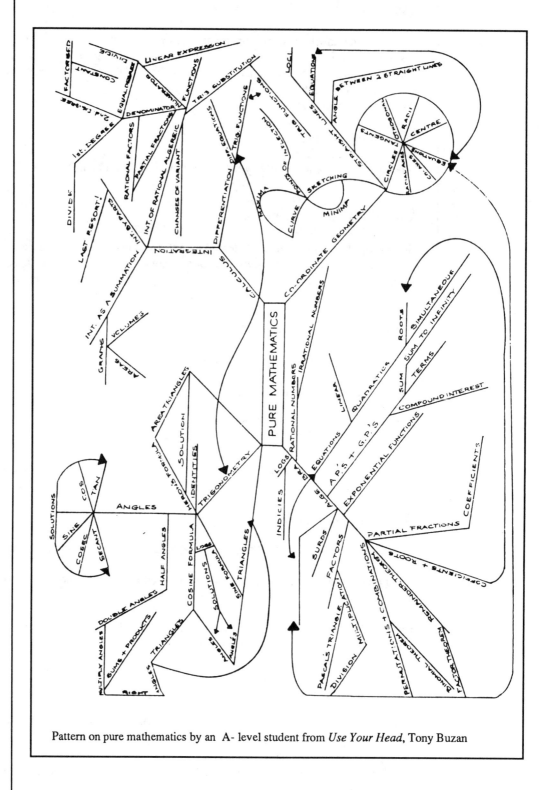

Figure. 1.6

Pattern on pure mathematics by an A- level student from *Use Your Head*, Tony Buzan

After reviewing the topic you should do the questions on objectives at the end. This is the best time to show your answers to Self-assessment Study and Development questions to your teacher, if you have not done so before.

Some people like to keep a separate part of a book or folder for experiments, and another part for definitions, equations, etc. which must be known. Others prefer to keep everything relating to a particular topic in one place. You must make up your own mind: you have to use the notes.

A general statement is better than a collection of examples. Your own language is preferable to someone else's.

Notes should be: CLEAR

                              CONCISE

                              SYSTEMATIC

Q 1.10 Study question

Using one or more of the recommended books about studying (see page 13), make a record in some form (diagram, list, headings and sub-headings for example) of aspects of making notes which seem to you to be important. This is essentially a personal exercise: your fellow-students may find rather different things important.■

Techniques of study

SQR³

This is not a mathematical formula, it is a 'code' for a widely-used system of study. It stands for Survey, Question, Read, Recall, Review.

Survey means start by getting an overall view of the topic you are studying, for example, by scanning one or more treatments of it, and thinking around the objectives.

Question means you should ask what you want to get from this book (or other material), which book deals with the topic in the most suitable way, or even whether you really need to study this topic at all. Again, the objectives of your study are important.

Read is obvious, and usually indicates 'mastery' reading. You could include other learning materials here too, by extending reading to cover listening to an audio tape, viewing a filmstrip or video, and other activities.

Recall reminds you that the purpose of reading is to remember, and you can judge the effectiveness of your reading only by bringing to mind the main points of what you have just read. Don't read too much before attempting to recall. This is usually a good time to make notes, that is, when you have made sure you understand and remember (see the section on making notes).

Review is a checking process. You should look back after completing a topic, to check that you follow the whole development and have not missed any important ideas. You will see the system has some built-in repetition, which is a good thing.

SQR³ is not the only way to study; however, it is simple to remember, and easy to follow, so it is worth trying. If you think you can improve on it, then do.

Discussion

Most people find that their understanding of a subject, particularly the tricky ideas which are fairly common in physics, is greatly helped by discussion with other students. Naturally this need not be confined to discussion questions! If you belong to a small group, you would probably find it very useful to meet at regular intervals with students from other schools. Ask if it can be arranged (or arrange it yourself).

Application

As was pointed out earlier, ideas are remembered more easily when they are used. One way of doing this is to find everyday applications of the topic you are studying. For example, if you are dealing with diffraction of waves, you might look carefully at the patterns seen when you look at street lights or car headlamps through an umbrella or net curtains. Or, if you are doing dynamics, you might consider the motion of the bus, train or car you travel in, and the forces on it.

Reorganisation

This is a very valuable technique which helps you to 'make knowledge your own'. Instead of just trying to absorb ideas in the form in which they are presented, try to find a new way to arrange them, a new structure for the ideas. For example, you might work out how a topic developed historically, or you could consider all the measurements involved, and how they relate together. By reorganising the ideas, you become actively involved in the learning process, which leads to better learning.

Look again at the diagram on page 16.

'The diagram shows a pattern on pure mathematics done by an A-level schoolgirl. When this pattern was shown to a Professor of Mathematics he estimated that it was done by a University Honours student and that it probably took two days to complete. In fact, it took the girl only twenty minutes. The pattern enabled her to display an extraordinary creativity in a subject which is normally considered dry, dull and oppressive. Her use of form and shape to augment the words will give an indication of the diversity possible in these structures.'

(From *Use Your Head*, Tony Buzan)

How APPIL helps

The following features of APPIL should enable you to use it as a way to learn effectively.

Clear objectives

Each topic has at the beginning a list of the things you should be able to do after studying it. Questions are provided at the end of the topic for you to check that you can actually do them.

Suitable standards

'The units are too generalised...all right for giving a basic knowledge...but not up to A-level standard.' (Student)

You will be aiming for A-level, but the standard needed to begin with has not been set too high. (The course is organised as a spiral; you will keep coming back to topics and each time going further into them. It's rather like climbing a spiral staircase instead of trying to jump straight up to the first floor.)

There is also optional work (called 'extensions') to enable you to develop your study of a topic.

Self-assessment questions

Throughout the units there are numerous questions to let you assess your own progress.
You should be able to answer these without difficulty if you have followed the work preceding them.

Organisation

Arrangements vary in different schools and colleges, but it is important that you are able to use the equipment for different activities when it is necessary (e.g. tape recorders, computers, projectors, experimental apparatus). It is best if any activity can be done at any time you take physics. You can help things to run smoothly by requesting what you need a few days ahead.

Motivation

This is largely up to you, but we have tried to make the units interesting, and to include points which you may not find in text books.

Many people find a little difficulty in the early stages of independent learning, presumably because it is so different from being taught. It feels strange when you first have to take the initiative for yourself. But most discover quite soon that the advantages are considerable, so don't give up!

The examination syllabus is not the whole of physics: you might call it the skeleton of the subject. It is up to you to put flesh on it by following up aspects which interest you.

Working systematically

Help is given in the units to enable you to develop good ways of studying, but as people differ so much you must work out what suits you best. Most important is to develop a system for yourself, rather than leaving it all to luck, or being haphazard about how you work.

Keeping up to schedule

It is obviously important not to fall behind in your study, or you will not cover the syllabus. A system has been worked out so that you can keep a regular check on your progress. You should be given a copy of the Progress Monitor for each unit when you start it.

'I work better when the teacher forces me... I feel the pressure...' (Student)

Q 1.11 Self-assessment question

You probably noticed in this section that some of the points had also been mentioned earlier. We did this deliberately. Why do you think we did? ∎

Part 2
Practical work

2.1 Why do experiments in physics?

Physics is a name which describes one way of looking at the physical world and finding ways of understanding it. Many of the things we study in physics are things which we can observe in the everyday world around us; other things we can only observe by setting up apparatus in a laboratory. But in both cases our study usually begins with observation.

Ancient scientists often proposed theories which were based only on speculation. Modern science might be said to have begun on the day Galileo used his telescope to observe the mountains on the moon and proposed theories about the universe which were no longer based on pure speculation but on the evidence of **observation**.

So a course in physics should help you to become a skilled observer and also give you the opportunity, whenever possible, to obtain direct evidence for yourself about the physical world. Reading about alpha particle tracks in a cloud chamber is no real substitute for seeing such events for yourself and much of the excitement of studying physics would be lost if there was no opportunity for direct observation of things like radioactive decay, the diffraction of light through a tiny hole or the polarisation of light reflected from a laboratory bench.

Many of the observations which you will make in practical work will require you to take measurements of important physical quantities. Indeed a famous scientist, Lord Kelvin, once said that there is no real science without measurement. So, one of the purposes of practical work in physics is to give you an opportunity to become familiar with different measuring instruments and with standard techniques for measuring important quantities like acceleration, resistance, wavelength, etc., to develop accuracy and yet be able to assess the possible errors involved in taking measurements.

Some practical work will give you the chance to verify for yourself well-known laws and relationships; but there will always be an important place in a physics course for probing a new idea, not by reading about it in a book, but by investigating it experimentally first. This will involve learning to design experiments so that, for example, some quantities are kept constant to allow you to investigate relationships between other variable quantities.

Experience of a wide variety of practical work will enable you to appreciate how scientists work but, above all, it will help you to understand physics. The combination of apparatus on the bench, and problems arising out of experiments to think about, has proved to be a powerful means of encouraging understanding. As you work through this course of experiments, being able to relate abstract ideas to practical situations will form a sound basis for understanding physics.

2.2 How to do experiments

The experiments in APPIL vary a good deal, from very simple ones to complicated and lengthy procedures involving complex apparatus, so it is not easy to generalise about how to organise your practical work. However, the following suggestions will usually be appropriate.

Look ahead

Plan the most suitable time, i.e. the time when the practical work will integrate most closely with your theoretical work. Make sure that apparatus and services are available. This may mean giving notice to your teacher or technician of your anticipated needs. Read through the experimental notes beforehand and plan the order in which you will do things within the experiment.

Look out for dangers

Most physics experiments are not very dangerous, but a few are. Apparatus must be securely supported: equipment falling over is a common cause of accidents. Some specific hazards such as radioactivity are considered later in sections 2.6 and 2.7.

Understand the aim

Make sure you understand the aim of the experiment. Keep this aim clearly in mind and don't allow it to be obscured by the details of the procedure.

Trial run

If possible, do a rapid preliminary run-through of the experiment before doing it thoroughly in order to get the 'feel' of the apparatus and to check the likely range of measurements involved.

Record observations

Keep a practical book or folder in which to record observations in a permanent form *as you make them*. Errors in copying are very easy to make. You can always write up the experiment carefully afterwards, but keep your original record and do not use scraps of rough paper for results.

Accuracy

Make a note of how accurate each measurement is, *as you make it*. Section 2.4 describes the meaning and significance of experimental errors.

Ensure completion of each task

Do not take the apparatus apart until you are sure you have *done everything necessary*. This may mean plotting a graph or calculating the entries in a table to check that the observations appear sensible and repeating observations in an independent way, where possible.

2.3 Writing up experiments

Your written account of the experiment should include the following components.

Aim

This provides a convenient reference for later revision but, above all, it serves to remind you of where the experiment should be leading.

Description

An uncomplicated labelled diagram is the best aid to describing how you performed the experiment (in an electrical experiment this would obviously be a circuit diagram). Your observations or measurements will also indicate what you actually did and so there is no need for any detailed, step by step description. It is more important to include difficulties encountered, detailed precautions and any ways in which you achieved greater accuracy in your final result.

Observations and measurements

Even when you are not required to take measurements with instruments, it is important to record what you observe. Record observations briefly and concentrate on describing the significant events.

F/N	x/mm
2.0	36
4.0	70
6.0	106

If you are making a series of related readings, these should be arranged in the form of a table in either columns or rows.

Make sure that columns or rows are available not only for the actual recorded results but also for any quantities that you will need to calculate from these results.

At the head of each column or row, write in words and/or symbols the quantity being recorded. Remember that most quantities you measure have units. You can record these quantities as pure numbers (without units) if you record the quantity divided by its unit.

For example, values of the force F exerted on a spring, and the corresponding extension x, can be recorded . This indicates that a force of 4 N produces an extension of 70 mm.

Quantities should usually be expressed in terms of SI units, and a lot of zeros before or after the decimal point should be avoided by expressing quantities in standard form, i.e. multiplying the units by the necessary power of ten. For example, readings for the volume of a gas, kept at constant temperature as the pressure is varied, could be recorded as

$p/10^5$ Pa	$V/10^{-5}$ m^3
1.1	5.3
1.4	4.2
1.7	3.4

This table records the fact that when the pressure is 1.1×10^5 Pa, the volume of the gas is 5.3×10^{-5} m^3 or 53 ml. This method of tabulating your results avoids the necessity of writing the unit after every recorded reading.

As you write down your results, you will have to keep in mind the accuracy of your observations.

This could be expressed in the above tabulated results, for example by recording volume/10^{-5} m^3 as 4.2 ± 0.1. This indicates that the volume was measured to the nearest 1×10^{-4} m^3 or nearest 1 ml. Even if the possible error is not written down each time, the number of significant figures recorded will indicate the accuracy. In the above example, it would be quite wrong to write $V/10^{-5}$ m^3 as 4.20 unless the experimenter was claiming to measure to the nearest 10^{-7} m^3 or 0.1 ml. Section 2.4 gives a full discussion about errors.

Usually, the most important way of displaying your observations is by drawing a graph which describes in a visual way the relationship between the variables you have been measuring. Section 2.5 gives guidance on the choice of suitable graphs and the interpretation of graphical results.

Conclusion

The most important part of this experimental report is the 'conclusion'. Before you write it, refer to the aims of the experiment and consider in your conclusion if, and to what extent, the aim has been realised.

The conclusion may be a numerical value calculated from your observations; it may be a relationship which you have deduced from your observations; or it may be the statement of a well-known law which you have confirmed by your experimental results. If the conclusion of the experiment is the determination of the value of a quantity, then make sure that:

(a) the result is expressed in the correct SI units;
(b) the relevant conditions under which it was obtained are stated (e.g. the temperature and pressure if these are significant);

(c) the number of significant figures quoted agrees with your estimate of the possible error involved in each measurement and in the final processed result.

Experiments never fail although they often produce results which are meaningless or unexpected! If you feel your results are unsatisfactory, then say so and try to suggest why, but make sure that every experiment performed is given a 'conclusion'.

2.4 Experimental errors

Look at the table which follows. It summarises a short chapter in the very long story of the determination of an accurate value for the speed of light - and incidentally it can teach us a lot about experimental errors.

Date	Investigator	Observed speed in kilometre per second
1875	Cornu	299 990 ± 200
1880	Michelson	299 910 ± 50
1883	Newcomb	299 860 ± 30
1883	Michelson	299 850 ± 60
1926	Michelson	299 796 ± 4

All these methods used a rotating mirror.

These results tell us that:

(a) no experiment gives the *right* answer;
(b) scientists aim to get nearer and nearer to the right answer;
(c) experimenters have to make a reasonable assessment of the accuracy of their experiments.

Significant figures

No meaning can be attached to the result of an experiment unless some estimate has been made of the possible error. This means that all the figures given in the answer must be **meaningful** or **significant**.

Notice that Michelson in 1880 could only give five significant figures in his answer because he estimated his error as ± 50 km s^{-1}.

In 1926 Michelson, well into his seventies, and after spending over 50 years measuring the speed of light, is saying through his results

'In my experiment I have calculated that the speed of light is 299 796 km s^{-1} and I bet my bottom dollar that the value is between 299 792 km s^{-1} and 299 800 km s^{-1}.'

The accepted value today is 299 792 459.0 ± 0.8 m s^{-1} - just within Michelson's estimated region of error. Notice that now ten digits in the answer (including the zero after the decimal) are all meaningful (ten significant figures) because the estimated error is so small.

Different kinds of error

Errors in a particular experiment may be due to the limitations of the observer, the measuring instruments used, or the method used (the experimental design). We can consider errors in two categories, **systematic** and **random** errors.

Systematic errors

This is the name given to the errors which will produce a result which is always wrong in the same way, e.g. a zero error in a meter produces a systematic error. Specific heat capacity of a metal can be measured by electrical heating of a metal block. If some heat intended for the metal is given to the surroundings, the calculated result will always be too big. This is a systematic error.

To measure how a gas expands when heated, the gas can be enclosed in a glass tube and heated in a water bath. The thermometer used to record the gas temperature will actually be in the water and so the observed temperature will be less than the actual temperature - another systematic error. What kind of error would be present if you took readings of gas temperature as the water bath cooled down? Your answer might suggest a way of reducing this kind of error. Fortunately, there are many ways of reducing or eliminating systematic errors by experimental techniques such as cooling corrections and control experiments.

Random errors

Some errors occur because of limitations in the accuracy of a particular measuring technique or because of the limited sensitivity of instruments. These errors will be random errors producing results which are both too large and too small. It is very important to be able to make good estimates of the possible error or uncertainty in each recorded reading. Let us consider the following two common examples of estimating errors.

(a) In a lens experiment the exact image position may be difficult to locate by focusing. An image distance might be recorded as 15.3 cm because the image on the screen was definitely out of focus at 15.0 cm and also at 15.6 cm. The image distance should be recorded as (15.3 ±0.3) cm, i.e. a possible error of 2%.
(b) When reading a thermometer which is marked in whole degrees Celsius, it is possible to read between the marks to the nearest one-fifth of a degree. The error or uncertainty would be 0.2 C. So a result would be written as

$$\text{initial temperature} = 17.4 \pm 0.2 \text{ °C (1% error).}$$

Percentage errors

A temperature difference found by subtracting two readings on the thermometer described above could be ±0.4 degrees in error. Of course, it is possible that two errors will cancel each other out when readings are added or subtracted but we cannot assume this, so in stating the possible error in a difference between two readings we must include the uncertainties. For example, if the two readings are 17.4 °C and 25.3 °C the temperature difference will be given as (7.9 ± 0.4) °C - a **percentage** error in this case of 5%.

What happens to the error when several quantities are multiplied or divided? Let's consider an experiment to find the Young modulus for brass by stretching a brass wire with a force of 4.0 N.

The expression for the Young modulus E is

$$E = \frac{\text{Stretching force per unit area of cross-section}}{\text{extension per unit length}}$$

$$= \frac{F/A}{x/l}$$

Here are the experimental results.

Quantity	Measurement	Estimated error	Approximate percentage error
extension x	1.00 mm	0.02 mm	2.0%
length of wire l	2.50 m	0.01 m	0.5 %
diameter of wire d	0.36 mm	0.01 mm	2.5%

Let's consider the error in calculating the cross-sectional area A of the wire.

$$A = \pi r^2 = \pi (d/2)^2 = \pi (0.18)^2 \text{ mm}^2 = 0.1202 \text{ mm}^2$$

However, A could be between $\pi (0.185)^2$ mm^2 and $(0.175)^2$ mm^2, i.e. between 0.107 mm^2 and 0.096 mm^2. So we should write $A = 0.102 \pm 0.0005$ mm^2. The percentage error is 5%.

Notice that an error of 2.5% in d (and in r) has produced an error of 5% in d^2 (and in r^2). The percentage error is doubld if a quantity is squared. This is a special case of a general rule that **when quantities are multiplied the percentage error of the product is the sum of all the percentage errors.**

What happens when quantities are divided? Consider the ratio x/l in the experiment.

The experimental results give

$$\frac{x}{l} = \frac{1.00 \times 10^{-3}\text{m}}{2.50 \text{ m}} = 4.00 \times 10^{-4}$$

But the estimated error allows that x/l could be between 0.98 x 10^{-3} m/2.51 m (lowest possible value) and 1.02 x 10^{-3} m/2.49 m (highest possible value) i.e. between 3.90 x 10^{-4} and 4.10 x 10^{-4}.

So we write $x/l = (4.0 \pm 0.1)$ x 10^{-4} (a possible error of 2.5%). But the estimated error in x was 2.0% and the estimated error in l was 0.5%. Again, the estimated **percentage error for a quotient x/l is found by adding up the percentage errors of each quantity.**

Q 2.1 Self-assessment question

(a) What will be the possible percentage error in the calculated value of the Young modulus of brass? Assume the error in F is negligible.
(b) What is the calculated value of E for brass?
(c) What is the possible error in the value for E?
(d) How should you quote the result of the experiment, including an indication of the possible error.■

Reducing the errors

Did you notice in our experimental example that the length of the wire was measured with a possible error of 1 cm? Not very accurate, you say, but measuring the length to the nearest mm (percentage error 0.05%) would be pointless since we must add to this error the very much larger percentage errors in A and x. Remember this when you do experiments and don't waste time measuring the mass of 100 g of water to the nearest mg (0.001%) if, after heating it, you measure its temperature change to the nearest 0.2 °C (5% error).

Instead, concentrate in experiments on trying to improve the accuracy of the readings which are most uncertain. The extension and the diameter of the wire are such quantities in the experiment we have considered. A vernier and a micrometer are used to measure these quantities but, even so, they contain the most error. Using a metre rule to measure r and x would be hopeless. How could the accuracy be improved in this experiment? Putting a bigger load on would help; a load of 40 N would give an extension of 1 cm with an error of only 0.2%. Taking more readings of the radius would provide a more accurate average value; in fact, as a general rule in experiments, try to repeat readings whenever this is possible.

Repeated measurement of the same quantity and averaging the result, will obviously improve the accuracy of the answer. However, a simple calculation of a mean value may not always be the best way of averaging because bad results which are a long way from the mean always have too great an influence on the final answer. If results are displayed graphically, it becomes more obvious which results are unreliable and the graph becomes a useful way of averaging or combining results. This is explained in section 2.5.

Q 2.2 Self-assessment question

Look back at the table of results for the speed of light. The accepted value for the speed of light tells us that in 1883 one famous experimenter got his estimated error right and the other got it wrong. Who was wrong? ∎

Take comfort, even famous experimenters get their estimates of error wrong but don't let that stop you from trying to get them right!

2.5   Plotting graphs

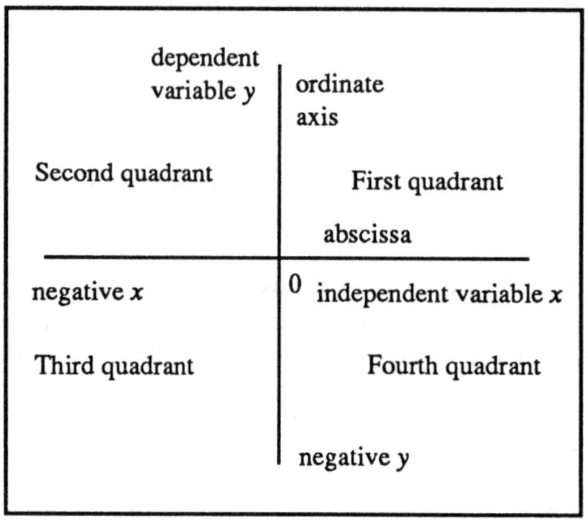

Figure 2.1

A graph provides an immediate visual picture of the results of an experiment and it can have a variety of functions. A graph can:

(a) display a relationship between two related variable quantities;
(b) show at what point a particular relationship ceases to be true (e.g. a straight line may turn into a curve);
(c) be used to determine the constants in an equation relating two variable quantities;
(d) provide the best way of combining a series of readings to improve the accuracy of the experiment.

How to plot a graph

(a) Plot the independent variable along the horizontal axis (x-axis or abscissa). This variable is the one which is controlled in the experiment and determines the value of the other (dependent variable) plotted on the vertical axis (y-axis or ordinate) (figure 2.1). For example, when describing how a particular quantity varies with time, it is obvious that 'time' is the independent variable (- plotted horizontally) and the value of the other quantity depends on the instant of time at which it was measured.

Positive values of the independent variable are plotted to the right of the origin (the point representing zero value of both variables) and positive values of the dependent variable (ordinate) are plotted above the origin.

In most experiments you will perform, the variables only have positive values and the points plotted are all in the 'first quadrant' (above and to the right of the origin). However, you must remember that a graph could extend over all four quadrants. The time variation of a pendulum's displacement will show both positive and negative values of the displacement (plotted as ordinate).

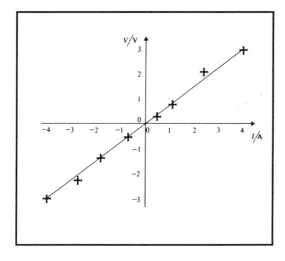

Figure 2.2

A graph is described by naming the **dependent** variable first. Thus, figure 2.2 is described as a graph of V against I. It shows how the p.d. V across a resistor depends on the current I through it. If the current I is reversed, it will have negative values which will be plotted to the left of the origin. In this case, the p.d. will also be reversed giving values of V which are plotted below the origin.

(b) Graphs are plots of **numbers** (rather than physical quantities). In physics, a symbol represents a quantity in an appropriate unit. For example, the statement

'The current is 1.5 ampere' can be expressed, using a symbol, as '$I = 1.5$ A', but it is incorrect to say 'the current is I A' since I includes the unit ampere.

So I/A is a pure number and V/V is a pure number. These numbers are plotted on the graph (figure 2.2).

The coordinates (that is the pair of numbers corresponding to a point on a graph) are always quoted in round brackets, the numbers separated by a comma, the abscissa (x-value) first. So (4,3) represents $x = 4$ and $y = 3$, or I/A = 4 and V/V = 3.

(c) When choosing the scales for the axes, the following points must be considered but the result will inevitably be a compromise.
(i) Choose scales so that points are distributed as widely as possible; this means choosing a suitable scale and deciding on the number at the beginning of the scale, i.e. whether to choose a true origin (0,0) or a false origin (e.g. $x = 4$, $y = 6$).
(ii) Choose simple scales to make calculations straightforward (e.g. don't choose 4 small squares to represent 7 units as a scale).
(iii) If the gradient is to be measured, try to obtain an angle of 30° to 60° between graph and axis.
(iv) If the intercept on the y axis is required, it may be necessary to start the scale of the x axis from 0.

(d) Plot points as crosses or circled dots.

(e) Plot the points as the experiment proceeds. This will enable you to retake readings which are suspect, obtain results which produce an even spread of points along the graph, and concentrate on obtaining enough readings in crucial regions, e.g. where the graph curves sharply.

(f) If possible, choose variables which are related by an equation which will produce a straight line graph. (Linear graphs are explained in part 3.)

(g) When you sketch the graph, do not join all the points together by a zig-zag. This would suggest that all the readings are free from any error which is obviously untrue. Instead use the points to draw a smooth curve which may not, in fact, pass through any of the plotted points but which will indicate how the two quantities are interdependent. Often the graph you draw will be a straight line and you will be required to draw the 'best straight line' (figure 2.3a) but you must resist the temptation to make every pattern of points conform to a straight line (figure 2.3b).

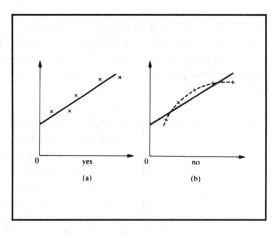

Figure 2.3

Drawing the 'best straight line' provides the best way of combining a series of readings to increase the accuracy of your experiment. This can be illustrated by considering a simple electrical experiment. It is possible to obtain a value for the resistance R of a wire by measuring one particular value of the p.d. V across the wire and dividing it by the current I passing through. The probable error in the determination of R can be reduced by taking several corresponding values of V and I, in each case calculating R and then obtaining an average of all these values of R. One disadvantage of this method of calculating R by obtaining an arithmetic mean is that results which differ widely from the mean have a bigger influence on the calculated average. Thus, one or two bad results can distort the answer considerably and cancel out the value of taking a series of readings.

If a graph (figure 2.1) is plotted with values of V/V as the ordinate (y-axis) and values of I/A as the abscissae (x-axis) then a straight line graph can be obtained with a gradient equal to R.

The amount of uncertainty or possible error in a reading can also be shown by the way readings are plotted. In the graph (figure 2.1) points are plotted and the short lines parallel to the axes indicate the possible error.

The plot of points will enable you to use your eyes to discriminate between those readings which are in agreement with each other, and should have greatest influence in the final result, and those readings which are in disagreement with the others and should be ignored or have less influence. You make this discrimination by drawing 'the best straight line' through the region of the points and so obtain the most accurate value of R available from your readings.

When choosing the best straight line, use a stretched piece of thread or plastic ruler. Manoeuvre it until you consider it lies along the ideal line and then lightly mark two well-separated points which will fix this line. Do not allow yourself to be over-influenced by the first and last points on your graph. If you have time, you could repeat the readings which produced points well off this line to obtain further confirmation that the graph you have drawn is 'best'.

2.6 Safety precautions

Physics laboratories are not places in which the accident rate is high - far more occur in playgrounds and corridors. There are, however, many *potential* hazards, and your safety depends on your understanding these, following safety procedures, and taking particular precautions, when required. Most of these matters will be dealt with as they arise, often in connection with an experiment, throughout the course. Here we summarise the types of hazard that can cause problems when studying physics.

You!

Any practical work should be approached sensibly and carefully and if there is anything you don't understand, ask your teacher first.

Mechanical

In studying machines we sometimes use objects which contain a lot of energy (e.g. massive and/or fast-moving objects) which they can give up to you - painfully - if a collision occurs. Most of these are fairly obvious and easily avoided (e.g. rifle pellets and falling heavy masses). Remember, however, that lots of energy can be stored in a stretched wire before it breaks, and that glass is brittle and sharp. Cuts from broken glass are among the most common accidents in science. Another source of hazard is a high or low pressure gas in, for example, a glass container which can explode or implode.

Chemical

Hazardous chemicals are used for various purposes in physics but not for their chemistry, so often safer alternatives can be found. The most frequent serious accidents are caused by flammable organic liquids such as meths (ethyl alcohol) and paraffins. Remember these are volatile and may give off toxic vapours, as can mercury and bromine. The chemical changes occurring in cells and electrolytic capacitors can produce toxic substances and explosions are possible if they are misused. Details of hazards of particular chemicals are given with the experiments in which they are used. If in doubt always ask your teacher or technician or consult a reference book.

Radiations

The hazard is dependent on the frequency of the electromagnetic wave. Low-frequency radio and microwaves are quite safe: infra-red can cause burns, but is familiar in all kinds of heating. The visible light of the sun and laser are of sufficient intensity to damage the eye; neither should be viewed directly. Radiations of higher frequency can cause ionisation, as their photons are more energetic. Ultraviolet can cause skin cancer, X- and gamma-radiation can cause a wide range of damage to the body. Alpha and beta particles are also called ionising radiations, and can be even more damaging if the body is exposed. Full details of the precautions to be followed when using radioisotopes which emit alpha, beta and gamma radiations are given in section 2.7.

Electricity

Although taken for granted as an essential service in homes and laboratories, the hazards from electricity are serious and varied. Firstly there is a danger of overheating, which normally occurs when there is a current overload; protection is by use of fuses. The second more sudden hazard is that of electric shock, by electricity passing through the body. The danger depends on the current which flows: a few hundredths of an ampere can be fatal. This current depends on the resistance (usually from the skin) and the voltage.

For this reason most laboratory equipment operates at voltages below 30 V. Mains (240 V) equipment should always be used with care; do not use faulty or d.i.y. apparatus. Experiments with extra high voltages (EHT), for example in electrostatics, can involve voltages of several thousand volts. In these cases, however, the current should be limited to a few milliamps so that any shock received, whilst it may be uncomfortable, is not dangerous. Electricity can also cause explosions by chemical change building up a gas pressure, for example if an electrolytic capacitor is connected the wrong way round. Capacitors can also give electric shocks, since their function is to store charge. A similar hazard is the basic e.m.f of some devices, though this is more likely to damage equipment than you.

Miscellaneous

Solid carbon dioxide can give a 'freeze-burn' in contact with the skin; it sublimes at -78.5 °C. Xenon stroboscopes can provoke fits in susceptible people at a frequency of about 10 Hz so always use a higher frequency.

2.7   Using radioactive sources

Safety regulations

The use of ionising radiations, that is, radioactive sources and X-rays, in schools is subject to strict and careful control. Many of the safety precautions listed below are taken from the regulations and recommendations of the Department of Education and Science. All are designed for your own and other people's safety. It is important that you follow them carefully.

Nature of sources

The sources used in cloud chambers, and naturally occurring salts of uranium, thorium and potassium, are relatively weak emitters. These are the only sources that can be used by pupils under the age of sixteen. The α, β and γ emitters you will use with GM tubes are called closed sources. They are mounted in metal holders, with one face open. The source is held in place with gauze or wire mesh. These sources are supplied in lead-lined boxes. The nature and strength of the sources is marked on the box, or on the source holder.

Laboratory rules

1 You may use a source only after being given permission by your teacher, and only when your teacher is present.

2 The sources must always be transported in their containers.

3 Always use only one source at a time; return one before using another.

4 Sources must *not* be handled except with tongs or similar holding tool.

5 Never look directly at the open face of a source, or point it at anyone.

6 Never tamper with a source. If one appears damaged, report this to your teacher immediately.

7 Do not use a source in an experiment close to someone who is not involved in the experiment. When a number of students are carrying out experiments, students should be spaced out as much as possible.

8 Do not rush when using sources, but work steadily to reduce the time a source is out of its container to a minimum.

9 Wash your hands thoroughly when you have finished using sources.

10 If in doubt about the safety of anything you are doing, or that anyone else is doing, ask your teacher.

Exposure levels

The regulations permit an exposure to radiation (including X-rays) of about one quarter the normal background radiation in any one year. The exposure on any one occasion must not exceed one-tenth of this. Exposure depends on the nature and strength of the radiation, the distance from the source and the time of exposure. If these factors are known the exposure can easily be calculated. For example, if you held a typical γ-source in tongs for 6 minutes while doing an experiment, the exposure you would receive would be approximately 1/500th of the permitted limit on any one occasion. If, however, you held the source in your hand you would exceed the limit after about 70 seconds! (The exposure is inversely proportional to the square of the distance between the source and you.)

2.8   Using electronic instruments

Developments in microelectronics have meant that there are a number of electronic devices available for making measurements. You have probably seen or used a digital multimeter. These instruments are very easy to use for the reading of voltage, current or resistance; they are reliable, fairly accurate and comparatively cheap.

In this course you may have the opportunity to use more complex electronic devices. A number of the experiments have sections that use electronic measurement. Because of the wide range of devices available, it is not possible to write instructions for all of them and so only two instruments are described. However, your science department may have other instruments that make the required measurements equally well. The two instruments described are the VELA and the North London Science Centre analogue to digital converter (NLSC ADC). Most of the quantities you will measure are termed 'analogue'. This means that the quantity can have any value between a minimum and a maximum value. A digital quantity can have only certain fixed values. You will learn more about this when studying the unit *Electronic systems*.

VELA

The VELA (this is formed from the phrase **VE**rsatile **L**aboratory **A**id) is a microprocessor based device that allows voltages to be sampled over a wide range of time intervals and the results stored in its memory. These measurements can then be displayed on an oscilloscope or a chart recorder (figure 2.4). If you have a suitable computer and the appropriate software then the measurements can be displayed on the screen of the monitor. There are four input channels but you will only be using one of them (channel 1). The analogue voltage to be measured is supplied to the input and is stored as a digital binary number in the memory. There are seventeen programs that can be called up via the keypad and these perform various functions on the incoming data so that the device can be used as a variety of standard laboratory instruments (these include scalers, timers, frequency meters and storage oscilloscopes and you will meet them in the course). For our purposes, the most useful programs are those where we can vary the time intervals between the readings. At its fastest, the machine can take 4092 readings at intervals of 30 ps. The largest time interval between readings is 15 minutes.

Using the VELA

There is a User Manual that is supplied with the instrument. The following instructions will be useful when you are using the VELA but, if there are any problems, you will need to refer to the User Manual. This also contains full details of all the seventeen programs. In your VELA you may have some additional programs.

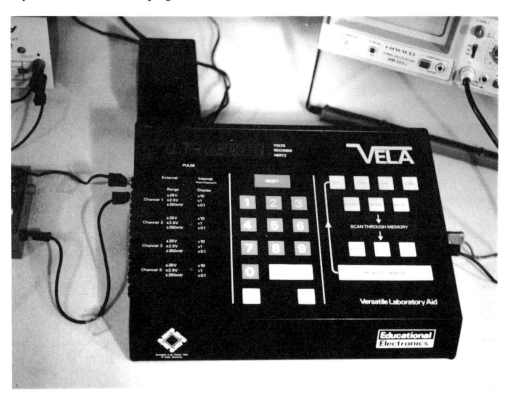

Figure 2.4

1 Before switching on the VELA, check that the power supply is within the range 8 to 12 V (either a.c. or d.c.).

2 Switch on and the display shows 'HELLO'. After a few seconds this changes to 'P'. If anything else appears, press the RESET key.

3 Connect the oscilloscope (or chart recorder) to the analogue output or the computer to the digital socket via the appropriate lead. Connect up the external circuit to the VELA, usually through Channel 1.

4 Often it is useful to get the incoming signal to start the VELA taking readings. To do this set the pulse switch to 'external' and connect the positive terminal of the pulse input to the positive of channel 1. The VELA will start taking readings when the input voltage reaches 1 V.

5 Use the keypad to select the required program. Often you will need to key in a parameter (for example to set the time interval between readings). The initial value used in each experiment will be given to you but for further details you should consult the appropriate program in the manual. After entering the parameter, press ENTER.

6 There are two ways of starting the VELA to take readings: (i) press START (pulse switch must be in 'internal' position), and (ii) using the external voltage (see instruction 4).

7 If you wish to stop the VELA at any stage, press STOP. Otherwise, when it has taken all its readings, the display will flash 'O-P'.

8 To display the readings on the oscilloscope, press CHI and then SCOPE. To download the data to the computer for display on the monitor, follow the instructions on the screen. At one point, you will need to press CHI and then MICRO.

NLSC ADC

As the name suggests, the device (figure 2.5) converts an analogue quantity to a digital quantity that can then be used by a computer (a computer can only process digital numbers). Unlike the VELA, the data cannot be stored in the ADC itself but must be sent to the computer to be stored in its memory.

Figure 2.5

The software controls the rate at which the readings are taken. There are two analogue input channels. Each channel has a variable gain so that small voltage signals can be amplified before conversion to digital quantities. The 'ideal' input voltage is one that varies in the range 0 to 2 V.

The bias control can shift the voltage levels so that this occurs. There are also two output channels containing relays but these are not used in any of the experiments. The User Guide that accompanies the ADC provides more details about how the device functions. Sensors such as those in the Philip Harris range can be directly attached to the inputs.

Using the NLSC ADC

1 Connect the ADC with its lead to the parallel part of the computer.

2 Connect up the external circuit to the ADC. If there is only one input, then it can be connected to either channel 0 or channel 1.

3 Run the appropriate program. All the operating instructions appear on the screen. However it is not possible to look back at previous instructions (without restarting the program) so make sure the instructions are fully understood before the screen is cleared.

Part 3
Mathematics

The international system (SI) of units

In physics we are concerned with making measurements. In order to measure the mass of an object we need some standard mass with which to compare it – the kilogram, for example. To measure time, we need another standard time – the second. It is convenient to have as few as possible of these standards.

Basic quantities and units

There are *seven* fundamental or basic quantities and *seven* basic units in the SI system. (The letters SI derive from the name Système International d'Unités.)

Physical quantity	Basic unit	Symbol for unit
length l	metre	m
mass m	kilogram	kg
time t	second	s
current of electricity I	ampere	A
temperature T	kelvin	K
amount of substance n	mole	mol
luminous intensity I	candela	cd

Note. (i) In using the thermodynamic scale for temperatures there is no degree sign included in the unit, e.g. 273 K *not* 273 °K.

(ii) The unit of luminous intensity is not used in the APPIL course.

Derived units

Some of the more important derived units are listed below.

Physical quantity	Unit	Symbol for unit
area	metre^2	m^2
density	kilogram/metre^3	kg m^{-3}
acceleration	metre/second^2	m s^{-2}
force	newton	N
power	watt	W
momentum	newton second or	N s
	kilogram metre/second	kg m s^{-1}
volume	metre^3	m^3
velocity	metre/second	m s^{-1}
frequency	hertz	Hz
energy	joule	J
pressure	pascal	Pa

Writing symbols

(a) Units may be written in full or by using the agreed symbols.

(b) The letter s is never added to the symbols to show the plural form, e.g. 100 kg *not* 100 kgs. This is to avoid the possible confusion with the abbreviation for seconds.

(c) A full stop is not written after symbols for units except at the end of a sentence.

(d) The names of units written in full do not have capital letters even when they commemorate the name of a person. Likewise symbols for units do not use capital letters except for a few special ones which commemorate the name of a person, e.g.

N (newton)   V (volt)
A (ampere)   Hz (hertz)
W (watt)   Pa (pascal)

(e) When two or more unit symbols are combined to indicate a derived unit a space is left between them, e.g. N m, J s, m s^{-1}.

(f) No space is left between a prefix (indicating powers of ten) and a symbol to which it applies, e.g. cm, kN, MJ, km s^{-1}.

(g) When unit symbols are combined as a quotient it is recommended that negative indices be used rather than the solidus sign (/), e.g. m s^{-1} rather than m/s.

Standard form

Quantities are sometimes expressed in fractions or multiples of an SI unit, e.g. g, mm, MW, although the basic or derived SI units are generally preferred.

The radius of the moon can be expressed as 1700 km but it is not clear in this case how many of the digits are significant, i.e. whether the measurement is made to the nearest kilometre or the nearest 100 km. This ambiguity is overcome if the quantity is expressed in **standard form**, in this case as

$$1.7 \times 10^6 \, \text{m}$$

Notice that:

(a) the quantity is expressed in terms of the appropriate SI unit;

(b) the value is stated as a number between 1 and 10 multiplied by a power of 10;

(c) in this form the digits given are all significant (in this case the accuracy of measurement of the moon's radius permits two significant figures to be given).

Standard form enables similar quantities to be compared more easily and makes clear the number of significant figures.

Prefixes for SI units

The following prefixes may be used to indicate decimal fractions, or multiples, of both basic and derived units.

Fraction	Prefix	Symbol
10^{-1}	deci	d
10^{-2}	centi	c
10^{-3}	milli	m
10^{-6}	micro	μ
10^{-9}	nano	n
10^{-12}	pico	p
10^{-15}	femto	f
10^{-18}	atto	a

Multiple	Prefix	Symbol
10^{1}	deca	da
10^{2}	hecto	h
10^{3}	kilo	k
10^{6}	mega	M
10^{9}	giga	G
10^{12}	tera	T

Units for inconsequential trivia

(Not required for any examinations!)

10^{12} bulls	= 1 terabull (and it gets worse!)
10^{9} les	= 1 gigale (don't laugh)
10^{6} phones	= 1 megaphone
10^{3} whales	= 1 kilowhale
10^{2} rings	= 1 hectoring
10^{1} cards	= 1 decacards
10^{-1} mate	= 1 decimate
10^{-2} mental	= 1 centimental
10^{-3} on	= 1 million
10^{-6} scope	= 1 microscope
10^{-9} goat	= 1 nanogoat
10^{-12} lo	= 1 picolo
10^{-15} mininity	= 1 femtomininity
10^{-18} boy	= 1 attoboy

Dimensions

The dimensions of a derived physical quantity show the way in which it is related, through its defining equation, to the basic quantities.

The use of square brackets [ ] around a physical quantity has the meaning 'dimensions of the quantity'. However, the square brackets are sometimes omitted, which can be rather confusing.

Every equation involving physical quantities must have the same dimensions on each side. This is called 'dimensional homogeneity'. It really means no more than the fact that you cannot equate things which are not similar in kind.

(a) **Volume** is calculated by multiplying together three lengths. (Volume of a cuboid is length × breadth × height; volume of a cylinder is $\pi r^2 h$).

So we write

$$[\text{volume}] = [L^3]$$

and this reminds us that volume is measured in metre cube (cubic metre), usually written m^3.

By writing down a dimensional equation it is possible to show how any physical quantity is related to the fundamental ones, and hence to derive its unit. Since any equation must be dimensionally homogeneous, clearly it must also be homogeneous in terms of unity of measurement.

(b) What are the dimensions and unit of **density**?

The density of a substance is defined by the equation

$$\text{density} = \frac{\text{mass}}{\text{volume}}$$

$$[\text{volume}] = [L^3] \qquad [\text{mass}] = [M]$$

Thus
$$[\text{density}] = \frac{[M]}{[L^3]} \quad \text{or} \quad [M\,L^{-3}]$$

The unit of density will be the kilogram per metre cube, kg m^{-3}.

(c) What are the dimensions and unit of **speed**?

Speed is defined as distance ÷ time.

Thus
$$[\text{speed}] = \frac{[L]}{[T]} \quad \text{or} \quad [L\,T^{-1}]$$

The unit of speed will be the metre per second, m s^{-1}.

Q 3.1 Self-assessment question

(a) What are the dimensions and unit of acceleration?
(b) What are the dimensions and unit of force?
(c) What are the dimensions of energy? What is the SI unit of energy, the joule J, equal to?

Solving physics problems

There are many different sorts of problems, but in physics the term is commonly used to mean the sort of question which involves mathematics. This section helps you develop a general way of approaching such problems – what could be called a *strategy* for solving physics problems.

> *'It isn't that they can't see the solution. It is that they can't see the problem.'*
> (G. K. Chesterton)

To start with it is worth thinking about the relationship between physics and mathematics. This relationship is a close one and is illustrated in figure 3.1.

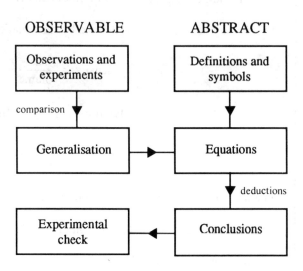

Figure 3.1

This is somewhat over-simplified, but makes the point that mathematics is really concerned with the right-hand side, that is with manipulating abstract symbols according to the rules of logic.

On the other hand, physics is principally concerned with the left-hand side, the observable world, but makes use of the techniques of mathematics. However, a conclusion reached by mathematical deduction always needs checking by experiment.

The process of formulating equations to represent physical situations is called 'mathematical modelling', and an equation relating physical quantities can be called a mathematical model. For example, the equation $F = ma$ is a simple mathematical model which you have already used.

The further you go with physics, the more important mathematical models become.

In order to solve physics problems, bearing in mind that there are many mathematical models for different aspects of physics, a good approach is as follows:

1 Make a list of the information given, and the information needed, if possible in the form of symbols.

2 Draw a diagram to help you visualise the situation.

3 Write down any equations which may be relevant, i.e. which connect several of the quantities given or needed.

4 See whether any of the equations give a direct way to solve the problem. This will only be true in simple cases.

5 If not, work out a route using two or more equations in turn. You may need to bring in additional quantities, neither given nor needed as answers, at this stage.

6 Write down the equations, and substitute the numerical values.

7 Make a rough estimate of the answer.

8 Calculate the result more accurately.

9 Check that your final answer is sensible (frequently an absurd answer is obtained due to faulty arithmetic).

It can be helpful at stage (5) to work out a route by writing down possible deductions. For example, if resistance R and current I are given, one could write:

knowing R and I then V can be found (using $V = IR$).

or more concisely $\qquad\qquad\qquad\qquad R, I \rightarrow V$

The symbol $\rightarrow$ is usually read as 'implies'.

The following worked example illustrates the suggested strategy.

Worked example

100 kW of power are supplied to a factory through wires of resistance $0.1\,\Omega$. What power is lost in the wires if the potential difference at the factory end is

(a) 230 V, (b) 10 000 V?

Stage 1

$$P = 100 \text{ kW}, \quad R = 0.1\,\Omega, \quad V = 230 \text{ V, or } 10000 \text{ V}$$

To be found: power lost.

Stage 2

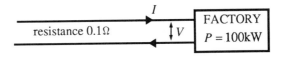

Stage 3

$$V = IR, \quad P = VI = I^2 R = V^2/R$$

Stage 4

No direct solution, because we need to know the current I in the wires and it is not given.

Stage 5

You might start by writing

$$
\begin{aligned}
&P, V \text{ give} &&I &&\text{using } P = VI \\
&I, R \text{ give} &&V \text{ (drop)} &&\text{using } V = IR \\
&I, V \text{ (drop) give} &&P \text{ (loss)} &&\text{using } P = VI
\end{aligned}
$$

indicating a three-stage calculation.

But then you would probably realise that the final two stages can be replaced by one

$$
\begin{aligned}
&P, V \text{ give } I &&\text{using } P = VI \\
&I, R \text{ give } P_{\text{loss}} &&\text{using } P = I^2 R
\end{aligned}
$$

Stage 6

Using $P = VI$,

$$I = P/V$$

(a) $I = \dfrac{100\,000}{230}\,\text{A}$ 	(b) $I = \dfrac{100\,000}{10\,000}\,\text{A}$

Using $P_{\text{loss}} = I^2 R$

(a) $P_{\text{loss}} = \left\{ \left(\dfrac{100\,000}{230} \right)^2 \times 0.1 \right\} \text{W}$ 	(b) $P_{\text{loss}} = (10^2 \times 0.1)\,\text{W}$

Stage 7

Approximating,

(a) $P_{\text{loss}} \approx \left\{ \left(\dfrac{100\,000}{200} \right)^2 \times 0.1 \right\} \text{W}$

$$= \left(\dfrac{10^6}{4} \times \dfrac{1}{10} \right) \text{W}$$

$$= 2.5 \times 10^4 \,\text{W}$$

(The correct answer will be smaller than this.)
For (b) no estimate is needed.

Stage 8

(a) $P_{\text{loss}} = \dfrac{10^7}{23^2}\,\text{W}$ 	(b) $P_{\text{loss}} = 10\,\text{W}$

$$P_{\text{loss}} = 1.89 \times 10^4 \,\text{W}$$

Stage 9

Thus in (a) a large amount of power is lost, while in (b) the loss is negligible, the sort of answer we should expect.

The strategy given above is slightly more detailed than the method given in a classic book on mathematics problems, *How to solve it* by George Polya. He says

FIRST	You have to **understand** the **problem**.
SECOND	Find the **connection** between the **data** and the **unknown**. You may be obliged to consider auxiliary problems if an immediate connection cannot be found.
	You should obtain eventually a **plan** of the solution.
THIRD	**Carry out** your **plan**.
FOURTH	**Examine** the **solution** obtained.

The whole book is an elaboration of this approach, in a variety of different cases, and you can see that it is basically similar to the strategy just given.

You will need to practise solving problems in order to become adept; with APPIL you will have plenty of opportunity.

3.3 | Indices and logarithms

Indices

'Power corrupts, but lack of power corrupts absolutely.' (Adlai Stevenson)

a^5 is shorthand for $a \times a \times a \times a \times a$. a^5 is called the fifth **power** of a and '5' is called the **index** or **exponent**.

The **rules for indices** are summarised below: use the examples which follow to check these general rules.

1   $a^m \times a^n = a^{m+n}$ 5 $(a^m)^n = a^{m \times n}$

2   $\dfrac{a^m}{a^n} = a^{m-n}$ 6 $a^{1/m} = \sqrt[m]{a}$

3   $a^{-m} = \dfrac{1}{a^m}$ 7 $(a^m)^{1/n} = a^{m/n}$

4   $a^0 = 1$ 8 $a^m \times b^m = (a \times b)^m$

Q 3.2 Development question

(a) Check that $a^5 \times a^3 = a^{5+3}$ by writing the expression without using indices. This is an example of rule 1.

(b) Check that $a^5 \div a^3 = a^{5-3}$. This is an example of rule 2. ∎

Applying rule 2 we can write

$$a^3 \div a^5 = a^{-2}$$

So a^{-2} must be defined as $1/a^2$ or, in general,

$$a^{-m} = \frac{1}{a^m} \quad \text{(rule 3)}$$

The reciprocal of a quantity is expressed by changing the sign of the index, e.g. $2^{-3} = 1/2^3 = 1/8$.

(c) What does $a^5 \div a^5$ give according to rule 2 or otherwise?

It gives $a^0 = 1$ whatever the value of a (rule 4).

(d) Check that $(a^3)^2 = a^6$. This illustrates rule 5. Since $2 \times 2 \times 2 = 8$, we say 2 is the cube root of 8, and we write

$$8^{1/3} = 2$$

since, by rule 1

$$8^{1/3} \times 8^{1/3} \times 8^{1/3} = 8^{1/3 + 1/3 + 1/3} = 8^1 = 8$$

Q 3.3 **Self-assessment question**

(a) Express without the use of indices $16^{1/4}$, $25^{1.5}$, 10^{-3}, $(\sqrt{2})^4$, $(\sqrt{3})^{-2}$.

(b) Which is the largest and which the smallest of $1/10^{-2}$, 2^6, $\sqrt[3]{(1000)}$?■

Sometimes the index may be expressed as a decimal fraction, e.g. $10^{0.3}$.

Using the rules for indices we can write

$$10^{0.3} = 10^{3/10} = \sqrt[10]{10^3} = \sqrt[10]{1000}$$

Thus $10^{0.3}$ is a number which, when multiplied by itself ten times, gives 1000.

This number is very near to 2 because $2^{10} = 1024$.

Thus $10^{0.3}$ is approximately equal to 2.

Q 3.4 **Self-assessment question**

Given that $10^{0.3} \approx 2$, and that $10^{0.5} = 10^{1/2} = \sqrt{10} \approx 3.16$, find the value of $10^{0.8}$ and $10^{0.2}$.■

Logarithms

If $y = a^x$, x is called the **index**. x is also called the **logarithm of y to the base a** and we write

$$x = \log_a y$$

Equivalent expressions can be written using indices or logarithms, e.g.

$$2^3 = 8 \quad \text{or} \quad \log_2 8 = 3$$

Q 3.5 **Self-assessment question**

Rewrite in logarithmic form the following identities

$$121 = 11^2, \quad 4^{5/2} = 32■$$

A logarithm can use any base but two types of logarithm are widely used:

(a) **common** logarithms to base 10,
(b) **natural** logarithms to base e (e ≈ 2.7183).

The symbol lg is often used for **common** logarithms, thus

$$\text{if } y = 10^x, x = \log_{10} y = \lg y$$

The symbol for **natural** logarithms is ln, thus

$$\text{if } y = e^x, x = \log_e y = \ln y$$

(e^x is a function of x having special properties as we shall see later.)

In question 3.4 you noted that $10^{0.3} \approx 2$, which can be expressed in logarithms as $\lg 2 \approx 0.3$. Check your answers to question 3.4 using a calculator.

You can easily verify that $\lg 2 = 0.3010$.

Since $20 = 2 \times 10$ we can write

$$20 = 10^{0.3010} \times 10^1 = 10^{1.3010}$$

i.e. $\qquad\qquad\qquad$ lg $20 = 1.3010$

2000 must equal $10^{0.3010} \times 10^3 = 10^{3.3010}$, i.e.

$$\text{lg } 2000 = 3.3010$$

These examples show that any number can be expressed as a power of 10 (or any other base).

Number	Logarithm
2	0.3010
20	1.3010
200	2.3010
2000	3.3010

$\qquad\qquad\qquad\qquad\quad\uparrow\quad\uparrow$
characteristic $\quad$ mantissa

The number after the decimal point is the logarithm of a number between 1 and 10. This is sometimes called the **mantissa**. To express larger numbers in logarithms we add a number (called the **characteristic**) before the decimal point. The same approach can be used for numbers smaller than 1, e.g.

$$0.2 = 2 \times 10^{-1} = 10^{0.3010} \times 10^{-1} = 10^{-0.6990}$$

Thus, lg $0.2 = -0.6990$ but it would usually be written

$$\text{lg } 0.2 = \bar{1}.3010 \quad \text{i.e. } -1 + 0.3010$$

(We say 'bar one point three zero one zero'.)

Note. Sometimes the logarithms of numbers are shown on graphs and for numbers less than 1 it is essential to use the resultant negative value of the logarithm and not a mixture of negative and positive quantities.

Since logarithms are the indices to which that base is raised, logarithms will obey the rules for indices discussed earlier.

This is why logarithms provide a useful method of finding products, quotients, powers and roots of quantities

$$\log(xy) = \log x + \log y$$

$$\log(x/y) = \log x - \log y$$

$$\log(1/y) = \log 1 - \log y = -\log y$$

$$\log x^n = n\log x$$

Worked example:

Evaluate $\sqrt[4]{0.2}$ using common logs.

$$\lg \sqrt[4]{0.2} = \lg (0.2)^{1/4}$$

$$= \frac{1}{4} \lg 0.2$$

$$= \frac{1}{4} \times \bar{1}.3010$$

$$= \frac{(-4 + 3.3010)}{4} = \bar{1}.8252$$

Using a calculator 10^x or antilog key $\sqrt[4]{0.2} = 0.6686$.

Q 3.6 Self-assessment question

(a) Evaluate without using a calculator or tables: $\log_4 64$, $\log_{10} 0.01$.

(b) Use a calculator or tables to evaluate $7.27 \times (0.277)^{-1/3}$. ■

The **natural** logarithm of a number can be obtained directly from a scientific calculator and the natural antilog is found by using the e^x function on the calculator.

Check the following example

$$\ln 0.06375 = \ln 6.375 \times 10^{-2}$$

$$= \ln 6.375 + \ln 10^{-2}$$

$$= 1.8524 + \bar{5}.3948$$

$$= \bar{3}.2472$$

Conversion from natural to common logarithms can be done using the relationship

$$\log_e x = (\log_e 10) \log_{10} x$$

or
$$\ln x = 2.303 \lg x$$

3.4 | Algebraic relationships

'What is algebra exactly; is it those three-cornered things?' (J. M. Barrie)

Mathematical sentences are used to express relationships between different quantities. Like all grammatical statements these sentences must have a subject and a verb. The following symbols are used to express the 'verb'

$=$ is equal to $\approx$ is approximately equal to

$<$ is less than $>$ is greater than

$\ll$ is much less than $\gg$ is much greater than

$\geq$ is greater than or equal to $\propto$ is proportional to

$\leq$ is less than or equal to

In addition, special symbols are used in standard ways to represent the result of certain mathematical operations.

Δx the difference between two values of x

Σx the sum of several values of x

$\langle x \rangle, \bar{x}$ the mean of several values of x

Note that if there are n values of x,

$$\langle x \rangle = \bar{x} = \Sigma x / n$$

Equations

In the equation

$$T = 2\pi \sqrt{\frac{l}{g}}$$

the period T of a simple pendulum is the **subject** of the equation. T may also be referred to as the **dependent variable** since its value depends on the quantities on the right-hand side of the equation. A quantity whose value can be chosen is called the **independent variable**. The equation can be rewritten with another subject, e.g. l, the length of the pendulum.

$$\frac{T}{2\pi} = \sqrt{\frac{l}{g}} \quad \text{(obtained by dividing both sides by } 2\pi\text{)}$$

$$\left(\frac{T}{2\pi}\right)^2 = \frac{l}{g} \quad \text{(squaring both sides)}$$

$$l = \frac{gT^2}{4\pi^2} \quad \text{(multiplying by } g\text{)}$$

When changing the subject of an equation remember that:

whatever you do to one side of an equation you *must* do the same to the other side to maintain the equality. You may:

(a) add the same quantity to both sides,
(b) subtract the same quantity from both sides,
(c) multiply *every term* in an equation by the same quantity,
(d) divide *every term* in an equation by the same quantity,
(e) raise both sides by the same power.

Use these results in the following questions.

Q 3.7 Self-assessment question

(a) Make y the subject of the equation if $x = 2y - 6$.
(b) Make v the subject of the equation given that

$$F = \frac{mv^2}{r} \blacksquare$$

Q 3.8 Self-assessment question

The p.d. V between the terminals of a cell is given by

$$V = \frac{R}{R + r} \cdot E$$

where E is the e.m.f., R is the resistance of the external circuit and r is the cell's internal resistance.

Make r the subject of the formula and find the internal resistance of a cell of e.m.f. 1.5 V which has a terminal p.d. of 1.2 V when connected to an external resistance of 2.0 Ω. $\blacksquare$

Solving equations

The solution to the last question was obtained by making the unknown quantity (the internal resistance) the subject of the equation and **substituting** the known values of all the other variables. It is, of course, equally correct to substitute first and then change the subject.

If there are two unknowns, then it is necessary to have enough information to construct two separate equations containing these same two variables. These are called **simultaneous equations** and to solve them it is necessary to:

(a) combine them to eliminate one of the unknown variables (this will produce a single equation with one unknown),
(b) solve this equation,
(c) substitute the result of step (b) in either equation to obtain the second unknown.

If you have learned about matrices you can also use them in solving simultaneous equations.

Q 3.9 Development question

$$2x + 4y = 19 \tag{1}$$

$$x - y = -1 \tag{2}$$

(a) Multiply equation (2) by 4 and add this equation to equation (1) to eliminate y. What is the value of x?
(b) Substitute this value of x in equation (2) and so find y. $\blacksquare$

Q 3.10 Self-assessment question

A cell has a p.d. of 2.5 V between its terminals when it supplies current to an external resistance of 2.0 Ω. The terminal p.d. changes to 2.8 V when the external resistance is 5.6 Ω. What is the internal resistance and e.m.f. of the cell? (*Hint.* Use the equation stated in question 3.8 and obtain simultaneous equations.)■

Proportionality

If x represents an independent variable and y the dependent variable (i.e. the value of y depends on the value of x) then if y is **directly proportional** to x, we write

$$y \propto x$$

This means that doubling the value of x will always result in a doubling of y, trebling x will treble y, when x is halved, y will be halved, etc. We can express this in another way: the ratio of y/x has a constant value, i.e.

$$y/x = k \quad \text{or} \quad y = kx$$

Q 3.11 Self-assessment question

(a) Given that $y \propto x$, fill in the blanks below.

x:	12	10	8	6	_	_	0	−2
y:	_	25	_	15	10	5	_	_

(b) Write an equation expressing y in terms of x.
(c) Write an equation expressing x in terms of y.■

Q 3.12 Self-assessment question

The following readings were taken in an experiment measuring current I in a wire when the p.d. across it is V.

I/A	1.25	2.15	3.15
V/V	1.37	2.35	3.45

(a) Is this an example of direct proportionality?
(b) What is the constant of proportionality k? What is the unit of k?
(c) What kind of graph would be obtained if V was plotted against I?■

Two variables are **inversely proportional** to each other if when one variable is doubled, the other is halved. As one variable increases, the other decreases, but the product has a constant value

$$xy = k \quad \text{or} \quad y = k\frac{1}{x}$$

i.e. y is proportional to the inverse or reciprocal of x.

Q 3.13 Self-assessment question

(a) The frequency of the note emitted by a stretched string plucked at its midpoint is inversely proportional to the length of the string. Here are some experimental results. Suggest what the missing readings might be.

Length/mm	500	—	—	250
Frequency/Hz	256	320	384	512

(b) Write an equation relating length *l* and frequency *f* and state the unit of the constant of proportionality.
(c) Sketch a graph of frequency against length.■

In this A-level Physics course you will be dealing with many different relationships involving proportionality, not just *x* proportional to *y*, but a quantity inversely proportional to the square of another

$$p \propto \frac{1}{q^2}$$

or a quantity directly proportional to the square root of another

$$l \propto m^{1/2}$$

Q 3.14 Self-assessment question

(a) The time of swing or period *T* of a pendulum of fixed length *l* is inversely proportional to the square root of the acceleration due to gravity *g*. Write an equation to express this relationship.
(b) If a pendulum on earth has a time of swing of 2 s what will its time of swing be on the moon where the acceleration due to gravity is 1/6 of the value on earth?■

Often a quantity depends on more than one variable. We can write proportionalities which are true, not only when two quantities vary, but which are true when several quantities vary.

Q 3.15 Development question*

(a) The gravitational force *F* between two points masses m_1 and m_2 is inversely proportional to the square of the distance *d* between them if masses m_1 and m_2 are constant.

Write down a proportionality which expresses the inverse square law relationship between *F* and *d*.
(b) If mass m_1 is doubled (keeping m_2 and *d* fixed) the gravitational attraction force is doubled. How can you express this relationship?
(c) If mass m_2 is doubled (keeping m_1 and *d* fixed) the attraction force is doubled. How can you express this relationship?
(d) Write a proportionality which shows how *F* depends on m_1, m_2 and *d* when all these quantities are varying.■

Q 3.16 Self-assessment question

The pressure of a fixed mass of gas is thought to be inversely proportional to its volume if the temperature is fixed, and directly proportional to its absolute temperature when the volume is kept constant. Suggest a relationship which shows how pressure *p* depends on volume *V* and absolute temperature *T*. Do the following results support this relationship?

Pressure/Pa $\times 10^5$	1.0	1.2	1.5
Volume/m^3 $\times 10^{-5}$	7.2	7.0	6.0
Temperature/K	300	350	375

■

3.5 | Graphs

(a) A graph can display a relationship between two variables.

(b) A graph also shows at what point a particular relationship ceases to be true (e.g. a straight line may change into a curve).

(c) A graph can be used to determine the constants in an equation relating two quantities.

Linear graphs

A straight line graph has a constant gradient. The gradient is the change in the value of the variable plotted on the vertical axis (ordinate or y-axis) divided by the corresponding change in the value of the variable plotted on the horizontal axis (abscissa or x-axis). In figure 3.2 the two parallel straight line graphs represent different relationships between x and y but both have a gradient of $\frac{1}{2}$ since variable y always changes by 1 when variable x changes by 2. (The **gradient** measures the rate at which y changes with x.)

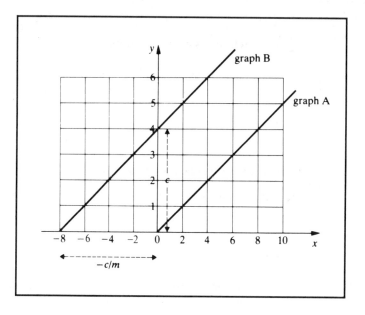

Figure 3.2

Note. The visual steepness of the line depends on what scales are used on the graph but the gradient does not, because lengths are measured from the scales on the axes (i.e. the gradient compares changes in the values of two variables and does *not* compare two *actual lengths*).

For graph A (figure 3.2) the value of y is always half the value of x and it presents the equation $y = \frac{1}{2}x$. $y = mx$ is the general equation of a straight line graph through the origin. A direct proportionality is indicated graphically by a straight line through the origin.

The equation of graph B (figure 3.2) must be

$$y = \tfrac{1}{2}x + 4$$

since the gradient is $\frac{1}{2}$ and when $x = 0, y = 4$. The general equation of a straight line graph is $y = mx + c$ where m is the gradient and c is the intercept on the y-axis.

Measuring the gradient of a straight line graph

Select two points A and B (see figure 3.3) on the line which you have drawn. These need not be points plotted from your observations. Choose points which are well separated.

Record from the graph the values of x_A, y_A, x_B and y_B and then the gradient

$$m = \frac{y_B - y_A}{x_B - x_A} = \frac{BN}{NA}$$

If possible, choose points A and B so that $x_B - x_A$ is a whole number or simple decimal (e.g. 2 or 0.5 or 0.005, not 2.73 or 0.0047) to avoid any unnecessary complication of the arithmetic when finding m.

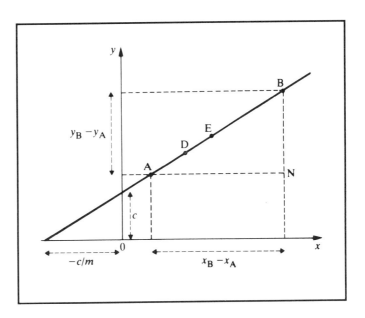

Figure 3.3

Q 3.17 Discussion question

Why should well-separated points A and B be chosen in preference to points D and E?■

Measuring the intercepts

The intercept on the y-axis is the constant c in the general equation $y = mx + c$. The intercept on the x-axis, that is, when y is zero, is $-c/m$.

It is easy to read off these values when the graph is plotted with the real origin $(x = 0, y = 0)$ on the paper.

However, to enable the plotted points to be spread across the whole graph paper, a graph is often plotted which does not include the true origin $(0,0)$, see figure 3.4.

To find the value of c in such instances:

(a) find the value of the gradient m using two points A and B on the line, then

(b) calculate c from this value of m and the coordinates of one point, e.g. x_B, y_B

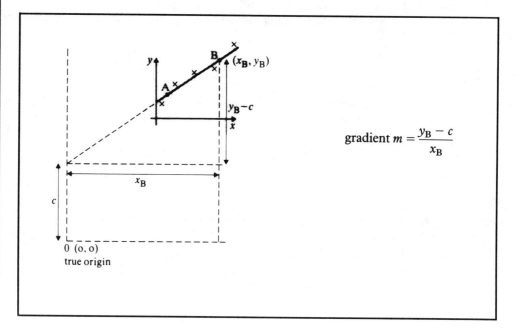

gradient $m = \dfrac{y_B - c}{x_B}$

Figure 3.4

Q 3.18 Development question

Use the above method to show that the graph shown in figure 3.5 has the same equation as graph B in figure 3.2.∎

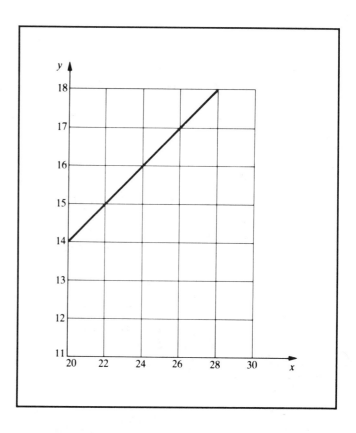

Figure 3.5

Q 3.19 Self-assessment question

The resistance R_θ of a coil at temperature θ can be expressed by the equation

$$R_\theta = R_0(1 + \alpha\theta)$$

where R_0 is the resistance at 0 °C and α is the temperature coefficient of resistance.

Use the following data to test the validity of this equation. Label the axes, choose suitable scales and from your graph obtain a value for α.

R_θ/Ω	$\theta/°C$
23.7	14
25.2	29
26.4	44
27.8	58
29.8	81
31.7	100

The results of an experiment may show that two variables are related by an equation (like that stated in question 3.19) at least within the range of values investigated in the experiment.

If we assume that the same relationship may be true beyond this range of values considered in the experiment, then we can extend the graph. This process is called **extrapolation**.

For example, if you obtain a straight line graph from a set of results, you can extend the straight line to obtain by extrapolation some values of the variables outside the range of your observations. This is often a useful way of predicting likely results but you must remember the big assumption on which extrapolation is based.

Q 3.20 Self-assessment question

Use the graph you drew in answer to question 3.19 to obtain by extrapolation the value of R_θ when the temperature is -100 °C.■

Non-linear graphs

Figure 3.6 shows sketch graphs of some familiar relationships in physics.

(a) An **inverse proportion** graph.
A graph (figure 3.6a) of p against V for an ideal gas at constant temperature expresses the relationship $p \propto 1/V$. Since

$$pV = k$$
$$AB \times EB = CD \times DF = k$$

(b) A **square law** graph.
A graph (figure 3.6b) of distance travelled s against time taken t for motion with constant acceleration has an equation $s = \frac{1}{2}at^2$.
(c) An **inverse square law** graph.
A graph (figure 3.6c) of force F between electric charges at different distances d has an equation $F = k/d^2$.

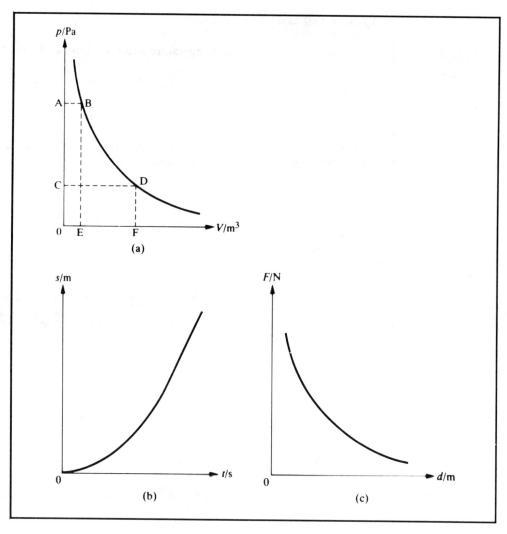

Figure 3.6

Q 3.21 Self-assessment question

Plot the graphs of:
(a) power consumption P in a constant 2.0 Ω resistor for different currents I if $P = I^2R$; plot I from 0 to 5.0 A;
(b) potential V against distance r if $V = 10/r$; plot r from 0 to 10 m. What is the value of r when $V = r$?■

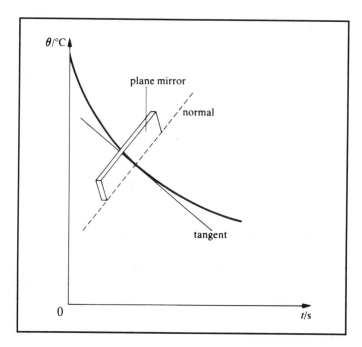

Figure 3.7

A non-linear graph indicates that one variable is not changing at a constant rate as the other variable changes. For example, if a hot object is cooling down, a graph of its temperature (the dependent variable – ordinate) against time (the independent variable – abscissa) will not be a straight line. The temperature will fall most steeply when the body is very hot and the slope will get less steep as it cools (figure 3.7). The gradient of the curve at a particular temperature will tell us the rate at which the temperature is falling at that point.

The gradient of the curve at a particular point is found by measuring the gradient of the tangent to the curve at that point. A good method for drawing a tangent is to use a plane mirror (figure 3.7). Turn the mirror until the curve and its reflection in the mirror appear as one continuous curve (no sharp kink). The mirror surface is then normal to the curve and the tangent can be drawn perpendicular to this normal. Another way is to use a piece of capillary tubing instead of a mirror. When the tubing lies along the normal the curve passes through it without any deviation being observed from above.

Linear graphs from non-linear equations

The aim of many experiments is to find an equation relating two variables. If the graph obtained by plotting these two variables is a straight line, it is an easy matter to measure the slope and intercept and write out an equation in the form $y = mx + c$. If the graph is a curve, the solution is not so simple but it is often possible to choose the variables so that a straight line is obtained. Here are distances moved by a trolley from rest after various times.

Time t/s	Distance s/m
0.8	0.141
1.3	0.372
1.9	0.794
2.3	1.113
2.9	1.850

By looking at the numbers given you can tell that if s is plotted against t the graph will not be a straight line since s increases much more rapidly than t because the trolley is accelerating. Can we discover whether the trolley has uniform acceleration? If it does, then $s = \frac{1}{2}at^2$ and a graph of s against t^2 would give a straight line of gradient $a/2$.

$$s = (\tfrac{1}{2}a)t^2$$
$$y = (m)x$$

Q 3.22 Self-assessment question

Use the above data to plot a graph of s against t^2 and test whether the motion shows uniform acceleration. ■

Q 3.23 Self-assessment question

How would you check graphically whether experimental results fit the following equations?

(a) $F = k/r^2$ where k is constant
(b) $E = \frac{1}{2}mv^2$ where m is constant
(c) $T = 2\pi\sqrt{\dfrac{l}{g}}$ where g is constant
(d) $V = \dfrac{RE}{R + r}$ when E and r are constant ■

Log graphs

Sometimes, two variables are related by an equation of the form

$$y = Ax^n$$

where A and n are unknown constants.

We can use trial and error to try to find n but this would involve graphing, for example,

y against x^2 y against $x^{1/3}$ y against $\dfrac{1}{x}$

to try to obtain a straight line and, in the end, we might give up without getting a solution.

However, we can say that

$$\log y = \log Ax^n$$
$$\therefore \log y = \log x^n + \log A$$
$$\therefore \log y = n\log x + \log A$$

A graph of $\log y$ against $\log x$ would be a straight line. The constant n is the gradient and the intercept is $\log A$. From this graph we would be able to deduce the expression relating y and x.

Q 3.24 Self-assessment question

Under certain conditions (when heat cannot flow into or out of the gas) the pressure p and volume V of a gas are related by the equation

$$pV^\gamma = k$$

where γ and k are constants.

If you obtained experimental data under these conditions, what graph would you plot to find the values of γ and k and how would the graph indicate these constants?∎

Distribution curves

Figure 3.8 is a typical graph of the relationship between two continuously varying quantities, in this case, the photon energy W and wavelength λ of electromagnetic radiation. It enables us to know the value of the energy for *any* value of wavelength over the range of the graph.

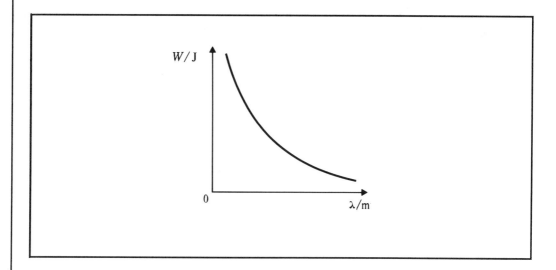

Figure 3.8

Figure 3.9 is a different kind of graph, called a **histogram**. It tells us about the speed of vehicles passing a recording point on a motorway. Suppose we count the number of cars passing in a fixed interval. The histogram records the number of cars passing during this interval in a particular speed range (e.g. 50–60 m s^{-1}). Each rectangle indicates by its height or area the number of vehicles in a particular speed range. Although the horizontal axis marks speed it cannot be read like an ordinary graph. The speed axis does not change continuously, but in steps from one speed range to the next. The graph cannot tell us whether any cars had a speed of 68.5 m s^{-1} past the recording point – only the number of cars in different groups. To obtain more detailed information we would need to divide the speed into smaller and smaller ranges and take readings for thousands of vehicles. Then we might get a graph like figure 3.10. In this graph the vertical axis is changed, so that now the *area* of each strip can be made to represent the number of cars passing in the given time in a very narrow speed range with speeds between 62 and 64 m s^{-1} (7 cars s m^{-1} × 2 m s^{-1} = 14 cars).

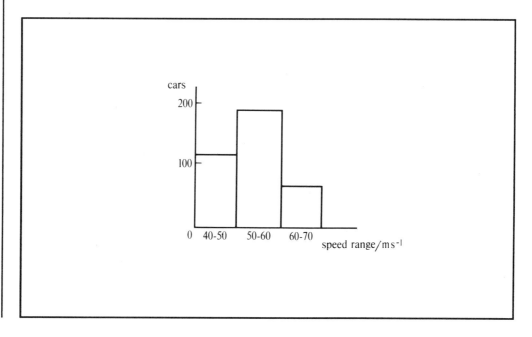

Figure 3.9

Q 3.25 Self-assessment question

What would the total area of all the strips in figure 3.10 represent? Use figure 3.10 to estimate this quantity and say whether figure 3.9 might be recording the same data in the 60–70 m.p.h. range.■

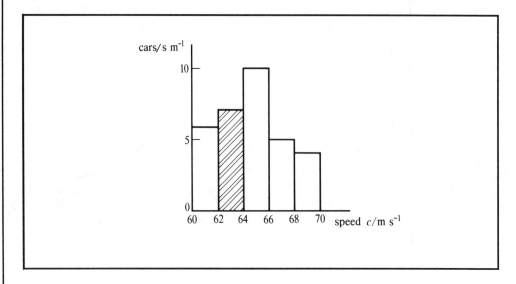

Figure 3.10

In studying gases we are dealing with so many molecules that their speeds can be represented by a smooth distribution curve, and the area of any strip under the curve represents the number of molecules in that speed range (figure 3.11). Consider what the vertical axis represents in figure 3.11. It is labelled number of molecules, N_c.

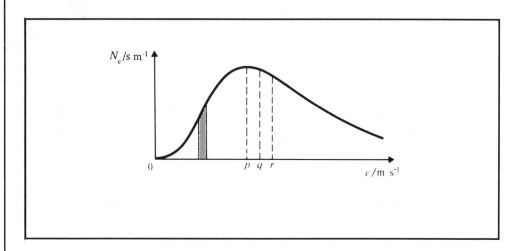

Figure 3.11

Since the number of molecules in a given speed range is represented by the area of a strip, we can write

$$\text{number of molecules with speeds between } c \text{ and } c + \Delta c = N_c \Delta c$$

The symbol Δ is used to indicate a small increase or increment so that $c + \Delta c$ is slightly larger than c. See section 3.8 for further details.

Q 3.26 Self-assessment question

The speed range Δc will have units m s^{-1}. What is the unit of N_c? What does the shaded area in figure 3.11 represent? What are the units of this area?■

3.7 | Geometry and trigonometry

'As no man is born an artist, so no man is born an angler.' (Izaac Walton, Compleat Angler)

The results below should be familiar and are quoted for convenient reference.

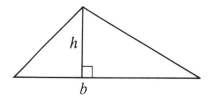

- Area of any triangle $= \frac{1}{2}bh$

- Area of a right-angled triangle $= \frac{1}{2}ab$

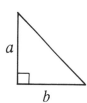

- Circumference of a circle $= 2\pi r$

- Area within a circle $= \pi r^2$

- Area of a surface of a cuboid $= 2(ab + bc + ca)$

- Volume of a cuboid $= abc$

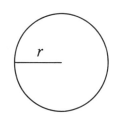

- Area of curved surface of a cylinder $= 2\pi rh$

- Area of ends of a cylinder $= \pi r^2$ each

- Total surface of a cylinder $= 2\pi r(r + h)$

- Volume of a cylinder $= \pi r^2 h$

- Volume of a sphere $= \frac{4}{3}\pi r^3$

- Surface area of a sphere $= 4\pi r^2$

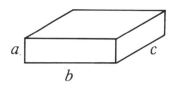

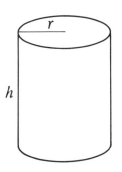

Figure 3.12

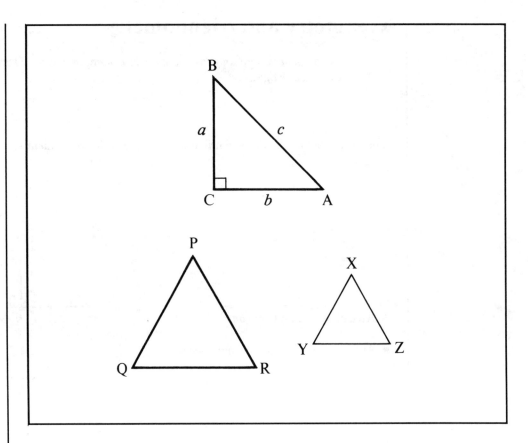

Figure 3.13

Triangles

- For a right-angled triangle

$$a^2 + b^2 = c^2 \text{ (Pythagoras' Theorem)}$$

- The angles of a triangle add up in all cases to two right angles

$$\hat{A} + \hat{B} + \hat{C} = 180° = \pi \text{ radians}$$

- Triangles are called **similar** when all the corresponding angles are equal, so they are the same shape.

△ PQR and △ XYZ are similar.

$$\text{if } \hat{P} = \hat{X} \quad \text{and} \quad \hat{Q} = \hat{Y} \quad \text{then} \quad \hat{R} = \hat{Z}$$

For similar triangles ratios of corresponding sides are equal. There are two versions:

$$PQ : QR : RP = XY : YZ : ZX$$

$$\frac{PQ}{XY} = \frac{QR}{YZ} = \frac{RP}{ZX}$$

For a right-angled triangle

$$\sin A = \frac{BC}{BA} = \frac{a}{c} \qquad \tan A = \frac{BC}{BA} = \frac{b}{a}$$

$$\cos A = \frac{AC}{BA} = \frac{b}{c}$$

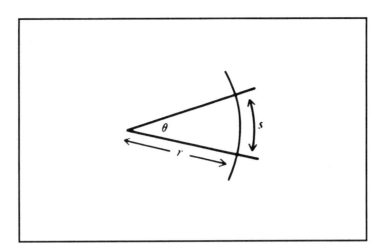

Figure 3.14

Angular measure

Angles are measured in radians or degrees.

Angle θ (figure 3.14) in radians is the ratio of the distance s along a circular arc subtended by θ divided by the radius r.

$$\theta = \frac{s}{r}$$

One **radian** is an angle subtended by the arc of a circle with length equal to the radius. If $s = r$, then $\theta = 1$ radian.

$$2\pi \text{ radian} \equiv 360°$$

Thus
$$1 \text{ radian} \equiv \frac{360°}{2\pi} = 57°18' \ (57.3°)$$

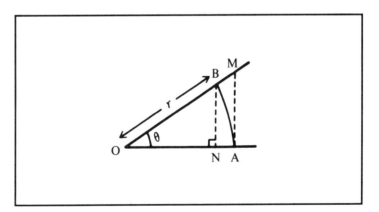

Figure 3.15

Trigonometrical relationships

In figure 3.15

$$\sin \theta = \frac{BN}{OB} = \frac{BN}{r}, \quad \tan \theta = \frac{AM}{OA}, \quad \theta = \frac{\text{arc } AB}{r}$$

For *very small* angles: $BN \approx$ arc $AB \approx AM$ and so

$$\sin \theta \approx \tan \theta \approx \theta \text{ (for very small angles)}$$

but
$$\cos \theta \approx 1$$

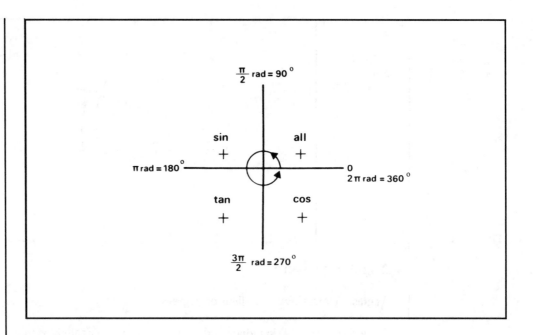

Figure 3.16

Figure 3.16 shows the quadrants in which a particular trigonometrical function is positive and figure 3.17 shows graphs of these functions from 0 to 2π.

For all angles

$$\tan \theta = \sin \theta / \cos \theta \quad \sin^2 \theta + \cos^2 \theta = 1$$

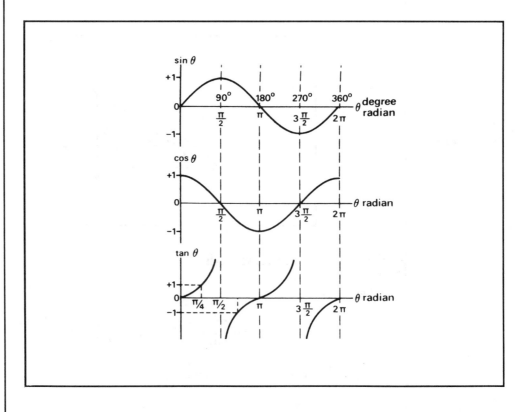

Figure 3.17

Angular velocity and angular acceleration

When a body is rotating about an axis its motion is described in terms of the angle moved through by a point on the body, i.e. the angular displacement θ (figure 3.18).

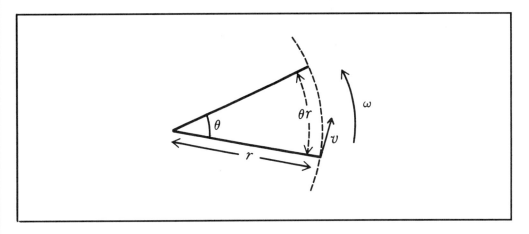

Figure 3.18

angular velocity ω = rate of change of angular displacement

The unit of angular velocity is the radian per second, rad s^{-1}.

For constant angular velocity

$$\omega = \frac{\text{angle moved through in time } t}{\text{time}}$$

$$\omega = \frac{\theta}{t}$$

If a point is distance r from the axis of rotation and has a linear speed v

$$\text{linear speed} = \frac{\text{distance travelled along an arc}}{\text{time taken}}$$

$$v = \frac{s}{t} = \frac{\theta r}{t}$$

Hence
$$v = r\omega$$

$$\text{linear speed} = \text{radius} \times \text{angular velocity}$$

The angular acceleration α is equal to the rate of change of angular velocity and is measured in radian per second squared, rad s^{-2}.

If the angular velocity is changing, then

$$\text{linear acceleration} = \text{radius} \times \text{angular acceleration}$$

$$a = r\alpha$$

Q 3.27 Self-assessment question

(a) If the edge of a disc is moving at a speed of 20 m s^{-1} and the radius of the disc is 0.5 m, what is its angular velocity?
(b) What is the rim speed in m s^{-1} of a 12″ LP record being played at 33 r.p.m. (assume 1″ = 2.5 cm)?■

3.8

Calculus

'The solution of the difficulties which formerly surrounded the mathematical infinite is probably the greatest achievement of which our age can boast.'
(Bertrand Russell)

Differential and integral calculus provide important tools for analysing and expressing relationships in physics. In this A-level course, there are sections which can be developed using calculus and these are treated as *extension* sections for those familiar with the methods of calculus.

Wherever possible, the physical concepts are developed without the need for a knowledge of methods of differentiation and integration.

However, the basic ideas in calculus and the notation developed provide a convenient way of expressing ideas in physics; these are outlined below as an introduction to their use in the units.

Rates of change

A straight line graph expresses a proportionality between two variables (see section 3.5) and the gradient of the straight line indicates the rate at which one variable changes with the other. How can the rate of change be obtained for a non-linear relationship?

Figure 3.19 shows a graph of displacement s (distance travelled from the start) against time t for a moving object.

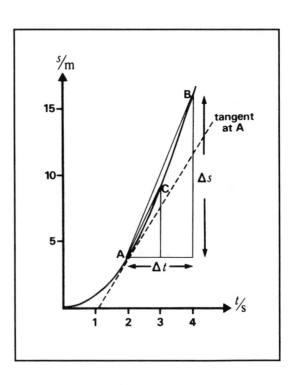

Figure 3.19

The rate of change of distance with time is the speed of the body. Can we find the speed at A when the time is 2.0 s from the start? We use the symbol Δt to indicate a change in time and Δs to indicate the change in displacement which occurs during that time.

Between 2.0 s and 4.0 s the object moves from 4.0 m to 16.0 m from the start.

Thus $\Delta s = 12.0\,\text{m}$ and $\Delta t = 2.0\,\text{s}$

The average speed in this interval is $6.0\,\text{m s}^{-1}$.

$\Delta s / \Delta t$ is the average speed in interval Δt and is the gradient of chord AB.

In the time between $t = 2.0$ s and $t = 3.0$ s the displacement changes from $s = 4.0$ m to $s = 9.0$ m.

The gradient of chord AC gives the average speed between 2.0 s and 3.0 s.

$$\frac{\Delta s}{\Delta t} = \frac{5}{1}\,\text{m s}^{-1} = 5\,\text{m s}^{-1}$$

Between $t = 2.0$ s and $t = 2.5$ s the displacement changes from 4.0 m to 6.25 m.

then $$\frac{\Delta s}{\Delta t} = \frac{2.25}{0.5}\,\text{m s}^{-1} = 4.5\,\text{m s}^{-1}$$

For the time interval between $t = 2.0$ s and $t = 2.1$ s

$$\text{average speed} = \frac{\Delta s}{\Delta t} = \frac{0.41}{0.1}\,\text{m s}^{-1} = 4.1\,\text{m s}^{-1}$$

If Δt is made smaller and smaller, the value of $\Delta s / \Delta t$ gets closer and closer to the speed when $t = 2.0$ s. This instantaneous speed is indicated by the slope of the tangent to the curve at A which is $4.0\,\text{m s}^{-1}$.

The limiting value of $\Delta s / \Delta t$ is written as ds/dt and is called the **differential coefficient**.

$$\frac{ds}{dt} = \lim_{\Delta t \to 0} \left(\frac{\Delta s}{\Delta t} \right)$$

ds/dt expresses the gradient of the graph of s against t and gives the instantaneous value of the speed at any point on the graph.

$$v = \frac{ds}{dt}$$

Q 3.28 Self-assessment question

Use calculus notation to express acceleration in terms of velocity and time. How does a graph of velocity against time indicate acceleration?■

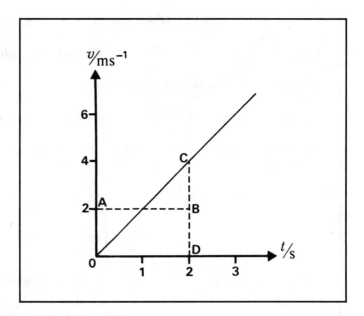

Figure 3.20

Areas and integration

The velocity of a moving body can be found (by differentiation) from a graph of displacement s against time t because $v = ds/dt$. Figure 3.20 shows the same motion as figure 3.19 but it is now represented on a graph of velocity v against time t. Can we obtain the distance travelled s from this graph by using a process which is the reverse of differentiation?

Since velocity is increasing steadily we can say

$$\text{distance travelled in 2.0 s} = \text{average speed} \times \text{time taken}$$
$$= 2.0 \text{ m s}^{-1} \times 2.0 \text{ s} = 4.0 \text{ m}$$

This is represented by the area of rectangle OABD or the area of triangle OCD ($\frac{1}{2} \times 4.0 \text{ m s}^{-1} \times 2.0 \text{ s}$).

Hence, in this case:

distance travelled in 2.0 s is represented by the area below the graph (between 0 and 2.0 s).

This is an important result but we must ask if it is true even when the graph is non-linear (figure 3.21).

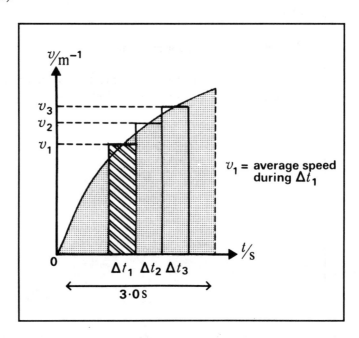

Figure 3.21

It is no use in this case to average over a long period because velocity does not change uniformly. However, if we consider a small time interval Δt_1 during which the average velocity is v_1 we can say that:

distance Δs_1 travelled in Δt_1 is approximately $v_1 \Delta t_1$.

This is only approximately true because the velocity v_1 does not change at a constant rate during the interval. The area of the line-shaded rectangle represents $v_1 \Delta t_1$.

The total distance s travelled in 3.0 s is approximately equal to $v_1 \Delta t_1 + v_2 \Delta t_2 + v_3 \Delta t_3 + \ldots$ added over three seconds. So we write:

$$s \approx \Sigma\, v\Delta t$$

(The symbol Σ means 'the sum of', and $\Sigma\, v\Delta t$ means the sum of all the quantities such as $v_1 \Delta t_1$.)

The distance travelled is thus represented approximately by the sum of the areas of all the strips.

By making the time intervals Δt smaller and so adding up more strips, the total area will more nearly represent the total distance travelled and will more nearly equal the area under the curve.

So we can say:

total distance travelled in 3.0 s is represented by the area under the curve between 0 and 3.0 s, and

$$\text{this area} = \int_0^{3.0} v\,\mathrm{d}t$$

where the sign $\int$ stands for a process of adding up an infinite number of small quantities.

$$\lim_{\Delta t \to 0} \sum_0^{3.0} v\Delta t = \int_0^{3.0} v\,\mathrm{d}t$$

This process is called **integration** and $\int_0^{3.0}$ means 'the integral between 0 and 3.0 s of v with respect to t'.

You will not need to know how to integrate mathematical expressions but in the A-level physics course you will use the fact that the area under the curve represents an integration and provides important data.

Figure 3.22 shows how the force F required to pull back a catapult sling varies with the distance x by which the sling is pulled back.

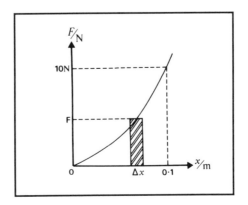

Figure 3.22

If, for a given extension, a nearly constant force F is required to pull back the catapult through a further distance Δx, the work which must be done is $F\Delta x$.

$\Delta W = F\Delta x$ and is represented by the area of the shaded strip.

If W is the total work done in pulling back the catapult by 0.1 m then W is represented by the total area under the curve from $x = 0$ to $x = 0.1$ m.

$$W = \lim_{x \to 0} \sum_0^{0.1} F\Delta x = \int_0^{0.1} F \, dx$$

Q 3.29 Self-assessment question

(a) By considering gradients and areas, what can you deduce from the graphs shown in figure 3.23a?

(b) The graphs as shown in figure 3.23b are obtained by stretching different wires. For each graph calculate the work done in increasing the extension from 3.0 mm to 6.0 mm. ■

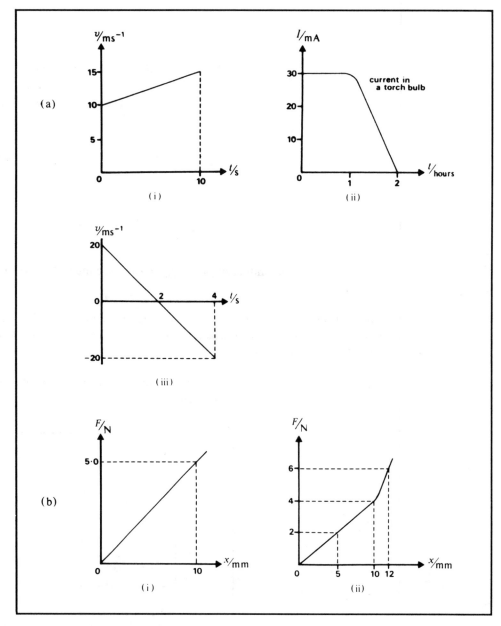

Figure 3.23

Vectors

> *"'Clearly"* the Time Traveller proceeded, *"any real body must have extension in four directions; it must have length, breadth, thickness and duration."'*
> (H. G. Wells, *The Time Machine*)

Many quantities are such that one number, and the unit, give a full statement of the quantity. They are called **scalar quantities**. Examples of these are time, mass and energy, and, in particular instances, these could have magnitudes 2.4 s, 3.81 kg or 7.63×10^6 J.

In contrast, some quantities are not fully specified unless a direction is also stated. These are called **vector quantities**. Examples of these are force, velocity and momentum. Full statements about them must include a direction, for example 9.81 N downwards, 15.3 m s^{-1} N 33°E, or 5.83×10^9 kg m s^{-1} at an angle 78° to the horizontal in a vertical plane 3.00° N of E.

While scalar quantities can be added algebraically, taking into account any negative values, vectors must be added geometrically. This is done according to the rules which apply to successive movements in space. In fact, vector quantities can be *defined* as those which are added in this way.

Adding displacements

The word 'displacement' is used to mean 'distance in a certain direction'. It is the simplest possible vector quantity. The addition of displacements is familiar. If you walk 30 m north and then 40 m east you end up in a position 50 m from your starting point, in a direction N 53°8' E (see figure 3.24). 53°8' = arctan (4/3) and distance from starting point = $(30^2 + 40^2)^{1/2}$ m = 50 m.

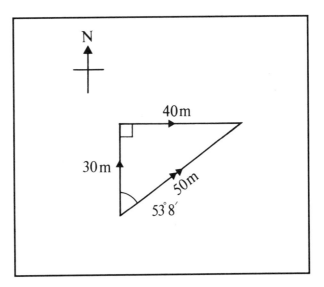

Figure 3.24

Similarly, any two successive displacements can be added by putting them 'nose to tail'.

Adding more than two displacements is simple. They are all put nose to tail in a scale drawing and the resultant R joins the start of the first to the end of the last as illustrated in figure 3.25.

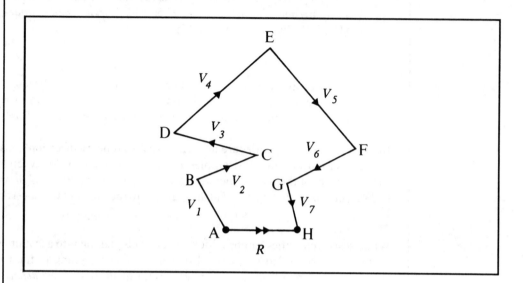

Figure 3.25

Q 3.30 Self-assessment question

What difference would it make if you put the displacements in figure 3.25 in a different order?■

Alternative symbols for vectors are bold letters, or letters with a line above them.

Q 3.31 Self-assessment question

How would you go about adding displacements which are not confined to one plane, for example, movements around a building with several floors?■

Resolving displacements

Often it is useful to split a vector quantity. We speak of 'resolving a vector' into its components in specified directions, usually at right angles to each other. (Oblique components are possible but not useful because they are not independent of each other.)

For example, the displacement of Liverpool Street Station L from Victoria Station V is 5.0 km N 61°23′ E, figure 3.26a. However, it is easier to use the component displacements east and north.

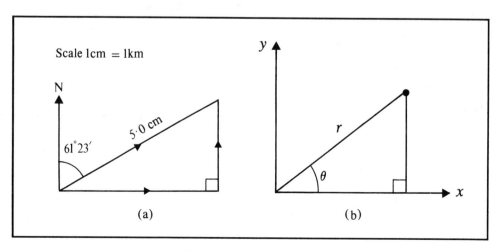

Figure 3.26

Q 3.32 Self-assessment question

(a) What are the easterly and northerly components of this displacement?
(b) In general, what are the components of a displacement of magnitude r in a direction making an angle θ with the x-axis (figure 3.26b)?■

The rule to be remembered is

$$x = r \cos \theta; \quad y = r \sin \theta$$

conversely

$$r^2 = x^2 + y^2; \quad \theta = \arctan(y/x)$$

Adding and resolving other vectors

The other vectors you are likely to meet are velocity, momentum, acceleration and force.

Each behaves in the same way as displacement, so a simple way to deal with them is by representing each individual vector quantity by a line on paper, i.e. by a displacement, to a given scale.

Q 3.33 Self-assessment question

An aircraft has an air speed of 350 knots in a westerly direction but experiences a cross-wind of 50 knots in a northerly direction. What is its ground speed and direction?■

In answering that question you may have seen that an accurate scale representation was not necessary: a sketch and calculation was a valid approach.

Q 3.34 Self-assessment question

A car of mass 1000 kg is at rest on a steep hill, gradient 1 in 4. What is (a) the force of the road on the car, normal to the road, (b) the frictional force along the road?■

Q 3.35 Self-assessment question

An aircraft of weight 250 kN experiences a thrust from its engines of 200 kN in a direction 20° above the horizontal, and a drag of 20 kN in the opposite direction. The lift from the wings is 240 kN at right-angles to the thrust. What is the net force on the aircraft?■

The **parallelogram of forces** can be used to add vectors. The lines of action of the forces pass through the same point and a parallelogram, to scale, is constructed: the diagonal through the same point represents the resultant. This is an alternative version of the vector diagram (see figures 3.27a and 3.27b).

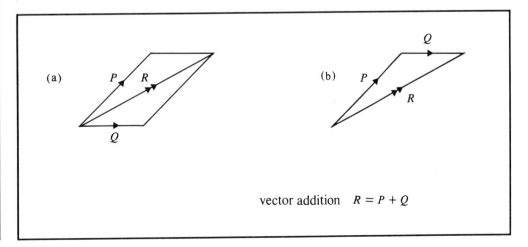

Figure 3.27

If more than two vectors are to be added, the parallelogram method is cumbersome.

The **polygon of forces** is a convenient method of solving problems involving bodies in equilibrium under a number of non-parallel forces.

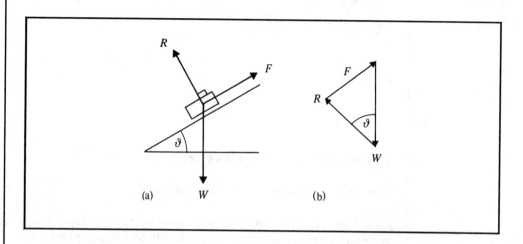

Figure 3.28

Consider the example in figure 3.28a: a body of weight W is held on a smooth slope by a force F, parallel to the slope.

A triangle of forces (figure 3.28b) can be drawn representing the three forces W, F and the normal reaction R, in magnitude and direction.

Problems can be solved for an unknown force by scale drawing or by trigonometry.

Q 3.35 Self-assessment question

What force is required, applied parallel to the slope, to hold a body of weight 10 N, on a smooth slope inclined at 30° to the horizontal?■

Equilibrium

A body is in equilibrium if there is no resultant force or moment on it. This means there is no linear or angular acceleration: the body may be at rest *or* moving with constant linear or angular velocity (or both).

Besides having a magnitude and a direction, a force has a line along which it acts: the force acts in a specific direction from a certain point (the point of application).

For example, the metre stick in figure 3.29a is in equilibrium, but that in figure 3.29b is not, even though the resultant force is zero: there is a net turning effect (couple).

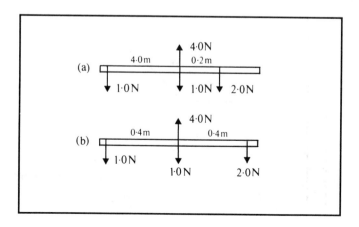

Figure 3.29

When there is a resultant force, we can say the line of action of two parallel forces is as indicated in figure 3.30.

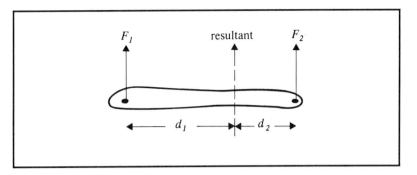

Figure 3.30

A force F, not through the centre of mass O of a body (figure 3.31a), may be resolved into a force F through the centre of mass and a couple Fd (figure 3.31b).

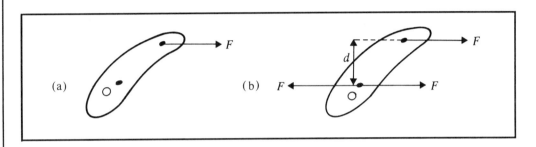

Figure 3.31

Then $F = ma$ and $T = I\alpha$, where m is the mass, a the linear acceleration, T the moment of the couple, I the moment of inertia and α the angular acceleration.

Q 3.37 Self-assessment question

A space station, of mass 3.0×10^4 kg and moment of inertia 3.0×10^5 kg m^2, experiences a rocket thrust of 100 N perpendicular to its radius at 10 m from its centre of mass. Calculate its linear and angular accelerations. ∎

Vectors and modern mathematics

The term **vector** is used in mathematics to mean a set of numbers in order, and the individual numbers are called **components**. There are row vectors, e.g. (12,5), and column vectors, e.g. $\begin{pmatrix} 12 \\ 5 \end{pmatrix}$. An essential feature is that vectors are added by adding the components

$$\begin{pmatrix} 12 \\ 5 \end{pmatrix} + \begin{pmatrix} -2 \\ 4 \end{pmatrix} = \begin{pmatrix} 10 \\ 9 \end{pmatrix}$$

It is obvious that mathematical vectors can form a useful representation of physical vector quantities. For vector quantities in three dimensions 3-vectors (with 3 components) are needed.

In displacements, row vectors are often used to represent positions (very similar to map references) and column vectors to represent actual displacements. For example, from (829,116) to (865,130) is $\begin{pmatrix} 36 \\ 14 \end{pmatrix}$.

It is possible to operate on vectors by means of matrices, and you may have learned something about matrix algebra. This can be applied in the context of physical vector quantities, but is beyond the scope of this book. If you are interested consult a book on applied mathematics.

Exponentials

'Change and decay in all around I see.' (H. F. Lyte, from the hymn *Abide with me*)

Quantities flow in and out of systems and very often the changes can be described by a fairly simple equation. If the rate of change of a quantity depends on its magnitude then the rate of change may well be exponential.

Situations that we might consider are:

• a water cistern with a leak in the bottom – the rate of leakage gets less as the pressure falls;

• a capacitor being charged to a given voltage – the charge grows more slowly as full charge is approached: when the capacitor is discharged through a resistor, its rate of decay shrinks as the charge declines;

• a pendulum swinging in air – the amplitude decreases but at a smaller and smaller rate as time goes by.

We look for an equation to describe such changes.

Consider a capacitor of capacitance C which is being discharged through a resistor of resistance R (figure 3.32a). The initial charge is Q_0. The remaining charge Q is measured at time t and a graph is plotted, figure 3.32b.

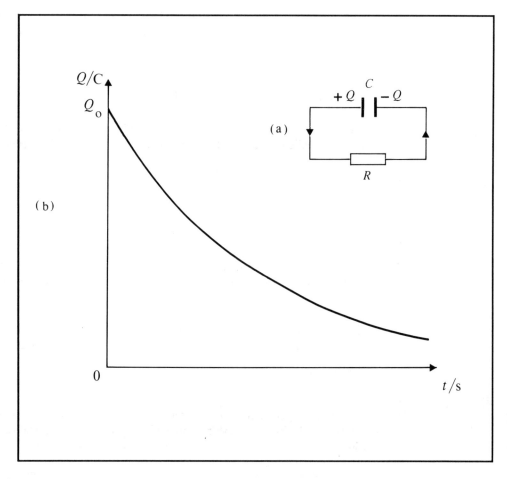

Figure 3.32

We may notice that:

(a) The charge halves every second. (For a different RC circuit it would halve at some other time interval.) For a quantity decaying exponentially there is a constant **half-life**.
(b) The (negative) gradient decreases as the charge decreases: in fact the gradient is proportional to the remaining charge.

We can say $dQ/dt = -kQ$ and, if we wish to test that this relationship is true, plot a graph of gradient (dQ/dt) against charge to see if it is a straight line of gradient $-k$. However, this method is clumsy.

Let us start again.

$$dQ/dt = -kQ \qquad (1)$$

$$\int \frac{dQ}{Q} = -k \int dt$$

$$\ln Q = -kt + c \text{ where } c \text{ is a constant of integration}$$

When $\qquad\qquad t = 0, \quad Q = Q_0 \quad \text{so} \quad \ln Q_0 = c$

and $\qquad\qquad \ln Q = -kt + \ln Q_0 \qquad (2)$

So an exponential decay will yield the graph shown in figure 3.33.

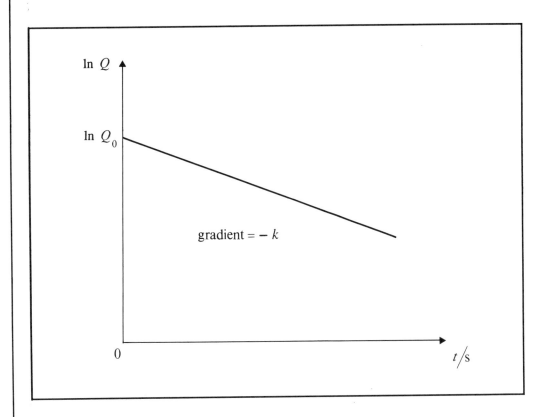

Figure 3.33

We can change equation (2) to

$$\ln \frac{Q}{Q_0} = -kt$$

or

$$\frac{Q}{Q_0} = e^{-kt}$$

so

$$Q = Q_0 e^{-kt} \qquad (3)$$

This is sometimes written $Q = Q_0 \exp(-kt)$.

We see that equations (1), (2) and (3) are equivalent and all represent exponential decay.

Less common in physics is growth with an increasing growth rate. Simple population growth appears to be of this kind, as when bacteria reproduce by doubling the number of cells N at regular intervals:

$$\frac{dN}{dt} = kN \qquad (4)$$

or

$$\ln N = kt + \ln N_0 \qquad (5)$$

where N_0 is the starting number

or

$$N = N_0 e^{kt} \qquad (6)$$

Finally, there may be growth towards an upper limit when $t = \infty$. An example of this is the charging of a capacitor in a circuit of total resistance R, figure 3.34a.

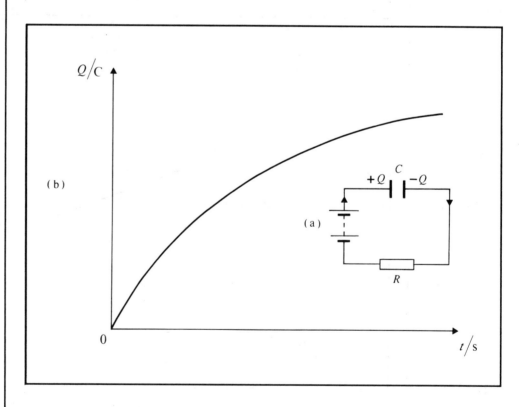

Figure 3.34

This curve (the mirror image of the discharge curve), figure 3.34b, has the equation

$$Q = Q_0(1 - e^{-kt})$$

$k = 1/RC$ where RC is known as the capacitative time constant τ_c.

Q 3.38 Self-assessment question

By considering the units of R and C, show that τ_c has the dimension of time. ■

Q 3.39 Self-assessment question

A bucket, originally full of water, has a hole in the bottom and water leaks out at a leakage rate which depends on the time as follows.

t/s	Rate/cm^3 s^{-1}
0	78
10	60
20	47
30	36
40	28
50	22

(a) Is this leakage an exponential decay? Explain your answer.

(**Hint.** Consider the changes in the rates during equal time intervals.)

(b) What is the rate of leakage when $t = 60$ s, 70 s and 80 s?

(c) If the volume remaining after 80 s was 320 cm^3, how much water was there at the beginning?

(**Hint.** The leakage rate will depend on the volume at any time.)■

Q 3.40 Self-assessment question

The intensity I of a beam of gamma rays after passing through an absorbing material decreases exponentially with the thickness x of the layer.

$$I = I_0\, e^{-\mu x}$$

where I_0 is the intensity of the beam before absorption occurs and μ is a constant for a particular absorber.

In an experiment, the intensity of gamma radiation decreases by 30% after passing through 50 mm of lead.

Calculate

(a) the value of μ for lead, and

(b) the thickness of lead which will reduce the intensity of the gamma ray beam by 50%.

(**Hint.** Express the equation in terms of natural logarithms.)■

Radioactive decay and absorption are two processes which show exponential decay (with time and distance respectively). The result of this is a smooth variation, enabling accurate predictions of radioactivity. This is despite the fact that the disintegration of a radioactive nucleus is a discontinuous and randomly occurring event. The population of nuclei in a sample is so enormous, however, as to make this statistical description valid.

Part 4
Resources for study

4.1 Bibliography

In order to study A-level physics successfully, you will need access to a range of resources. Those particularly recommended are referred to in the student's units. Details of these are given here. Your teacher has an additional list of recommended resources which you may want to consult.

(a) Course texts

These are referred to in the unit by the name in bold print.

AKRILL, T.B., BENNET, G.A.G. and MILLAR, C.J.
Physics.
Edward Arnold, 1979.
ISBN 0 7131 0297 7

BOLTON, W. *Patterns in physics.*
McGraw Hill, 1986 (Second edition).
ISBN 0 0708 4961 7

DUNCAN, T. *Physics: A textbook for advanced level students.*
John Murray, 1987 (Second edition).
ISBN 0 7195 4336 3

MUNCASTER, R. *A-level physics.*
Stanley Thornes, 1985 (Second edition).
ISBN 0 85950 224 4

NELKON, M. and PARKER, P. *Advanced level physics.*
Heinemann Education, 1987 (Sixth edition).
ISBN 0 435 68668 2

ROGERS, E.M. *Physics for the enquiring mind.*
OUP, 1960.
ISBN 0 19 69 0183 9

WENHAM, E.J., DORLING, G. W. SNELL, J. TAYLOR, B.
Physics: Concepts and models.
Longman, 1986 (Second edition).
ISBN 0 582 35580 X

WHELAN, P.M. and HODGSON, M.J. *Essential principles of physics.*
John Murray, 1989 (Second edition)
ISBN 0 7195 4566 8

(b) Books for particular units

Behaviour of matter

COOKE, B. and SANG, D. *Physics of materials for A-level students.*
University of Leeds, 1986.
ISBN 0 9044 2115 5

GORDON, J.E. *The new science of strong materials.*
Penguin, 1976 (second edition).
ISBN 0 14 020920 4

GUINIER, A. *The structure of matter.*
Edward Arnold, 1984.
ISBN 0 7131 3489 5

RAITT, G. Electricity 1 *Circuits.*
CUP, 1987
ISBN 0 521 31085 7

Forces and motion

AKRILL, T.B. and MILLAR, C.J. *Mechanics, vibrations and waves.*
John Murray, 1974.
ISBN 0 7195 2882 8

RAITT, G. Forces: *Building a cantilever bridge.*
CUP, 1987
ISBN 0 521 31084 9

SIMMONDS, D.J and NUNN, P.E. *Essential mechanics for A-level.*
Nelson, 1984.
ISBN 0 17 431281 4

TAO, P.K. *The physics of traffic accident investigation.*
OUP, 1987.
Out of print

WILLIAMS, D.J. *Force, matter and energy.*
Hodder & Stoughton, 1974.
ISBN 0 340 12374 5

Waves and vibrations

AKRILL, T.B. and MILLAR, C.J. *Mechanics, vibrations and waves.*
John Murray, 1974.
ISBN 0 7195 2882 8

BOULIND, H.F. *Waves or particles.*
Longman, 1972. (Physics topics).
Out of print

CHAUNDY, D. *Waves.*
Longman, 1972 (Physics topics).
ISBN 0 582 32212 X

NEWTON, R.E.I. *Wave physics.*
Edward Arnold, 1986.
ISBN 0 7131 2656 6

RAITT, G. *Vibrations and radiations.*
CUP, 1987.
ISBN 0 521 31088 1

Electronic systems

DUNCAN, T. *Success in electronics.*
John Murray, 1983.
ISBN 0 7195 4015 1

GREGORY, J.M. et al. *A practical approach to systems electronics.*
Longman, 1985.
ISBN 0 582 35500 1

HARTLEY, J.R. & MISELL, D.L. *Physics by experiment*
Stanley Thornes, 1987.
ISBN 0 85950 191 4

SPARKES, R.A. *Microelectronics: A practical introduction.*
Hutchinson, 1985.
ISBN 0 09 154581 1

Forces and fields

FEYNMAN, R. *The character of physical law.*
BBC, 1965.
Out of print.

GAMOW, G. *Gravity; Classic and modern views.*
Heinemann, 1962. (Science study series.)
Out of print

HOBSONS Science Support Series *Dielectric heating.*
Hobsons, 1986.
ISBN 0 8602 1759 0

NARLIKAR, J.V. *The lighter side of gravity.*
W.H. Freeman, 1982.
ISBN 0 7167 1344 6

Thermal properties

ADKINS, C.J. *Thermal physics.*
Hodder & Stoughton, 1976.
Out of print

ASE - SATIS 303: *Physics and looking.*
ASE, 1986.

RAITT, G. *Heat and temperature.*
CUP, 1987.
ISBN 0 521 31087 3

RAMAGE, J. *Energy: A guidebook.*
Oxford, 1983.
ISBN 0 19 289157 X

Electromagnetism

BENNET, G.A.G. *Electricity and modern physics.*
Edward Arnold. (Second edition.)
ISBN 0 7131 2459 8

RAITT, G. *Electricity 2: Electromagnetism*
CUP, 1987
ISBN 0 521 31086 5

Electrons and the nucleus

CARO, D.E., McDONELL, J.A. and SPICER, B.M. *Modern physics: An introduction to atomic and nuclear physics.*
Edward Arnold, 1978 (Third edition).
ISBN 0 7131 2704 X

GAMOW, G. *Mr. Tompkins in paperback.*
CUP, 1965.
ISBN 0 5210 9355 4

LEWIS, J.L. *Electrons and atoms.*
Longman, 1973. (Physics topics.)
ISBN 0 582 32215 4

LEWIS, J.L. and WENHAM, E.J. *Radioactivity.*
Longman, 1970. (Physics topics.)
ISBN 0 582 32206 5

NRPB. *Living with radiation.*
HMSO, 1986. (Third edition.)
ISBN 0 8595 1255 X

ROMER, A.S. *The restless atom.*
Heinemann, 1961. (Science study.)
Out of print

SHIRE, E.S. *Rutherford and the nuclear atom.*
Longman, 1972.
Out of print

UKAEA. *Glossary of atomic terms.*
UKAEA, 1984.

(c) Books for GCSE revision

AVISON, J.H. *The world of physics.*
Thomas Nelson, 1984.
ISBN 0 17 438238 3

DUNCAN, T. *GCSE physics.*
John Murray ,1987 (second edition).
ISBN 0 7195 4380 0

DUNCAN, T. *Success in physics.*
John Murray ,1985.
ISBN 0 7195 4191 3

(d) Additional books for option topics

Energy and its uses

RAMAGE, J. *Energy - a guidebook*
OUP,1983
ISBN 0 19 289157 X

Medical physics

HOBSONS *Science Support Series Noise*:
Hobsons ,1986.
ISBN 0 86021 860 0

POPE, J.A. *Medical physics.*
Heinemann 1984.
ISBN 0 435 68681 X

Astronomy

McGILLIVRAY, D. *Physics and astronomy*
Macmillan, 1987
ISBN 0 333 42861 7

WAXMAN, J. *Workbook for astronomy*
CUP, 1985
ISBN 0 521 25312 8

Rotational dynamics

McGILLIVRAY, D. *Rotational dynamics.*
Heinemann, 1984.
ISBN 0 435 68270 9

Solid materials

GORDON, J.E. *Structures.*
Penguin, 1978.
ISBN 0 14 021961 7

Telecommunications

NICHOLL, B. and SELFE, J. Ed. *Telecommunications in practice.*
British Telecom/ASE 1985.
ISBN 0 863 57018 6

(e) Books for study skills

BARRASS, R. *Study: A guide to effective study, revision and examination techniques.*
Chapman & Hall
ISBN 0 412 25690 8

BUZAN, T .*Use your head.*
BBC Publications
ISBN 0 563 16552 9

BUZAN, T. *Use your memory*
BBC Publications
ISBN 0 563 20476 1

FREEMAN, R. *Mastering study skills.*
Macmillan
ISBN 0 333 30448 9

HARMAN, C. and FREEMAN, R. *How to study effectively.*
National Extension College
ISBN 0 86082 446 2

MADDOX, H. *How to study*
Pan Books
ISBN 0 330 30144 6

Comprehension and data analysis exercises

Comprehension exercise BM 1
MODELS AND CRYSTALLOGRAPHY

Introduction

Models play an important part in science, particularly in the areas of work where the scale of the investigation is so immense or minute that our normal senses cannot assimilate information properly and routine observations become useless. For example, in *Behaviour of matter* , the atom is first considered as a tiny sphere. This model is then refined as we consider the sub-atomic particles and even further refined in *Electrons and the nucleus* as our understanding of the sub-atomic particles increases. But why have models only to keep changing them?

The following extract is based on an article by Sir Lawrence Bragg.

X-ray crystallography

X-ray crystallography is a strange branch of science. The results of an investigation lasting many years can be summed up in a 'model'. I have often been asked 'Why are you always showing and talking about models? Other kinds of scientists do not do this.' The answer is that what the investigations have been seeking all along is simply a structural plan, a map if you will, that shows all the atoms in their relative positions in space. No other branch of science is so completely geographical: a list of spatial coordinates is all that is needed to tell the world what has been discovered.

The atomic structure of a crystal is deduced from the way it diffracts a beam of X-rays in different directions. A crystal is built of countless small structural units, each consisting of the same arrangement of atoms; the units are repeated regularly like the pattern of a wallpaper, except that in a crystal the pattern extends in three dimensions in space. The directions of the diffracted beams depend on the repeat distance of the pattern. The strengths of the diffracted beams, on the other hand, depend on the arrangement of atoms in each unit. The wavelets scattered by the atoms interfere to give a strong resultant in some directions and a weak resultant in others. The goal of X-ray analysis is to find the atomic arrangement that accounts for the observed strengths of the many diffracted beams.

This brings us to the question of why X-rays, of all the available forms of electromagnetic radiation, are indispensable for this method of investigation. In order for the interference of the diffracted beams to produce marked changes in the amount of scattering in different directions, the differences in path taken by refracted beams must be of the order of a wavelength. Only X-rays have wavelengths short enough to satisfy this condition. For example, the distance between neighbouring sodium and chlorine atoms in a crystal of sodium chloride (ordinary table salt) is 2.81×10^{-10} m, whereas the most commonly used wavelength in X-ray analysis is 1.54×10^{-10} m.

Actual crystals come into the picture only because they are a convenient means to an end. The resultant scattering of X-rays would be hopelessly confused and impossible to interpret if the scattering units were randomly distributed in all orientations. In a crystal, the units are all similarly orientated and hence scatter the X-rays in the same way; as a result, a total scattering measurement made with a whole crystal leads directly to a determination of the amount scattered by an individual unit.

(Bragg, Sir L., *X-ray crystallography*, 1969. *Scientific American* offprint no 325. Reproduced by courtesy of the Royal Institution.)

In answering the questions, you may wish to leave questions 5 to 9 until you have completed topic 3 of the unit *Behaviour of matter.*

Questions

1 Why did Bragg rely so much on 'models' in his work (second paragraph)?

2 There are some models whose job is to remind one of what things are like; a model of a petrol engine, a circuit diagram, a sketch map, etc. Can you see any difference between this type of model and Bragg's models?

3 Is it true that other scientists do not use models? If they do, describe a useful model in physics and try to explain why it is useful.

4 What evidence is there to support the statement (third paragraph) that 'a crystal is built of countless small structural units, each consisting of the same arrangement of atoms'?

5 How and why are X-ray diffraction photographs quite unlike the X-ray shadow photographs of bones taken by radiologists or by metallurgists examining flawed castings?

6 Why must 'the difference in the paths taken by refracted beams ... be of the order of a wavelength' (third paragaph)?

7 '... X-rays, of all the available forms of electromagnetic radiation, are indispensible for this method of investigation' (fourth paragraph). Why not use light?

8 The fourth paragraph says why crystals, with their orderly arrangement of atoms, are used with X-rays for diffraction experiments. Can you say something about how X-rays might be diffracted by water? (Molecules in a liquid are not tidily arranged.)

9 X-rays are well-known for their ability to penetrate deep inside solids. Is this property essential for the success of X-ray diffraction?

(Adapted from Nuffield Advanced Physics Students' Book, Unit 1 Materials and structure. Longman 1971.)

Comprehension exercise BM 2
DESIGNING NEW ENGINEERING MATERIALS

Up to now metals have been the predominant materials for engineering use, but other types of materials are likely to become increasingly important in the future. An important consideration in the future use of metals is the availability of the raw materials - metallic ores. Although the earth's crust contains vast quantities of most elements, iron and aluminium being particularly abundant, there are complicating factors. In the first place, many of these raw materials are very unevenly distributed over the earth. The supply of copper, for example, has been greatly affected by political changes in the few countries which contain large reserves. Secondly, much of this raw material is in a dilute form, and there comes a time when its extraction is not economic.

Engineering materials can be roughly categorised by four properties: the modulus, or how much they deflect under load; the yield strength, or how far they deflect before distorting permanently; the toughness, or how difficult they are to fracture; and the melting point. For most engineering uses materials must not bend too much, yield, fracture or melt. Metals and their alloys fulfil these requirements quite well but, in some cases, they may have reached their limits. An example of this is the nickel-based alloys used in gas turbines. Development of these alloys has allowed the operating temperatures to rise from 50°C in 1950 to 1250°C at present. Further advances are unlikely, since the melting point of nickel is 1455°C, and blades based on other metals have not been successful. Engineers are, therefore, looking to other materials, particularly those which may offer advantages such as reduced weight.

There are three groups of materials which might replace metals and alloys for some engineering purposes: polymers, ceramics and glasses. Polymers are tough and do not yield easily, but they have a low modulus. The reason for this is that polymers are made up of long molecules in which a simple pattern based on the carbon atom, repeats itself many times. A material such as bulk polyethylene (polythene) has a structure part-way between a perfectly aligned parallel set of chains (rather like a packet of spaghetti) and a totally random collection of chains (rather like cooked spaghetti on a plate). The chains are partly folded round each other, and the forces keeping the material together are strong within the chains and at the intersections of chains, but very weak between the chains, so the material bends easily.

There are several ways of increasing the stiffness of polymers. One is to form polymers with stronger cohesive forces between the chains. Another is to draw or extrude the material so that the chains are less tangled and the strong forces along the chains determine the strength of the material. A third way is to mix the polymer with a stiffer material to make a composite. Wood is a natural composite, with stiff cellulose fibre aligned and embedded in the amorphous lignin. Fibre-glass is another composite: twenty per cent of glass threads can stiffen the resin in which they lie by a factor of ten. The fibres also add to the toughness of the material, by resisting the spread of cracks.

A composite in everyday use is rubber-roughened polystyrene, which is used for making telephones. In this instance, the rubber is not used to stiffen the polystyrene, but to increase its resistance to fracture, since telephones are frequently dropped. A crack, once started, can only grow by stretching the rubber spheres in its path. As rubber can distort to a very large extent without breaking, the spheres act as a sort of clamp, discouraging fracture.

Ceramics, such as porcelain, brick and concrete, fracture very easily. However, they have high moduli, yield strengths and melting points, and are also light, cheap and chemically stable. One way of increasing their toughness is the incorporation of wires or rods: an example of this is reinforced concrete. A different method is used in the ceramic composites called cermets, which are used in cutting tools. Cermets consist of very small ceramic particles (tungsten carbide is the commonest) separated by a thin metallic film (usually cobalt). The modulus is high, since it depends mainly on the dominant material, tungsten carbide. The yield strength is also high because, although cobalt by itself would yield easily, the tungsten carbide particles inhibit flow. The toughness is increased because a local fracture in a tungsten carbide particle runs into cobalt, which does not fracture easily. This material, therefore, meets the criteria for engineering materials. However, few composites of this kind have yet been investigated.

Questions

1 Why is it necessary to seek non-metallic substitutes for metals?

2 (a) List the four important characteristics of engineering materials mentioned in paragraph 2.
(b) The terms *modulus* and *yield strength* are not fully defined. Write brief statements explaining the meaning of each term.

3 How has the operating temperature of gas turbines been increased over the past thirty years, and what now limits further advance?

4 Comment on the 'spaghetti model' of the structure of polyethylene.

5 Why do polymers bend easily? What are three ways of overcoming this problem?

6 Why are fibre structures strong? Give two further examples of fibre structures.

7 What is a cermet? What property of ceramic materials have they been designed to overcome, and how does the formation of a composite do this?

Further reading
Gordon, J.E. *The new science of strong materials.*
Cooke, B. and Sang, D. *Physics of materials.* Case study. Materials for turbine blades.

Comprehension exercise BM 3
150 YEARS FROM OHM'S LAW

The delight of school teachers and the plague of pupils, crammed into minds late at night, written on the backs of hands, Ohm's Law should rank as one of the most widely remembered pieces of school physics. Ironically the discoverer, Georg Simon Ohm (1769-1854) was a school teacher, but not by choice.

Bavarian by birth, Ohm came from a large family and received his early education at home from his father who was by profession a locksmith and whose bent for the sciences gave his sons an early aptitude in mathematics. When he was 11 Georg went to school and progressed from there to university in his home town of Erlangen. At 22 he graduated with a PhD and began to teach mathematics at the university. This was a poorly paid job with few prospects and, wanting more in life than this drudgery, Ohm became a school teacher for the extra pay it offered. Although he hated it he stayed and when, in 1817, he got the chance to teach in a better school, the Jesuit School in Cologne, he took it. Here in the enthusiastic atmosphere of a newly founded school Ohm was stimulated and, as he had been asked to teach physics as well as mathematics, his interest began to shift more to the former.

He read avidly from the French classics of Lagrange, Legendre, Laplace, Biot, Poisson, Fresnel and Fourier, books whose abstruse mathematical style he was later to try to emulate. But the turning point came in 1820 when Oersted made his great discovery that an electric current flowing along a straight wire produces a magnetic field which will turn a compass needle held beneath it. The significance for Ohm was that it turned his mind to electricity. The school laboratory at Cologne was well equipped with apparatus and Ohm began to experiment.

However, it was not until 1825 that he got the idea of doing research with an eye to publication leading, he hoped, to recognition and an escape from the life of a school teacher. The problem to which he addressed himself was to discover how the connecting wire between the two poles of a battery affected the current flowing through it. Ohm measured the current with a compass needle suspended by a thin torsion wire over a fixed straight portion of the circuit, an arrangement in direct descent from the classic experiments of Oersted and Coulomb, and one capable of great accuracy. When a current was flowing Ohm would adjust the twist in the torsion wire to give no deflection. The angle of twist was then a measure of the current.

At first Ohm used a voltaic pile as his source but it gave him a lot of trouble. Not only was there a current surge every time he connected it but the generation of gas in the pile reduced the current as the experiment proceeded. With much trouble Ohm managed to get consistent results which he published in 1825 and it was his editor who gave him a new and crucial idea. Poggendorf suggested he use Seebeck's recently discovered thermo-electric effect to generate the voltaic force as this would not change with time nor give current surges. Ohm started out again in 1826, the crucial year, to re-experiment using a thermocouple - this time with success.

Keeping one junction in ice and the other in boiling water, Ohm varied the length of wire x between the thermocouple terminals, measuring the current X each time. Ohm found that the equation which fitted his results was of the form

$$X = \frac{a}{x + b}$$

By varying the thermocouple temperatures he found that a was proportional to the e.m.f. of the source, and b a constant for the source. In modern symbols we recognise this as the school-book formula

$$I = \frac{E}{R + r}$$

with I the current, E the battery e.m.f., R the circuit resistance, and r the battery resistance. As he had so far used only one kind of wire of fixed diameter he went on to experiment with the dimensions and composition of the wire and found that its 'resistance' varied in proportion to its length and inversely as its cross-sectional area with a constant factor dependent on its composition.

Failure in communication

Later, Ohm was offered sabbatical leave in Berlin, which gave him a welcome relief from his teaching duties. Here Ohm wrote a book, in the style of the great French mathematicians, on the mathematical theory of the electric circuit. Published the following year, it contained no account of the experimental work from which it derived. Ohm was so influenced by those French texts that he failed to emphasise the practical aspects which might have brought him the early recognition he was seeking and deserved. The book fell on stony ground, its format and length disguising the simplicity of its message. As we shall see, when revealed and put to use by others, Ohm's Law was destined to become of enormous importance later in the century, both in the development of the telegraph and in the invention of the electric light bulb which shone the way to the 'electric age'. But Ohm never saw the full fruits of his discovery for he died in 1854. Only in the last 10 years of his life were honours bestowed on him by some of the world's scientific societies in recognition of his work. He finally attained a chair of physics at the University of Munich.

Ohm's work languished for almost 15 years before it received a staunch adherent in Charles Wheatstone, professor of physics at University College, London, who was quick to recognise its significance. It had been translated into English under the auspices of the British Association and published in 1841. Wheatstone was on the translation committee and must have been delighted to find that Ohm held the solution to his own problem, which was to find the best circuit configuration for producing electrical effects over long distances - the telegraph. He used to the law to discover the best construction of battery and wires to produce a needle deflection at a given distance.

Wheatstone's first practical telegraph was set up parallel to Brunel's Great Western Railway from Paddington to West Drayton. By the 1850s the telegraph was a well-established communication between major centres. However, the great challenge of the age was yet to come - the spanning of the Atlantic by telegraph cable. Ohm's seminal work was to show its influence here too. While the practical imagination was fired by the problem of finding a ship big enough to hold the cable, with landing gear strong enough to support two miles of cable dangling from ship to ocean bottom, the intellect of one man was stimulated to consider how an electric signal would pass through such a cable. This man was William Thomson (later Lord Kelvin). Thomson used the analogy between the flow of electricity and of heat to solve this problem, a comparison first recognised by Ohm, who had been greatly influenced by Fourier's book *The Theory of Heat* in writing about electricity.

The importance of the analogy is that for heat flow it is natural to include the storage of heat in the bar. Charge storage is just what is pronounced in the flow of electricity through a cable surrounded by water. So Thomson, using Fourier's equations, was able to solve the problem. He discovered that a sharp pulse dispatched from one end of the cable becomes spread out into a long slow quiver at the other, a fact which severely reduces the rate of sending if the received signals are not to overlap. The equations also told him that if the resistance of the cable is reduced the rate of sending can be increased. Therefore, a scientific approach to cable design required pure copper in as thick a core as possible. Unfortunately, the cable was already made and, when laid in 1858, was a failure. As Thomson's ideas became accepted he was able to influence the design of a second cable giving it three times as much copper per nautical mile as the first cable with proper choice of purity. This cable was laid by Brunel's great ship 'The Great Eastern' and completed in 1866. It was a success. Within 24 hours of connection the line was at capacity with messages to and from the New World.

More practical applications

The telegraph obtained its electric power from batteries, that is from chemical reactions, but in 1931 Michael Faraday had made the momentous discovery that electricity could be generated mechanically. It was a discovery that remained under-developed for many years for, although electricity had many uses, none of these was so universal as to augur a return on investment in development. It was Edison, a great admirer of Faraday, who perceived that if a profit were to be made it would be necessary not only to develop an efficient dynamo but also to create an electrical distribution system and a universal use for electricity. For Edison that meant the electric light bulb and, possessed of the imagination and initiative necessary to develop the complete system, he started work.

Once he had grasped the idea Edison was guided in his calculations by Ohm's Law. First, since each light must be independent, the bulbs would be wired in parallel - a departure from the arc-light practice of the time. Secondly, he calculated the weight of copper in the wires necessary to light a given housing area with lamps of one ohm resistance each, a typical value for lamps being patented at this time by others. The result was impossibly expensive. He then did the calculation with hundred ohm lamps and the system began to look feasible. This then was the crux, a high-resistance lamp filament was needed. Edison, directing his research team at Menlo Park , set out to find a suitable filament. They concentrated on carbon which has inherent high resistivity, and on making the filament as thin as possible consistent with strength and long life. When they finally succeeded, Edison and his workers just sat watching the filament blaze for its record 40-hour duration. That was in 1879. Three years later, when Edison started up the steam engines at the Pearl St. generator in New York City and the electric light shone in distant offices, the electric age had begun.

Electrical science in the 19th century was dominated by materials which obeyed Ohm's Law but the 20th century has seen the development of circuitry far from ohmic in its operation. The starting point was again the light bulb and Edison.

One of the problems with the carbon filament lamps was that, after a time, the glass became blackened and this so reduced the lamp life that Edison became interested. He noticed that the black shadow of carbon contained one clear line in the shape of the projection of one side of the filament. It appeared, therefore, that carbon was being emitted by only one side of the filament loop, the negative side. The 'Edison effect' remained unexplained until the discovery of the electron which, emitted from a negative hot wire, travels freely in a vacuum, in straight lines.

Thus, the triumph of the application of Ohm's Law in the 19th century, the light bulb, provided the link with the new 'bulbs' of the 20th century. First the valve, giving us radio, and then the cathode ray tube for television, not to mention the insides of pocket calculators or computers which owe everything to the transistor whose electrical properties are certainly a long way on from Ohm.

(Article by Christopher Farrell from *New Scientist*, 30th September, 1976.)

Questions

1 What problems did Ohm have to overcome in doing his experiments? How did he overcome them?

2 Why did he omit his experiments from the book that he wrote? Why are experiments important in physics?

3 Explain why the mathematical relationship found by Ohm was essential to the development of (a) the telegraph; (b) the electric light bulb.

4 Write a brief summary of the article to emphasise how Ohm's work is typical of any advance in physics.

Data analysis exercise FM 1
ANALYSIS OF A SIMULATED ACCIDENT

Figure 4.1

In their investigations into passenger safety, the Transport and Road Research Laboratory simulate accidents by using remotely controlled test cars which they direct at rigid concrete barriers. Drivers and passengers are simulated by the use of carefully designed models. Cars and models are fitted with instruments which enable the observers to measure velocities, accelerations and strains. Strategically placed cameras enable position changes to be recorded throughout the impact (figure 4.1). The results then have to be translated into the practical situations which are encountered on the road, with cars controlled and occupied by human beings.

Before considering methods of reducing the risk of injury, we need to examine the main changes which occur in the collision. After hitting the wall, the car moves through a small distance before coming to rest. During this motion the front of the car crumples. Meanwhile, the driver continues to move forward until his body strikes the object immediately in front of him.

It is this latter impact which causes injury. *The extent of the injury might be expected to depend on*:

the speed of impact,
the mass of the driver,
the resistance exerted by the object struck.

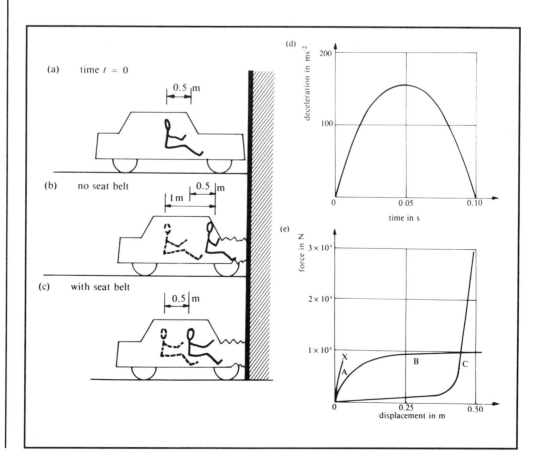

Figure 4.2

A car travelling at about 10 m s^{-1} crashes into a rigid wall. Between the time (reckoned as $t = 0$) at which the car first makes contact with the wall (figure 4.2a) and the time at which it comes to rest (figure 4.2b) the engine compartment at the front is crushed so that its length is shortened by 0.5 m, whilst the main body of the car, including the padding and dashboard, is decelerating. The graph in figure 4.2d shows how this deceleration of the main body of the car varies with time.

Questions

1 Explain, in terms of the laws of motion, the sentence in *italics*.

2 A scientist says 'the area under the graph is roughly 100 x 0.1 which gives about 10 m s^{-1} so that's consistent'. Explain her statement.

3 Sketch a graph of the velocity of the main body of the car against time over the time interval shown in figure 4.2d. Label the axes and explain how your sketch is related to figure 4.2d.

4 Consider a passenger in the car who is *not* wearing a safety belt. The dashboard padding is 0.5 m away from him before the crash (figure 4.2a) so that he moves a total distance of 1 m, relative to the ground, between time $t = 0$ and the moment that he hits the dashboard (figure 4.2b). Assuming that he moves forward freely during this interval and that he is then stopped by the padding which deforms a total of 15 cm, draw a sketch graph, using the same axes as for question 3, of his velocity relative to the ground as a function of time.

What is his velocity relative to the padding when he hits it?

5 Consider a passenger who *is* wearing a safety belt. Assume first that it holds her *very firmly* to the car seat throughout the crash (figure 4.2c). If her mass is 70 kg, estimate the maximum force exerted on her during the crash and explain at what time during the crash this maximum force is exerted.

6 The curves A, B,C (figure 4.2e) are curves of force exerted on the passenger by a seat belt against the forward displacement of the passenger relative to the seat as the seat belt 'gives'. Curve A is for a belt which breaks at the point X: discuss whether this belt will give complete protection, some protection, or no protection at all.

7 Curves B and C are for seat belts of different design and made of different materials. Compare B and C in terms of the forces experienced by passengers when a car decelerates as in figure 4.2d. Explain the advantages of the belt which you think is the more suitable.

Oxford and Cambridge Examination Board (1975)

Comprehension exercise FM 2
BUILDING THE WIND-UP TUBE TRAIN

A child's spinning top, known technically as a flywheel, is an efficient energy-storage device. It will be used experimentally for the first time late this year (1972) to capture some of the kinetic energy lost when a tube train stops at a station and re-use that energy to start the train again.

In the experiment, a pair of 270 kg, 60 cm steel discs rotating in an evacuated (30 mmHg) chamber will be installed in each of two New York tube carriages. Each carriage will still have its normal electric motors and power-collection system; an electric motor will also be attached to each flywheel. Before beginning to run, the flywheels will be brought up to 14 000 rev/min by their motors. During train acceleration, the flywheel motors will be used as generators to produce electricity for the carriage motors. During braking, all motor fields are reversed and the carriage motors act as generators to power the flywheel motors.

The bulk of the electricity used by a tube system is for accelerating trains out of stations, and the New York Metropolitan Transportation Authority estimates that flywheels could save enough energy from braking to provide half the acceleration energy. The New York underground requires 10% of the city's electricity generating capacity; peak demand in New York City is during the evening rush hour, just when the underground is also consuming the most electricity. Thus, if the flywheel is successful, it could reduce power consumption just at the time of day when there is least spare capacity.

Energy-storing flywheels are not new - they have been used to power torpedoes since 1870 and are used for industrial applications such as punch presses where power surges are needed without putting a drain on the electrical system.

But there has been interest recently in 'regenerative' flywheels for vehicles because of the demand for pollution control, studies of hybrid vehicles, and the improving flywheel technology. At present, flywheels such as those to be used in New York store as much energy per kilogram as the best available batteries. But battery technology has been pushed to the limit, with no significant improvements in sight for the near future, while available technology could more than double the energy storage capacity of the flywheel, and research has really only just begun.

A flywheel has been tried in a vehicle before - the Swiss Electrogyro Omnibus successfully carried passengers from 1953 until 1969. But the flywheel was the sole source of power - effectively it was a wind-up bus - which limited its range. The flywheel only stored one-fifth the energy of the present systems, so the bus had to stop at a 'power-point' every half mile to speed up the flywheel again. Recently, interest has switched to the more practical hybrids, such as the New York underground carriages, where a traditional motor provides normal running power and the flywheel provides acceleration boosts.

Although simple in theory, the flywheel has a large number of technical problems. Rapidly spinning objects are subject to many forces - for example, if the flywheel is horizontal and rotates clockwise, when the vehicle drives uphill the gyroscopic couple generated forces the flywheel to the left. (In the New York underground carriage, this effect is avoided by mounting the flywheel vertically under the floor, which restricts its size.)

Gravitational effects will cause the flywheel to want to precess like a gyroscope. And there is the danger that, during a skid, the vehicle will counter rotate around the flywheel axis. Thus, one is forced to employ complicated gimballed mountings or to use two oppositely rotating flywheels on the same shaft.

The need for a vacuum to reduce drag means that either the flywheel bearings must be airtight, or a magnetic suspension system must be employed, or a vacuum pump must be included.

Finally, the rapidly spinning flywheel could be a serious danger in event of an accident. Researchers at the Johns Hopkins University Applied Physics Laboratory recently concluded that 'it is not feasible' to use flywheel systems in which the flywheel case is used to absorb all of the flywheel energy in case of accident. Instead, they propose using a brittle composite material made of glass or graphite that would be self-pulverising in event of failure.

(From an article by Dr. J. Hanlon, 'Building the wind-up tube train', in *New Scientist*, 10 February, 1972).

Questions

1 Re-phrase the second sentence, explaining in more precise scientific language the phrases 'to capture kinetic energy' and 're-use energy'.

2 Calculate how much energy will be stored by the flywheels before the train starts (paragraph 2).

continued

3 If all this energy is used to accelerate a train of mass 1.0×10^4 kg, what speed will it acquire? Comment on your answer. (The moment of inertia of a flywheel is $Mr^2/2$.)

4 Why is the chamber containing the flywheel evacuated? What design features are suggested for maintaining this low pressure around the flywheels?

5 Explain the different functions of 'carriage motors' and 'flywheel motors'. When is one of these types of motor required to act as a generator? How is this possible?

6 How is it possible to increase the energy per kilogram stored by a flywheel, and how might modern technology be used to increase this quantity?

7 How did the Swiss 'wind-up bus' system function and what was the limitation of this system? Why, in contrast, is the New York system described as a 'practical hybrid'?

8 Why might a flywheel system be dangerous? How can this danger be minimised?

Comprehension exercise WV 1
THE BIG WAVE

The tsunami or tidal wave is one of the most destructive natural phenomena known to man. It has produced some of the worst disasters in recorded history. Perhaps the most famous tsunami in recent times was that formed by the explosion of the volcanic island of Krakatoa in 1883. It raced across the western Pacific Ocean at nearly 500 km/h, raising waves 30 to 40 metres high on the coasts of Java and Sumatra that killed over 27 000 people and swept everything away before them. One or two such disasters occur in the Pacific each century, while several tsunamis every decade cause loss of life, greater property damage and extensive flooding.

The popular name 'tidal wave' is a misnomer. The wave is not produced by any solar or lunar tide effects, but is generated as a result of underwater earthquakes, volcanic eruptions or land-slides. Nor is the idea of a single giant wave correct. A tsunami is a series of waves with the largest crest in the middle. Moreover, these giant waves are produced only as the sea disturbance approaches the land.

Everything about these waves is extraordinary. Their wavelengths in deep ocean may be 150 km to 250 km (compared with 300 m for the longest wind-produced sea wave). Wind waves rarely travel at more than 90 km/h but the velocity of tsunamis varies as the square of the water depth, and in the deepest waters of the Pacific they reach a staggering 800 km/h. One final unique feature of these waves is that in the deepest parts of the ocean their amplitude may be only three metres or so.

As a tsunami approaches land, the forward region of the wave pulse is slowed down as the depth decreases. The wavelength is dramatically reduced, causing a build-up of the crests. In this way, a 5 m high crest travelling at 600 km/h becomes a 30 m high wave travelling at 50 km/h. When such a wave struck Hilo Bay in Hawaii in 1946, the crews of ships moored 2 km offshore watched horrified as a wave which had passed them as a wave of amplitude 1.5 m then built up into a 10 m wall of water as it reached the shore. This particular wave, generated by an earthquake in the Aleutian Islands, had travelled 3400 km in only five hours.

The first effect of the arrival of a tsunami on a coast is a minor wave, which raises the sea level by a metre or two (figure 4.3). This is followed about 15 minutes later by a trough, which appears to take the sea out to low tide (hence the term tidal wave). The heights of incoming crests and troughs increase, until the sea retreats well below low tide level just before the arrival of the main giant wave.

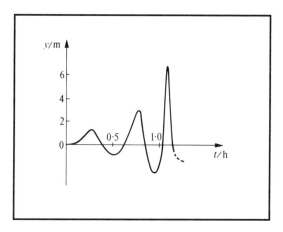

Figure 4.3

Although we will never prevent the occurrence of destructive tsunamis, warning systems have now been set up which enable endangered populations to be evacuated from threatened coastlines. When a large earthquake occurs, tsunami-watchers calculate its epicentre. If it is likely to produce a tsunami wave, stations all over the Pacific are alerted to detect shock waves and predict the possible arrival times of the tsunami at hundreds of populated areas. In this wave, warning was given of the 1960 tsunami generated by an earthquake in Chile, and though it caused extensive damage the death toll was dramatically reduced because of the warning system.

Questions

1 Explain how the amplitude of a tsunami increases, and indicate why this does not contradict the principle of energy conservation.

2 A tsunami had a speed of 47 km/h where the ocean depth was 1300 m. Its maximum speed reached 750 km/h. What can you deduce from this?

3 Using any relevant data, estimate a typical wavelength in the forward part of a tsunami as it approaches land.

Comprehension exercise WV 2
WAVY RADIO

Striking evidence for the wave nature of electromagnetic radiation can occasionally be noted by motorway drivers with car radios. The following true account is an example.

Observation

Driving on the M4 from Bristol to London at a steady 65 miles per hour (29 m s^{-1}). Radio tuned to BBC Radio 2 (wavelength 330 metres). Very noticeable and regular cyclic variation of volume from radio. Interval, as roughly timed with wristwatch over a number of cycles: approximately 6 seconds. Volume variation most marked in the region of motorway junction 16 (figure 4.4).

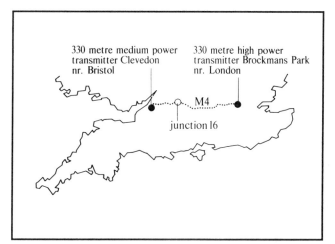

Interpretation

A superposition effect: with 330 metres broadcast the stationary wave pattern repeats every 165 metres. Time interval between successive maxima approximately 5.75 seconds.

Figure 4.4

Questions

1 Why is this evidence that radio transmissions have a wave nature?

2 What would you hear on the radio of a car as you drove along the M4 near junction 16 listening to the radio? Write your answer as if explaining to a non-scientist what he would hear.

3 Explain, again as if to a non-scientist, why the amplitude and hence the intensity of the radio signal rises and falls.

4 Is it the audio modulation of the radio waves or the radio waves themselves that are superimposed to produce the stationary wave pattern?

Comprehension exercise WV 3
DIFFRACTION RULES THE WAVES

Most ideas for the generation of power from waves have centred around various oscillating mechanisms which tap the energy from the waveform itself and involve still developing technology which could prove too costly or complicated. An approach which is both simple and uses proven technology has, however, been suggested by the Central Institute for Industrial Research in Oslo. The researchers have proposed that a series of blocks could be moored offshore, in such a position that waves are diffracted to concentrate most of their energy onto a stretch of coastline approximately 400 metres long. The waves, now 15-30 metres high, would be funnelled into a channel leading to a reservoir which could be as much as 100 metres above sea level. Generation of electricity would follow by a conventional hydroelectric power station. The Norwegians estimate that such a power station, utilising approximately 10 kilometres of the Norwegian coastline for wave gathering, could have an annual output of 800-2000 gigawatt hours. (By comparison, Oslo, with a population of 472 000, uses 2900 GW h per year.) The Institute is recommending that an experimental wave power station should be constructed in one of the bays of the Oslo Fjord. If this is successful a prototype power station could be in use by 1985.

(From an article in *New Scientist* , February 1978)

Questions

1 What important quantities must be known before it is possible to design a 'grating' such as this ?

2 Assuming all the energy of the waves along a 10 km stretch of coastline is used to produce waves 20 m high (amplitude 10 m) concentrated along a 400 m length of beach, estimate what value this implies as typical for the amplitude of a sea wave off Norway. Is this value realistic?

3 If a diffraction maximum is to be produced at F (figure 4.5b) by constructive superposition, suggest values for the lengths AF, BF, CF, etc. Will the grating have equally spaced slits? Explain.

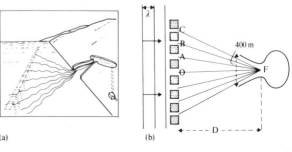

(a)   (b)

Figure 4.5

98 | Student's Resource Book
Part 4 Resources for study

Comprehension exercise WV 4
SPECTROSCOPY AT WORK

Consider three important but very different ways in which the spectra of electromagnetic waves provide valuable information.

1 Emission spectra in steel working

At a critical moment in the manufacture of steel, the prepared melt has to be analysed before it is poured into moulds and its composition must be modified if necessary. Very speedy analysis is required. A tiny sample is poured into a mould, cooled, and a slice is cut and polished and placed in a spark chamber (figure 4.6). The spark source produces radiation which includes the characteristic ultraviolet emission of the elements in the disc. This radiation is dispersed by two fluorite prisms and produces a spectrum along a curved focal surface. Slits are positioned so that the particular wavelengths of radiation which are required for the steelmaker's analysis are passed through the slits and reflected into a set of photomultiplier tubes (which produce an electron current when ultraviolet is incident on them). The signals from the photomultiplier are fed into a computer which prints out the percentage composition of the steel based on information given to it about the intensity of the characteristic ultraviolet emissions of different elements. Six minutes after pouring the sample, the decision can be taken whether to pour or modify the melt.

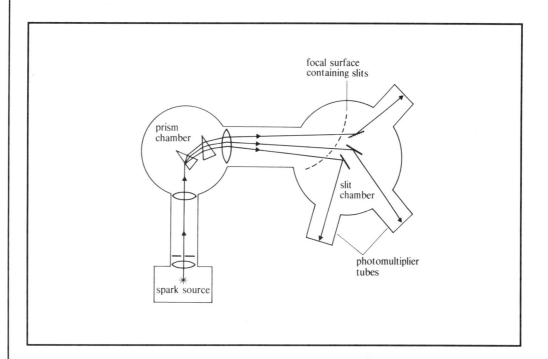

Figure 4.6

2 Molecular absorption spectra

Figure 4.7 lists the components required to produce molecular absorption spectra in different parts of the e.m. spectrum. When ultraviolet or visible radiation is absorbed by a complex molecule, it is used to change the energy of the electrons and also to change the vibration and rotation of the whole molecule (see topic 1 of *Waves and vibrations* on resonance). This explains why molecular spectra are complex band spectra, in contrast to the simpler line spectra of atoms. When infra-red radiation is absorbed by molecules, the radiation can affect only changes in the rotational and vibrational energy of the whole molecule. If microwaves were used, with wavelengths of about 3 cm, molecules could only absorb energy which would affect their rotation. The measurement of the wavelengths at which molecules absorb different radiations (i.e. their absorption spectra) in different regions of the electromagnetic spectrum will provide a lot of information about the structure and grouping of atoms in a very complex molecule.

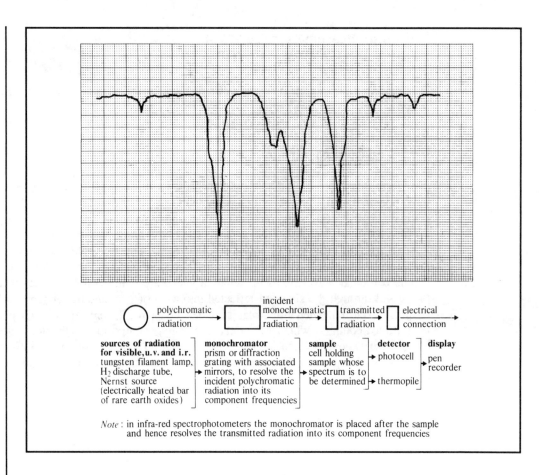

Figure 4.7

3 Flash photolysis

This is a method of studying fast chemical reactions. In 1967 Professor G. Porter and R.G.W. Norrish were awarded the Nobel Prize for Chemistry for their work in developing this method.

Some chemical reactions can be initiated by light energy, and in the flash photolysis method the reaction is triggered off by an intense light flash from the photoflash tube (figure 4.8). The progress of the rapid reaction taking place in the reaction tube is observed by sending light from a second flash tube (the spectroscopic flash) through the reaction vessel and into the spectrograph. By photographing the absorption spectrum at very rapid intervals, using the spectroscopic flash, information can be obtained about the progress of the reaction and the free radicals produced in the tube.

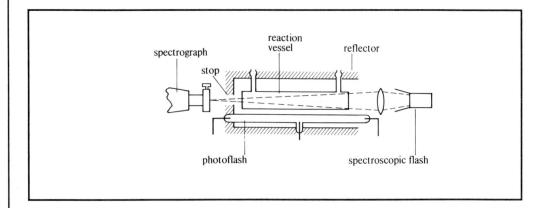

Figure 4.8

In the past few years, the ability to time-resolve molecular events in photochemistry has improved enormously. Until recently, the resolution of events by flash photolysis has been limited to a few microseconds. Now, through new techniques, flash photolysis may be applied to species lasting a few nanoseconds. These improvements depended on the introduction of the laser into photochemistry.

Questions

Emission spectra in steel making

1 Suggest reasons why *fluorite* prisms are used, and why *two*.

2 Why is the slit plate curved?

3 Why is the sample disc polished?

4 Why is it necessary to use the sample disc in a spark source instead of just heating it until it is white hot?

Molecular spectroscopy

5 Why are molecular spectra more complex than atomic spectra?

6 Choose from the lists in figure 4.7 a set of components suitable for obtaining an infrared spectrogram.

7 Molecules only absorb energy from radiation of particular frequencies. Mention an analogous example of resonance occurring in sound or in the mechanical vibrations of a system.

Flash photolysis

8 Give two reasons why capacitors are needed in the circuits controlling the flash tubes.

9 Why are two flash tubes used? How do their functions differ?

10 The term *kinetic spectroscopy* is used for methods like this. Why is the term appropriate?

Data analysis exercise FF 1
PART A KEPLER

Table 4.1 shows the data obtained by Kepler.

Planet	Radius of planet's orbit r (km) x 10^7	Time of revolution T (days)
Mercury	5.754	87.97
Venus	10.752	224.7
Earth	15.886	365.3
Mars	22.656	687.0
Jupiter	77.328	4332.0
Saturn	141.776	10760.0

Table 4.1

Use a calculator or a computer spreadsheet to test whether r^3 is directly proportional to T^2.

PART B APOLLO SPACEFLIGHT (*answer given)

The data in table 4.2 were taken during a period when the spacecraft was travelling directly away from the earth, with the motors off.

(a) In table 4.2 the pair of values (2) and (2A) are only ten minutes apart in time. In this time the speed of the spacecraft decreased by 272 ms⁻¹. At what mean rate was the speed changing?

(b) Write down (without further calculation) an estimate for the gravitational pull of the earth on each kilogram of the spacecraft at a distance of 27.7×10^6 m from the earth, this being the average of the distances at points (2) and (2A).

(c) Use the other pairs of data points to plot a graph which tests whether the gravitational force on one kilogram varies as the inverse square of the distance.

(d) Plot a second graph to check by means of a possible straight line whether the data corresponds to an inverse square law relation.

Time from launch/ h: min: s:	Distance from Earth's centre $r/10^6$ m	Speed v/m s-1
03:58:00 (2)	26.3	5374
04:08:00 (2A)	29.0	5102
05:58:00 (3)	54.4	3633
06:08:00 (3A)	56.4	3560
09:58:00 (4)	95.7	2619
10:08:00 (4A)	97.2	2594
19:58:00 (50)	169.9	1796
20:08:00 (5A)	170.9	1788

Table 4.2

Comprehension exercise FF 2
EINSTEIN'S EXPLANATION FOR GRAVITY

The parable of the apple

Once upon a time a student lay in a garden under an apple tree reflecting on the difference between Einstein's and Newton's views about gravity. He was startled by the fall of an apple nearby. As he looked at the apple, he noticed ants beginning to run along its surface. His curiosity aroused, he thought to investigate the principles of navigation followed by an ant. With his magnifying glass, he noted one track carefully, and taking his knife, made a cut in the apple skin one mm above the track and another cut one mm below it. He peeled off the resulting little highway of skin and laid it out on the face of his book. The track ran as straight as a laser beam along this highway. No more economical path could the ant have found to cover the ten cm from start to end of that strip of skin. Any zigs and zags or even any smooth bend in the path on its way along the apple peel from starting point to end point would have increased its length.

"What a beautiful geodesic", the student commented.

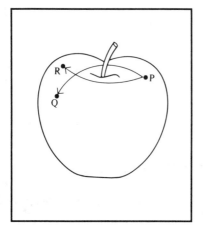

His eye fell on two ants starting off from a common point P in slightly different directions. Their route happened to carry them through the region of the dimple at the top of the apple, one on each side of it, as illustrated in figure 4.9. Each ant conscientiously pursued his geodesic. Each went as straight on his strip of appleskin as he possibly could. Yet because of the curvature of the dimple itself, the two tracks not only crossed but emerged in very different directions.

Ants Q and R following the straightest possible track on an apple's surface. Starting from a common point P their paths diverge and cross because of the stem's dimple.

Figure 4.9

"What happier illustration of Einstein's geometric theory of gravity could one possibly ask?" murmured the student. "The ants move as if they were attracted by the apple stem. One might have believed in a Newtonian force at a distance. Yet from nowhere does an ant get his moving orders except from the local geometry along his track. This is surely Einstein's concept that all physics takes place by 'local action'. What a difference from Newton's 'action at a distance' view of physics! Now I understand better what this book means".

And so saying, he opened his book and read, "Don't try to describe motion relative to faraway objects. *Physics is simple only when analysed locally*. And locally the world line that a satellite follows (in spacetime, around the earth) is already as straight as any world line can be. Forget all this talk about 'deflection'and 'force of gravitation'. I'm inside a spaceship. Or I'm floating outside and near it. Do I feel any 'force of gravitation'? Not at all. Does the spaceship 'feel' such a force? No. Then why talk about it? Recognise that the spaceship and I traverse a region of spacetime free of all force. Acknowledge that the motion through that region is already ideally straight".

The dinner bell was ringing, but still the student sat, musing to himself. "Let me see if I can summarise Einstein's geometric theory of gravity in three ideas: (1) locally, geodesics appear straight; (2) over more extended regions of space and time, geodesics originally receding from each other begin to approach at a rate governed by the curvature of spacetime, and this effect of geometry on matter is what we mean today by that old word 'gravitation'; (3) matter, in turn, warps geometry. The dimple arises in the apple because the stem is there. I think I see how to put the whole story even more briefly: *Space acts on matter, telling it how to move*. In turn, matter reacts back on space, telling it how to curve. In other words, matter here," he said, rising and picking up the apple by its stem, "curves space here. To produce a curvature in space here is to force a curvature in space there, " he went on, as he watched a lingering ant busily following its geodesic a finger's breadth away from the apple's stem. "Thus, matter here influences matter there. That is Einstein's explanation for 'gravitation'".

Then the dinner bell was quiet, and he was gone, with book, magnifying glass - and apple.

(From Gravitation, Misner *et al.*, Freeman 1973)

Questions

1 What is a 'geodesic'?

2 Is there any gravitational force acting

(a) in orbit around the earth;
(b) in deep space?

3 Draw a diagram of the apple to explain what the student means.

4 Discuss whether this is a 'better' explanation for gravity.

Comprehension excercise TP1
HOW TO STOP THE GREENHOUSE EFFECT

Now we know the greenhouse effect is real, the world has two ways forward: dumping millions of tonnes of carbon dioxide on the ocean beds, or creating a new energy-efficient world.

1 The greenhouse effect is now established scientific fact. Evidence published in the US earlier this year [1986] leaves little room for doubt. Carbon dioxide sent into the air whenever fossil fuels are burnt traps reflected heat from the earth's surface and prevents it from escaping into space - just as a greenhouse traps heat on a summer's day.

2   The ensuing 'global warming' can now be measured. Scientists working for the US's Department of Energy warn that the greenhouse effect could, within the next century, raise the world's temperatures to levels that have not been reached for 100 000 years. They have come up with two solutions: a technological fix, and something rather more sensible.

3 About 13 per cent of the gas that disappears up the chimney of a typical coal-fired power station is carbon dioxide. It could be removed, rather as sulphur dioxide can be at the base of the chimney stack. If every power station in the US installed equipment to remove carbon dioxde from waste products, it would cut the annual global addition of carbon dioxide to the atmosphere by 10 per cent. If the whole world did it, the reduction would be about 30 per cent.

4   A pioneer of the process of 'decarbonisation' is M. Steinberg of Brookhaven National Laboratory process science divison. He has proposed bubbling the gas through an organic solvent. Steinberg's original process required roughly half the energy produced by the power station to remove the carbon dioxide. A new system developed by Dow Chemicals uses a heat exchanger to extract latent heat from steam produced in the process and so radically reduces the energy cost of the system. Steinberg says: "Assuming a conventional power plant efficiency of 38 per cent ... integrating the carbon dioxide recovery system with the power plant in this manner lowers the coal- and gas-fired power plant efficiencies to 35-36 per cent". This is a significant improvement on a previous estimate that the efficiency of a coal-fired plant might plummet to 14 per cent. The net result of this process, however, is an awful lot of carbon dioxide, which has to be disposed of.

5 Steinberg and his colleagues propose three routes: injection into the deep ocean, storage in empty gas and oil wells, and storage in excavated salt caverns. They envisage an elaborate network of pipes across the US (and other countries), carrying liquid carbon dioxide from power stations to the dumping grounds. The cheapest disposal method, however, for most of the US, and for many other countries, is the sea. The problem with this method is that if the carbon dioxide is disgorged from pipes into shallow water, it would eventually reach the atmosphere and a lot of money spent stopping it going up the power station chimney would have been wasted.

6 Liquid carbon dioxide is less dense than seawater at shallow depths. But, says Steinberg, carbon dioxide is much more compressible and its density increases rapidly in deeper water, where the water pressures are higher. The gas becomes denser than seawater at about 3000 metres below sea level. At that depth "it could be expected to form a pool of liquid carbon di-oxide and sink to the ocean floor". In the northeast of the US, this would require a pipeline 300 kilometres long, threading its way along the seabed.

7 This massive infrastructure to get rid of unwanted carbon dioxide and prevent the gas from reaching the atmosphere would use up to 16 per cent of the output of the power stations across the country and increase the capital investment of building a power station by anything from 70 per cent to 150 per cent. Overall, electricity would cost 50-70 per cent more to produce, says Steinberg.

8   This sounds like the economics of the madhouse, and Steinberg, the chief architect of the technological fix for the greenhouse effect, is inclined to agree. In recent months he has switched his attention to looking at ways of creating less carbon dioxide by designing more efficient power stations and making better use of energy in factories, homes, offices and on the roads. The results are very encouraging.

9 Without allowing for any change in the overall pattern in energy use, or possible moves away from generating power by fossil fuels towards nuclear or renewable resources, Steinberg says that his proposals "amount to a 58 per cent reduction in the demand for fossil fuel in the year 2050 compared with the demand based on the technologies and energy efficiencies of the mid-1970s". In other words, it would reduced the predicted emissions of carbon dioxide from power station chimneys from 17 billion tonnes to 7 billion tonnes.

10 Steinberg has set his planning horizon at 2050 because, by then, "most of the present and emerging technologies will probably be fully developed up to their achievable efficiencies and will be available globally". It will also be about the time when, unless something is done to stop it, there will be twice as much carbon dioxide in the atmosphere.

11 Large reductions in energy demand from both industrial and domestic users are expected to result from improvements in the recovery of waste heat. New heating systems for buildings could use 30 per cent less fuel. The major industrial use of energy is the 'process heat' needed in the production of metals, chemicals, cement and oil refining. Improvements include new heat exchangers and heat pumps, and the process of 'energy cascading', in which several processes requiring successively lesser quantities of energy are placed in sequence so that each takes waste heat from the previous one.

12 Energy savings in the factories of the 2050s could, by these kinds of methods, amount to 48 per cent of the oil that might otherwise be used, 67 per cent of gas, 33 per cent of electricity and no less than 70 per cent of coal.

13 Cars and trucks have also caught the eyes of Steinberg and co. The efficiency of existing car engines could be increased by 15 per cent, they say, by reducing the vehicle's power:weight ratio, cutting internal friction, eliminating idling and the like. Of the useful energy output of an automobile, about 20 per cent is lost to friction inside the engine and 12 per cent to transmission and axle friction. Higher gear ratios and continuously variable transmission would bring more gains, as would radial tyres. New light composite materials will reduce vehicle weight, and more efficient engines, such as gas turbines, could recover energy from exhaust gases. Fuel consumption for the US's entire fleet of cars could be reduced by 65 per cent by the year 2050.

14 An increasing amount of the world's energy is ultimately consumed in the form of electricity. Steinberg sees no end to this "continuing trend towards a more electrified world". So, a second key of the energy-saving drive lies in improvements to technologies for generating electricity. On the face of it, electricity generation is a wasteful form of power. The overall efficiency of energy conversion in even the best modern power station is less than 40 per cent.

The new technologies which will give greater efficiencies are under development: fluidised beds, gasification of coal, fuel cells and magnetohydrodynamics (MHD).

15 Britain leads the world in the development of fluidised beds. Tiny particles of coal are mixed with ash at high pressure. Air is forced through the mixture, which acts as a fluid, transmitting heat from the burning coal throughout the mixture. Both fluidised beds and gasification can be hooked up to 'combined cycle' technology. This means the exhaust heat of a gas turbine is used to raise steam through a heat-recovery boiler for a steam turbine.

16 Fuel cells convert chemical energy directly into electrical energy, rather like a battery, except that the chemicals are fed continuously to the cell and the waste products are continually removed. Fuel cells use phosphoric acid or molten carbonate as the electrolyte. Hydrogen from naphtha or natural gas is pumped to the anode side of the cell where the electrolyte strips the hydrogen atoms of electrons, which provide electricity, while the surviving hydrogen ion reacts with oxygen being passed over the cathode to yield water. The cells have efficiencies of more than 50 per cent and, theoretically, could approach an efficiency of 100 per cent. New systems being developed use gasified coal as a source of hydrogen ions for the fuel.

17 In MHD, a gas or plasma, seeded with electrically charged particles and heated to around 3000 °C, produces electricity directly when passed through a strong magnetic field.

18 All this may sound fine for the developed world, but what about the developing nations? Traditional rural life may not tune in to the new high-tech low-CO_2 world, but by 2050 the majority of the people in the Third World will be in urban areas, and hooked up to the growing national electricity grids.

19 In much of the Third World, including most of China, Africa and Latin America, hydroelectric power is abundant. Steinberg believes that with the improvements in energy efficiency in giant factories and office blocks by 2050, many of these countries will be able to meet their entire electricity needs from this source.

20 Perhaps the most extraordinary and encouraging result of Steinberg's analysis is the conclusion that most of the savings will be cost effective. True, the bill is huge. "The total capital cost for implementing major energy-efficient technologies for the year 2050 is about six

trillion (million million) dollars for the US and 24 trillion dollars for the whole world", says Steinberg. But the return on investment looks good, too, he says. In the industrial sector, where some of the biggest savings will be made by recycling process heat, the return on investment is around 40 per cent. Building new power stations that are more efficient and production lines for energy-efficient cars is more expensive and yields a return of around 78 per cent and 5 per cent respectively, according to Steinberg's calculations.

(A shortened version of an article by Fred Pearce, in *New Scientist*, September 1986.)

Figure 4.10

Questions

1 What is the 'technological fix' mentioned in paragraph 2?

2 Paragraph 4 describes the power needed to remove carbon dioxide emissions by an older and an improved method. What is wrong with the figures quoted for power station efficiency?

3 How would carbon dioxide, discharged into shallow sea, get back into the atmosphere? (Paragraph 5.)

4 What are the 'emerging technologies' in paragraph 10 which are described in the remainder of the article? Can you list some that are not mentioned?

5 How does a fuel cell work, and why is it one attractive new technology? (Paragraph 16.)

6 Explain the statement 'Traditional rural life may not tune in to the new high-tech, low CO_2 world'. (Paragraph 18.)

7 Do you think the measures suggested will be useful to developing nations?

8 What is meant by a 'return on investment of 40 per cent'? (Paragraph 20.)

Comprehension exercise EM 1
PHYSICS IN THE KITCHEN

The applications of science in the kitchen have been growing steadily and almost unnoticed over the years. Time switches and thermostatically controlled cookers are commonplace and the idea of cooking with infra-red and microwaves nowadays barely raises an eyebrow. One of the latest developments is to make use of electromagnetic induction in cooking. A current is induced in the pans but the cooker itself never gets hot - you can only burn yourself on the saucepans.

Inside the stove are coils, each one corresponding to one of the cooking areas marked out on the glass-ceramic top. To start cooking, a rapidly alternating current is passed through a coil; this generates an oscillating magnetic field around the coil which, in turn, induces an electric current in the saucepan. Obviously, an electric current can be induced in anything metallic but, since a pan of optimum resistance is needed, copper is ruled out. Iron or steel can be used and these materials have the advantage that the induced current tends to be confined to a thinner layer which increases the resistance and hence power dissipated in the utensil. If a copper kettle is used, a device automatically cuts in to limit the current, and the stove turns itself off if a pan boils dry. An oscillator produces the high frequency current needed, which is over 18 kHz, and the device runs off a standard 240 V, 60 A power supply.

Some of the above principles are also used on a different scale in an attempt to solve a problem which seems to have caused a great deal of trouble - that of lighting a gas jet. This latest in a long line of different gadgets is now transistorised. It produces a spark within 30 μs which means that the gas is ignited almost immediately, avoiding a massive and dangerous build-up of gas. The whole unit is powered by a 1.5 V battery which drives an oscillator circuit connected to a coil. A second coil steps up the 20 V pulses from the oscillator to 300 V which are used to charge the main 1.5 μF capacitor.

The oscillator produces some 5000 pulses per second and it takes about 1000 pulses before the capacitor is fully charged. When the charge reaches a pre-determined level the capacitor is discharged rapidly (via a gas-filled gap set to break down at a preset voltage) through the primary of a transformer giving up to 15 kV at the spark gap. The typical energy of each spark is 1 mJ and the device will continue sparking at regular intervals. One interesting point is that the energy supplied at the spark gap is independent of the state of the battery, thus always ensuring a successful ignition.

(Freely adapted from C.J. Myers 'Domestic Science', *Physics Bulletin*, 1973, **24**, pp.350-52.)

Questions

1 (a) A cook using the electromagnetic induction stove can put a hand on one of the cooking areas before putting a pan on it and not get burnt. Write a few sentences explaining the principle on which the stove works and why a prospective user would not get burnt.
(b) The cook might also wonder about the wisdom of having electric currents flowing in cooking utensils. Explain why an electric shock would not occur if the metal part of a saucepan were touched while being heated on the stove.
(c) Discuss whether or not it would be dangerous to wear a wedding ring or bracelet while using the stove.

2 Figure 4.11 shows a saucepan being placed on one of the coils of the stove.
(a) Draw an enlarged diagram of the coil and then add to it a sketch of the magnetic field when the current in the coil is a maximum.
(b) Draw a separate diagram of the saucepan and on it show the paths of the currents induced (i) in the base of the saucepan, (ii) in the walls of the saucepan.
(c) At what stage in the cycle of changes in the magnetic field will the current in the saucepan be at a maximum? Give your reasoning.
(d) If there are electric currents in the coil and the pan, there may be a force (or forces) on the pan. Comment on this suggestion, saying what you can about the direction of any such forces.

continued

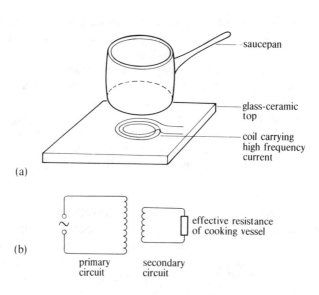

saucepan

glass-ceramic top

coil carrying high frequency current

(a)

effective resistance of cooking vessel

(b)

primary circuit   secondary circuit

Figure 4.11

3 The combination of cooking vessel and high frequency coil can be considered as a transformer in which the cooking utensil is both the secondary coil and the load resistor (figure 4.11b).

(a) Assuming a cooking vessel (secondary coil and load) to have an effective resistance of $0.2\,\Omega$, estimate how much current must flow in the vessel if power is being transformed at a rate of 2 kW.

(b) In the second paragraph it says there is an optimum value (i.e. neither too high nor too low) for the resistance of the cooking vessel. However, the passage does not give a clear or consistent explanation about this.

Make suggestions about the possible effects of having a cooking utensil the resistance of which is (i) very high, (ii) very low.

4 Draw a diagram to illustrate the various stages of the gas lighter as described in the passage. Components should be shown using the usual symbols but 'blocks' can be drawn for the oscillator circuit and for the gas-filled gap and the spark gap.

5 (a) An error has occurred in the article. The time of 30 μs (3rd paragaph) should refer to the *duration* of the spark and not to the *frequency* of sparking. What information in the article makes it apparent that the frequency of sparking is about once every 0.2 s?

(b) Use the information given in paragraph 4 to show that the maximum energy stored in the main 1.5 μF capacitor is about 70 mJ. (For a capacitor $Q = VC$ and the energy stored = $CV^2/2$.) Suggest why this value is different from the 1 mJ of energy of each spark .

(c) If the 1.5 μF capacitor stores an energy of 70 mJ, show that a frequency of sparking of once every 30 μs is not possible if the gas lighter is powered by a 1.5 V torch battery.

Oxford and Cambridge Examination Board (1975)

Comprehension exercise EN 1
THE DISCOVERY OF THE ELECTRON

The following passage is an extract from an article written by Sir George Thomson who was the son of Sir J.J. Thomson.

Every research turns up odd effects which might repay study. If one was to study them all each would lead in turn to other oddities in endless process and one would never get anywhere. Yet if one refuses to be deflected from the immediate object of research one risks imitating the notorious physicist of the [18]90s who found the photographic plates were fogged near a discharge tube and very quickly moved them away and so was able to continue his planned research undisturbed by the discovery of X-rays!

This ability to separate the significantly odd from the really trivial is one of the most valuable qualities a research scientist can have, for it not only helps him to take advantages of the breaks that nature may offer him but enables him to use those made by others. It frequently happens that the main development of a discovery is due to those who saw its significance quickly after the first announcement. Rutherford did not discovery radioactivity, nor the Braggs X-ray diffraction. Rutherford indeed abandoned in succession two very worthwhile lines in which he was doing excellent work, radio telegraphy and conduction in gases ionised by X-rays, to settle eventually on radioactivity. The main results from the original discovery of the Viennese ladies Blau and Wambacher that photographic plates left on a mountain showed microscopically visible tracks, were achieved in Britain, not in Austria.

The choice of an hypothesis is of great importance in any research. Getting hold of the right end of the stick, as my father used to call it. If one starts with the wrong idea it is terribly difficult to change. I have recently been studying the work on cathode rays in the [18]80s and early [18]90s which led to the discovery of the electron. Cathode rays are a phenomenon which appears when an electric discharge is sent through a gas at very reduced pressure, about 1/10 000th of an atmosphere. They appear as tracks of light in the gas diverging from one of the plates connected to the electric supply, but more brightly as patches of phosphorescence when they strike the glass walls of the vessel, particularly if these are coated with certain materials.

Hertz did a series of experiments in which he started with the idea that cathode rays are a phenomenon in the ether. This was a natural enough theory for the man who was later to discover the waves predicted by Maxwell. Hertz was an excellent experimenter but he found, among other things, that cathode rays are not deflected by an electric field set up between parallel plates placed outside the flat discharge vessel he was using, as one would expect if they were moving electrified particles. He thought of the possibility that the applied field might be neutralised by charges on the glass and put the plates inside the vessel. Still no deflection. At this point he stopped, his induction coil (a method of producing a very high voltage) was not working well and he had entirely satisfied himself by a long series of experiments, which I cannot now describe in detail, that his original hypothesis was correct. He seems not to have thought that there might be compensating charges near the plates even when these were inside the discharge vessel. If one had suggested it, he would probably have replied that the gas was a conductor so that such accumulations could not have occurred. Unfortunately for him, they do.

Later on, his pupil followed up another of Hertz's observations, namely that cathode rays can make a screen phosphoresce even when it is covered by gold leaf, a difficult thing to explain if, as the English and French supposed, the cathode rays were charged particles. It was surprisingly hard for physicists of those days to imagine that any particles could pass through a solid body without making a visible hole. Lenard was able to get the cathode rays clear to the discharge by passing them through a thin window into the atmosphere, where they showed as a diffuse luminous beam, capable of producing the characteristic phosphorescence. He made a number of experiments with these 'Lenard rays', sometimes in air, sometimes in an evacuated tube into which they passed through the window from the discharge vessel where the cathode rays were made.

Lenard was a superb experimenter, perhaps even better than Hertz, but he too started with the same wrong hypothesis and all his results seemed to him to fit it, including his very accurate measurements of the absorption of the rays by different materials which were one of the chief reasons that made my father believe that the particles of the cathode rays are a universal constituent of matter. Lenard did not, in fact, try Hertz's deflection experiment with the plates placed in his exhausted tube, when it would probably have succeeded, for the degree of exhaustion seems to have been high, so one can only guess whether it would have changed his view. It was left for J.J., by improving the vacuum, to show that the electric deflection really exists and to make it the basis for his proof of the electron.

There is an epilogue. After electrons, of which the cathode rays are one manifestation, had dominated physics for thirty years as particles, it became clear that they also have wave properties.

Questions

1 Explain what 'the notorious physicist of the[18]90s, (paragraph 1) failed to discover, and why.

2 X-rays (paragraph 1) and cathode rays (paragraph 3) are both produced using discharge tubes. What do we now believe cathode rays and X-rays to be?

3 Copy figure 4.12 and mark on your copy

(a) where you would expect to see tracks produced by cathode rays,
(b) the position of the parallel plates referred to in paragraph 4,
(c) the sign of the potential difference applied to the parallel plates and the corresponding direction in which the cathode rays *ought* to be deflected, and
(d) the charges which could cause the applied field to be neutralised.

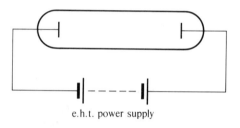

e.h.t. power supply

Figure 4.12

4 Paragraph 4 mentions a gas as being a conductor. Some people are surprised that a gas should be considered as a conductor. Outline an experiment to investigate the conditions which affect the conduction of electricity through gases.

5 (a) Suggest why it is that *nowadays* scientists do not think it quite so surprising that 'particles could pass through a solid body without making a visible hole' (paragraph 5).
(b) Name an experiment which gives evidence of a particle passing through a solid without leaving a hole.

6 In paragraph 3 the author asserts that the choice of an hypothesis is of great importance in research. Summarise briefly the main point of his argument in the rest of the passage which supports this assertion.

Comprehension exercise EN 2
THE ELECTRON PROBES THE NUCLEUS

The electron remained the lightest known particle for 35 years. Then, in 1932, studies of cosmic rays - showers of particles produced in the atmosphere by energetic particles from outer space - revealed the positron, a positively charged particle with the same mass as the negatively charged electron. The positron was the electron's complete antithesis - its antimatter counterpart, the first antiparticle to be observed. The experiments with cosmic rays showed pairs of electrons and positrons produced simultaneously from gamma rays that had been radiated by electrons passing through dense matter.

When electron and positron came close enough to each other the reverse process occurred: the two particles would annihilate to produce a gamma ray.

Electrons (and positrons) appear to be completely stable. Provided an electron does not encounter a positron, or vice versa, the particles should live for ever. However, electrons can be made in a variety of ways, and studying how electrons are produced has provided physicists with a rich view of the nature of matter. Thomson showed that the particles of the photoelectric effect and cathode rays were one and the same, and we now know that in these instances the electrons are knocked from orbiting within atoms, either by light or by strong electric fields. By the opening years of the 20th century, experimenters had also shown that the so-called beta rays, emitted by certain radioactive substances, also consist of energetic electrons. However, it was to be a number of years before physicists fully understood how electrons are produced in radioactive decays.

In 1932, the discovery of the neutron put paid to the idea that electrons exist *within* the nucleus at the heart of the atom, as well as in orbitals extending throughout the atom. The nucleus could now be understood in terms of positively charged protons and neutral neutrons, each weighing some 2000 times as much as the tiny electron. The neutron also cast light on the process of beta decay because it too was radioactive. A single neutron, free from the forces at work within the nucleus, lives for only 15 minutes before decaying into a proton, an electron and a virtually invisible particle, the neutrino (or strictly, in the case of the decay of a neutron, an antineutrino).

In the first reasonably successful attempt at a theory for beta decay, the Italian physicist Enrico Fermi imagined that the neutron radiates an electron and an antineutrino simultaneously, rather as a charged particle such as an electron can radiate a photon of light. In the process, the neutron loses a unit of negative electric charge, and so becomes a positively charged particle - a proton. Fermi based his theory on the quantum theory of the electron, which successfully explained how electrons could radiate photons.

Physicists now know that Fermi, in 1934, did not have the story quite right. The decaying neutron, in fact, emits a so-called W particle, which then almost instantly materialises as an electron and an antineutrino. In this case, the W is a 'virtual' particle. This means that the particle's creation apparently defies the law of energy conservation, as the W's mass is some 90 times greater than the mass of a neutron. But the W exists for such a short period of time that this discrepancy is shrouded by the uncertainty inherent in quantum phenomena.

In recent years, physicists have successfully created 'real' W particles, but even these are detected only via the electrons and antineutrinos into which they decay. In the same experiments, physicists have also created the related Z particles, which are electrically neutral - a kind of 'heavy light'. Z particles can decay into electron-positron pairs, rather as gamma-ray photons materialise in this way, and these pairs provide a distinctive 'signature' for the Zs.

The electron's stability means that it often provides the only lasting record of the existence of some short-lived particles. In another form of beta decay, the particle known as the muon decays to an electron, a neutrino and an antineutrino. This decay can leave a characteristic pattern in detectors that record the tracks of particles, particularly when the muon itself is born in the decay of another short-lived particle, such as the pion.

The muon has more clues to offer, however. It is some 210 times heavier than the electron, has a lifetime of only 2.2 microseconds, but in other respects behaves just like an electron. Physicists now recognise the muon as a 'heavy electron'.

The muon was discovered in cosmic-ray experiments in the mid-1930s; indeed, it is a major component of the cosmic radiation. More recently, however, experimenters working at particle accelerators, which can reproduce the effects of cosmic-ray showers under more controlled conditions, have found a third electron-like particle, called the tau. The tau is even heavier than the muon, with a mass some 3600 times greater than the electron's - greater even than the mass of the proton. It lives for a mere 10^{-13} seconds or so, but is in every other respect like a heavy electron. Why three versions of the electron should exist in this way remains one of the puzzles of particle physics.

The electron is very small (and so are its relations). It is smaller than experimenters can measure even with their most sophisticated techniques, which implies that it is less than 10^{-18} metres in size. The proton and the neutron, on the other hand, are much bigger, with a radius of about 10^{-15} metres. This difference has made the electron an ideal probe for studying the structure of larger particles such as protons and neutrons.

In the 1960s, SLAC built its first famous machine, a linear electron accelerator, which at 3 kilometres in length is still the longest in the world. In their experiments in the 1890s, physicists such as Thomas and Wiechert had observed what happens when electrons cross evacuated tubes about 50 centimetres long. The electric field set up between the electrodes of one of these tubes accelerated the electrons to energies of roughly a thousand electronvolts (1 keV). (One electronvolt is the energy an electron gains crossing an electric potential of one volt.) By 1967, the machine at SLAC was accelerating electrons to 20 thousand million electron volts, that is, 20 GeV. Now [1987] it has reached 50 GeV.

The physicists at SLAC have used this enormous 'peashooter' to fire energetic electrons at protons and neutrons. Not long after the machine first started up, the researchers discovered that although the electrons often travelled through the larger particles, deviating only slightly, on many occasions they were scattered through large angles. This was the first direct evidence for a 'hard' structure within the proton and the neutron - structure that physicists now recognise as the elementary building bricks called quarks, and the gluons that bind the quarks together. In particular, because the electron doesnot feel the strong force that acts on quarks, the experiments revealed the electromagnetic properties of the quarks, confirming the idea that they carry charges that are fractions - 1/3 and 2/3 - the charge of the electron.

The 1970s proved exciting years at SLAC. First, there were the results from the linear accelerator. Then, the laboratory built its first version of a new type of machine - an electron-positron collider, called SPEAR. Such a machine has a number of advantages over a linear accelerator - although there are also disadvantages. In firing electrons at protons sitting in a 'target', much of the electrons' hard-won energy is dissipated in simply knocking the protons (or more precisely, the quarks) forwards, as in a game of subatomic billiards. This is because the collisions must conserve momentum - a fundamental law of physics. However, in bringing bunches of particles into a head-on collision, where the particles have equal but opposite momentum, the total momentum is zero. So, no energy need be 'wasted' in motion necessary to conserve the momentum. Instead, all the energy of the collision is available to probe the forces between the particles and to create new particles.

When an electron and a positron collide they annihilate and create for an instant a 'virtual' photon - a burst of energy - which rapidly materialises as particles and antiparticles. The photon can convert into an electron and a positron, or a muon and its antiparticle, or a tau and an antitau. Alternatively, the photon can rematerialise as a quark and an antiquark. The quark and antiquark cannot exist for long as individual particles - the strong force prevents this. Instead, additional quarks and antiquarks quickly materialise from the energy of the collision, and form particles such as protons and pions.

(From 'Ninety years around the atom' by Christine Sutton, *New Scientist,* 8.1.87.)

Questions

1 Giving examples where you think them helpful, what do you understand by the following:

positron, antiparticle, beta decay, W particle, Z particle, electron-like particle, virtual photon?

2 Explain the relationship between electrons and gamma rays.

3 When a neutron decays, energy is apparently not conserved. Why is this and how is it explained?

continued

4 Define the electronvolt (eV). What energy, in joules, has an electron accelerated to 50 GeV? What is its speed? What is its mass at this energy?

Use $m = \dfrac{m_0}{\sqrt{\left(1 - \dfrac{v^2}{c^2}\right)}}$

where m_0 is the rest mass of the electron and c is the speed of light.

5 Calculate the mass of the proton in GeV.

6 What direct evidence is there for substructure in protons and neutrons?

Comprehension exercise EN 3
WHAT IS THERMONUCLEAR FUSION?

Take two light atoms: bang them together hard enough and they will overcome the natural repulsion that their nuclei have for each other. The nuclei will combine. The result will be a larger nucleus and a number of nuclear particles. These particles will carry with them some energy. This process, thermonuclear fusion, is the opposite of nuclear fission - in which nuclei fall apart, delivering particles and energy in the process. Fission is what drives the atom bomb: fusion drives the hydrogen bomb.

Deuterium and tritium will probably be the first fusion fuels because they are the easiest to coax together. Unfortunately, forcing two atoms together is extremely difficult - it requires very high temperatures, over 100 million, kelvin and some tough 'confinement' conditions. At present, fusion researchers expend more energy in trying to coax atoms to fuse than the fusion reactions can hope to deliver. This is why it has taken more than 30 years to progress from machines that could sit on a laboratory bench to machines that need a building bigger than a cathedral. Nuclear fission took less than a decade to go from bomb to power station. Thirty years ago, the first H-bomb exploded: we still don't know if we can build a fusion power station.

To make deuterium and tritium fuse, their temperature has to be around 100 million kelvin. At this temperature both are completely ionised: the electrons and the nuclei are completely dissociated. Physicists call this state of matter a 'plasma', effectively a mixture of negatively charged electrons and positively charged nuclei. The properties of a plasma are such that a complex configuration of magnetic fields can kept it together. This is just as well because no physical container could possibly keep together a gas at 100 million degrees.

Even so, plasma has the annoying habit of wriggling out of any magnetic container, or of leaking through it. As well as achieving the right temperature, a fusion reactor has to stem this flow, in other words, it has to get the 'containment' right. Plasma physicists describe the quality of containment in terms of the 'energy confinement time', the time for which the plasma holds its energy. If this time is too low - either because particles escape or radiation drains away energy - fusion reactions cannot hope to generate more energy than went into setting up the system, ionising the gas and heating it. The goal of fusion research since it began around 1950 has been to building magnetic containers with smaller and smaller leaks.

The third important factor, after the temperature and the confinement time, is the density of the plasma. There must be enough nuclei if fusion reactions are to happen quickly enough to keep up the temperature and to beat the inevitable exodus of energy from the system as neutrons and radiation escape.

The density and the confinement time are combined in a factor known as the Lawson number. The Lawson number has to reach a crucial level for fusion to be a feasible process for a reactor - for obvious reasons, this level is known as the Lawson criterion.

Over the past 30 years, the Lawson number has risen gradually as fusion researchers have built bigger and better - and much more expensive - containment devices. Different machines have achieved one or other of the goals of fusion - the right temperature or the right Lawson number - but no machine has managed to get both right. The current generation of tokamaks - JT-60, JET and TFTR - just might do it, if all goes well. Then we will face the problem of turning these physics experiments into commercial reactors.

Inertial confinement is different. This is really no more than a miniature H-bomb. Here the problem is to get the plasma hot enough and quickly enough for fusion reactions to take place and deliver their energy before the deuterium and tritium fly apart because of the kinetic energy they acquire from the laser heater.

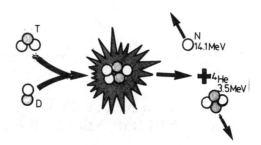

Hydrogen is the most likely fuel for the first fusion reactors. There are three isotopes of hydrogen: ordinary hydrogen, deuterium and tritium. All have a single proton in their nucleus: they differ in the neutron complement. Hydrogen has one neutron, deuterium has two and tritium three.

Fuse tritium (T) and deuterium (D) together and the result is a helium nucleus (an alpha particle) and a neutron. Both of these particles carry some energy.

(From 'Japan's rising man-made Sun'. Bob Johnstone, *New Scientist*, 26.2.87.)

Questions

1 Explain in your own words:

(a) thermonuclear fusion,
(b) plasma,
(c) containment,
(d) containment time,
(e) plasma density.

2 (a) What three factors necessary to achieve thermonuclear fusion are difficult to achieve simultaneously?
(b) Which of these are combined to give the Lawson number?

3 (a) Write down the nuclear equation of the reaction shown in the diagram.
(b) Where has the energy liberated in this reaction come from?
(c) By reference to appropriate tables, calculate how much energy is liberated in the reaction.

Comprehension excerise ES 1
MOLECULAR BEAM EPITAXY

Molecular beam epitaxy (MBE) describes the growth of thin films (< 10 μm) on crystalline surfaces, known as substrates, from beams of molecules produced by heating and evaporating suitable materials. The films may be formed of elements or compounds. The whole process takes place at very low pressures (< 10^{-9} torr), conditions known as ultra high vacua. The single crystal substrate influences the film growth to produce an 'orientated overgrowth', a process known as epitaxy, so that the film generally has the same crystalline structure as the substrate but not necessarily the same chemical composition.

The preparation of semiconductor materials and devices represents the major application of the technique.

Early work

Simple evaporation of elements and compounds to form films on various surfaces has been achieved in medium to high vacua (about 10^{-6} torr) for some time. With such vacuum conditions, however, molecules from the residual gas in the vacuum chamber may be incorporated in the growing film as impurities.

Thus, a major difference between the early work and modern MBE is that, in the latter, the ultra high vacuum allows the growth of single crystal films on clean substrates and any impurities in the films due to the residual gas in the vacuum chamber are minimised. The importance of such cleanliness for obtaining good epitaxial films only become evident when special instruments for analysing the structure and composition of the films as they were growing were incorporated in the vacuum chamber.

Kinetic theory shows that the number of gas molecules striking unit area of surface per unit time is given by

$$b \frac{p}{\sqrt{MT}}$$

where b is a constant of value 2.63 x 10^{24} SI units, p is the residual gas pressure in pascal, M is the relative molecular mass of the gas and T is the temperature in kelvin. It follows that at pressures of about 10^{-6} torr, exposed surfaces can be covered with gas molecules within a few seconds. In ultra high vacua (about 10^{-10} torr) this can take several hours. There is thus a clear need to know the pressure and the nature of any residual gas. The residual gases are analysed using a mass spectrometer.

Substrates and film growth

The material of the substrate is chosen so that its crystalline structure is closely similar to that of the film. Any mismatch of lattice sizes may cause strains in the film which in semiconductor films can lead to a worsening of electrical properties. This problem can be overcome by 'grading' the growth, the film composition being varied as deposition takes place so that there is a gradual transition from the crystal structure to that of the film.

In most MBE work, growth rates are 0.1 μm per hour to 1 μm per hour. The molecular beams, from which the films are formed, are produced from small ovens sited within the chamber. In these ovens the materials to be evaporated are raised to appropriately high and controlled temperatures. Several such ovens are needed if multi-component films are required. Substrate temperatures are also controlled. In general, MBE offers lower growth temperatures than any other technique, a factor which is important if diffusion effects need to be minimised. As well as producing smooth thin layers, these slow growth rates allow good control over layer thicknesses. Thus, MBE can produce sharp or abrupt interfaces between semiconductor film and substrate or between successive films of different semiconductor materials so that abrupt doping profiles (i.e. the variation of carrier concentration with distance from the substrate) can be formed.

[*Note*. Many scientists and vacuum technologists use the torr as the unit of gas pressure. 1 torr $\equiv$ 1 mm of Hg = 133.32 Pa (or N m^{-2}).]

(Extract from 'Device Fabrication for the Future?', J.D. Grange and E.H.C. Parker, *Physics Bulletin*, Vol. 30 (1979).

Questions

1 Explain in your own words the terms

(a) *substrate,*
(b) *orientated overgrowth,*
(c) *residual gas.*

2 The residual gas in a certain vacuum system at 10^{-8} torr and 300 K consists mainly of traces of water vapour. How long will it take for a clean surface of area 10^{-4} m^2 to become covered with 10^{15} molecules of water? State any assumption you have made. (Relative molecular mass of water = 18.)

3 A semiconductor thin film is grown for 40 minutes by MBE on to a crystalline substrate of another semiconductor at a rate of 0.6 μm per hour. How thick is the deposit? By estimating the size of the atoms involved determine the number of atom-layers to which the thickness corresponds.

4 What are the main advantages of modern MBE techniques over earlier evaporation methods for the fabrication of thin film semiconductor devices?

5 List the various quantities which you think need to be measured or monitored in a modern MBE system. Name the instruments or devices which you would use to measure or monitor two of these quantities.

6 A semiconductor is to be grown as a thin film on a single crystal substrate. Describe the nature of the film which might be expected if the film were grown

(a) in ultra high vacuum and the lattice size of the susbtrate closely matched that of the semiconductor,
(b) in ultra high vacuum and the lattice size of the substrate differed from that of the semiconductor.

London Examination Board (1984)

Data analysis excerise ES 2
THE RECTIFIER EQUATION

Corresponding measured values of potential difference V, and current I, for a semiconductor diode are given in table 4.3

Potential difference, V/V	Current, I/μA
0.255	0.40
0.315	1.60
0.345	3.6
0.385	8.9
0.410	18.2
0.455	52.2
0.475	90.3
0.495	140
0.505	182
0.515	223
0.530	310

Table 4.3

Questions

1 Using the values in table 4.3 plot a graph with I as ordinate against V as abscissa. Determine, for the point on the graph corresponding to $V = 0.500$ V

(a) the rate of change of I with V, and hence
(b) the percentage change in I corresponding to a 1% change in V.

2 The following theoretical equation (the 'rectifier equation') applies for certain types of semi-conductor diode:

$$I = I_0 (e^{\alpha V} - 1) \qquad (3)$$

where I_0 and α are constants.

If V is sufficiently large, $\quad I \approx I_0 e^{\alpha V} \quad$ (4)

so that $\qquad \ln I \approx \ln I_0 + \alpha V$

or $\qquad \log_{10} I \approx \log_{10} I_0 + 0.434\, \alpha V$

From an appropriate table of values plot

either a graph of ln (I/μA) as ordinate against V as abscissa,

or a graph of $\log_{10}$ (I/μA) as ordinate against V as abscissa.

From your graph derive values for I_0 and α.

3 Explain for which value of potential difference in table 4.3 the approximation made in equation (4) will be most serious. Using the values of I_0 and α derived in question 2, calculate the current at this p.d. using the exact equation (3) (e = 2.72). Plot the corresponding point on your second graph.

continued

State, giving your reasons, whether you consider that use of the approximate equation (4) was justified in analysing the results in table 4.3.

University of London Examination Board (1980)

Part 5
Option topic study guides

Introduction

Certain syllabuses include a study of a number of topics in physics as an extension to the core. The aim is either to go into more depth in a theoretical topic or to study the applications of physics principles in some technical detail, which may also include social and economic implications.

The topics dealt with here are:

5.1   Electronics
5.2   Energy and its uses
5.3   Fluids and waves
5.4   Medical physics
5.5   Nuclearphysics
5.6   Optical instruments
5.7   Physics of astronomy
5.8   Rotational dynamics
5.9   Solid materials
5.10   Telecommunications

Each topic is divided into themes with the following features:

> objectives;
> study questions and references;
> self-assessment questions.

Answers to the self-assessment questions are given at the end of each topic.

Your teacher has a list of additional resources and suggested practical work for some of the options.

The choice of topics to study should be made in discussion with your teacher with reference to the syllabus. The precise requirements of the syllabuses of the different boards may vary from year to year, and additional topics may be added. The content of a topic for one board may differ from that of another, with the same title. For example, the Medical Physics of London contains three main themes and requires about two-and-a-half weeks study, whereas JMB has four themes and requires about five weeks study.

5.1 Electronics

Theme 1 Operational amplifiers

Study time 1.5 weeks

Objectives

When you have completed the work in this theme you should be able to:

1 Use the following terms correctly: amplification, inverting and non-inverting amplifiers, transfer characteristics, negative feedback, frequency response, integration, analogue computing.

2 Understand the basic characteristics of a perfect op-amp.

3 Understand the use of negative feedback in the following amplifier circuits: inverting, non-inverting and summing.

4 Recall and use the relationships between the output and input voltages in the circuits mentioned in objective 3.

5 Understand that a voltage follower is a non-inverting amplifier with a gain of 1.

6 Describe uses of the circuits mentioned in objectives 3 and 5.

7 Describe the relationship between frequency response and gain for an op-amp amplifier.

8 Understand the use of an op-amp as an integrator.

9 Be able to use the op-amp integrator circuit in the solution of first - order differential equations involving exponential decay or growth.

Study questions and references

Basic references

Duncan (SIE)	Chapter 13
Gregory	Chapters 4 and 8
Hartley	Chapter 15
Sparkes	Chapter 4

1 Make notes on the terms used in objective 1.

2 Describe the basic characteristics of an ideal op-amp and then compare them with a commercially available device.

3 Describe the operation, and give examples of their use, of the op-amp circuits mentioned in objectives 3 and 5.

4 Explain how the op-amp integrator circuit works and describe some practical applications for it.

5 Describe how the op-amp can be used for the solution of a first order differential equation for (a) exponential decay, and (b) exponential growth.

Experimental work

You will need apparatus similar to that used in *Electronic systems*, experiments 13, 14 and 15. Do not forget the power-lines for the op-amp. If you are using a manufactured op-amp module, you will have to use its component values for resistors and capacitors.

1 Transfer characteristics of the non-inverting amplifier

(a) Set up the circuit as shown in figure E1. Set the gain $= (R_a + R_f)/R_a$ to a convenient value.

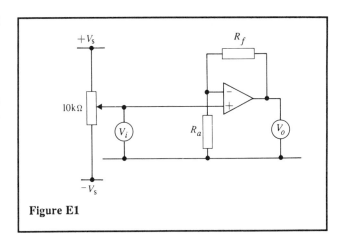

Figure E1

(b) By varying V_i and measuring V_i and V_o, the transfer characteristics can be plotted.

(c) With a gain of 10 (or more) connect a frequency generator to the input and use a double-beam oscilloscope to monitor V_i and V_o. Ensure that V_o does not reach the saturation voltage. Investigate the relationship between the frequency response and the gain. It may be helpful to plot the frequency as a logarithm.

(d) You may like to repeat steps 2 and 3 using an inverting amplifier.

Student's Resource Book
Part 5 Option topic study guides | 121

2 The summing amplifier

(a) With $R_f = R_{a1} = R_{a2} = 10^4 \ \Omega$, set up the circuit shown in figure E2. The gain is -1, i.e. $V_o = - (V_i' + V_i'')$. Ensure that V_o does not reach the saturation voltage.

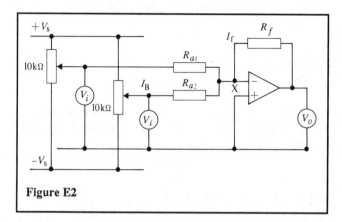

Figure E2

(b) By using various values of V_i' and V_i'', check that $V_o = -(V_i' + V_i'')$. Ensure that V_o does not reach the saturation voltage.

(c) It is possible to multiply and divide the input voltages. Using the fact that

$$V_0 = -\left(\frac{R_f}{R_{a1}}\right)V_i' - \left(\frac{R_f}{R_{a2}}\right)V_i''$$

set up the relationship $V_0 = 2V_i' + 0.5V_i''$

3 The voltage follower

(a) Set up the circuit shown in figure E3. Since $R_f = 0$ and $R_a = \infty$, the gain = 1.

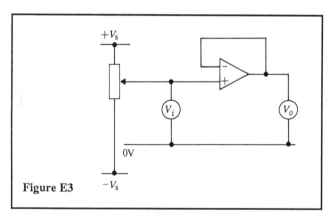

Figure E3

(b) By plotting the transfer characteristic, check that V_o 'follows' V_i.

(c) Cne of the uses of this circuit is when no current can be taken from the voltage source. Connect a moving-coil voltmeter across a charged capacitor. Note what happens. Use the same voltmeter in place of V_o as shown in figure E4. Connect the recharged capacitor to the input. Explain what is observed.

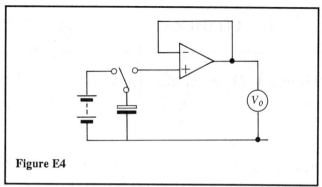

Figure E4

4 Integrating with the op-amp

(a) The circuit is shown in figure E5. V_o is related to V_i by the equation

$$V_0 = -\frac{1}{CR} \int V_i \, dt$$

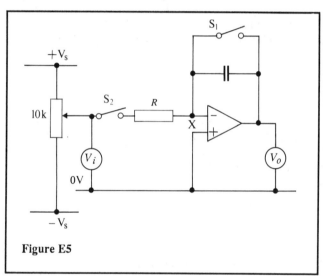

Figure E5

(b) With $C = 1 \ \mu F$, $R = 1 \ M\Omega$ and V_i constant, the relationship becomes $V_o = -V_i t$ (in seconds).

(c) Set V_i to a convenient value, say 1V. Briefly close S_1 (this discharges C) and then close S_2. Does $V_o = V_i t$?

(d) The relationship can be investigated with other positive or negative values of V_o.

(e) The output can be displayed on an oscilloscope using the square wave function of a signal generator. Note that the value of CR (the time constant) must be very much less than the period of the square wave.

5 Exponential decay - I

(a) The circuit is shown in figure E6. The output can be read with a voltmeter if the following component values are used.

(b) With $C = 1 \ \mu F$ and $R = 1 \ M\Omega$, close the switch to charge the capacitor to a p.d. V'.

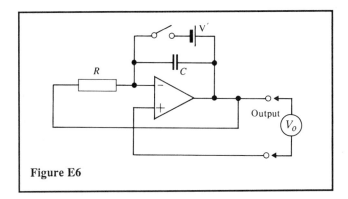

Figure E6

7 Exponential growth

(a) The circuit shown in figure E8 can be used. Note the use of the inverting amplifier to provide a gain of -1. The output can be read with a voltmeter.

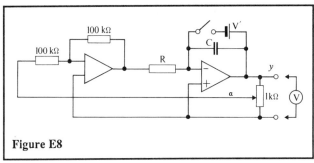

Figure E8

(c) Open the switch and record the variation of output voltage with time. If you have access to a VELA this will make the recording process easier. Use program O2.

(d) The output voltage V is given by

$$V = V' \, e^{-t/CR} \text{ where } V' = \text{voltage at } t = 0$$

How would you check that the output voltage does represent an exponential decay?

(b) The output voltage is given by $V = V' \, e^{t/CR}$ (if the output is connected directly to the inverting input of the left-hand op-amp).

(c) With $C = 1 \, \mu\text{F}$, $R = 1 \, \text{M}\Omega$ and a known fraction (α) of the output p.d. being fed back,

$$V = V' \, e^{\alpha t}$$

(d) Investigate this relationship. It is advisable to keep V' fairly small as the output voltage will take longer to saturate.

6 Exponential decay - II

(a) The circuit is shown in figure E7. The output can be read with a voltmeter if the suggested component values are used.

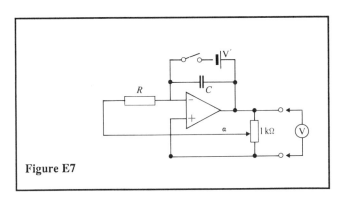

Figure E7

(b) It is possible to vary the rate of the decay by varying C and/or R or using the arrangement shown in figure E7. It is easier to use the arrangement shown in figure E7.

(c) With $C = 1 \, \mu\text{F}$ and $R = 1 \, \text{M}\Omega$, $CR = 1 \, \text{s}$, i.e. $V = V' e^{-t}$ in the circuit shown in figure E7. A known fraction (α) of the output voltage across the 1 kΩ potentiometer can be fed back to the inverting input via R. The equation for exponential decay becomes

$$V = V' \, e^{-\alpha t} \text{ (with } C = 1 \, \mu\text{F and } R = 1 \, \text{M}\Omega)$$

(d) Investigate this relationship. It is necessary to know α. This can be done by separately measuring the resistance of the 'tapped off' sections of the potentiomer using a multimeter.

Self-assessment questions

The operational amplifier in the circuit diagram in figure E9 (a) has supply voltages of ±15 V and can be considered ideal.

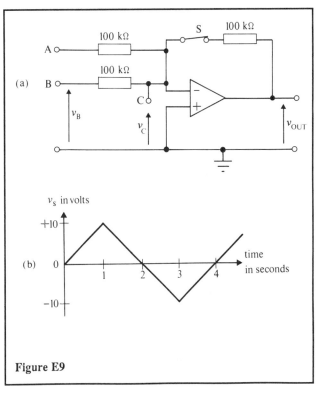

Figure E9

1 In each of the following three cases the voltage waveform shown in figure E9(b) is applied to the input B. Sketch waveforms to show the resulting output voltage v_{out} and the voltage v_C at the point C:

(a) when the switch S is closed and the input A is left unconnected;
(b) when the switch S is open and the input A is left unconnected;
(c) when the switch S is closed and a steady +1.0 V d.c. is applied to the input A.

2 In the circuit shown in figure E10, the operational amplifier is connected to power supply lines at +15 V and -15 V, and $V_1 = 1.5$ V, $V_2 = 10$ mV and $V_3 = 10$ V. All switches remain open unless otherwise stated.

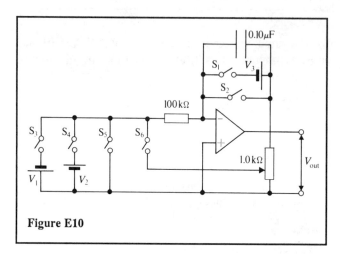

Figure E10

For each of the following settings of the switches, use appropriate equations to explain how V_{out} occurs. Illustrate each of your answers with a sketch graph on which each axis is labelled with an appropriate scale.

(a) S_2 briefly closed then S_3 closed.
(b) S_2 briefly closed then S_4 closed. After 5 seconds S_4 is opened again as S_5 is closed.
(c) S_1 briefly closed and then S_4 closed.
(d) S_1 briefly closed and then S_6 closed. Indicate on your graph the effect of adjusting the 1.0 kΩ potentiometer. With the potentiometer set at the mid-point position, calculate the value of V_{out} 4.0 s after S_6 is closed.

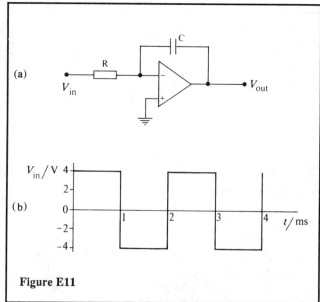

Figure E11

3 (a) Name the circuit shown in figure E11(a) and derive an expression for the output voltage, V_{out} in terms of the input voltage V_{in} the resistance R and the capacitance C.

(b) If $R = 10$ kΩ and $C = 0.1$ μF in the circuit shown in part (a), draw a graph showing the variation of the output voltage with time when the input voltage varies as shown in figure E11(b). (Assume that $V_{out} = 0$ when $t = 0$.)

(c) Show by means of a diagram how the circuit in (a) can be combined with a potential divider to satisfy the condition

$$V_{in} = \frac{V_{out}}{5}$$

Indicate on your diagram how V_{out} can be set initially to +6V.

Assuming that $C = 1$ μF and $R = 1$ MΩ, sketch a graph of V_{out} against time. Calculate the value of V_{out} after 5 s have elapsed.

Theme 2   Logic circuits

Study time 1.5 weeks

Objectives

When you have completed the work in this theme you should be able to:

1 Use the following terms correctly: logic gate, positive logic, truth table, binary system, binary number, bit, flip-flop, asynchronous, module

2 Recall the truth tables of the following logic gates:

NOT, AND, NAND, OR, NOR, exclusive OR and exclusive NOR gates

3 Construct truth tables for any combination of the above gates.

4 Using NAND gates only, construct binary half- and full-adders and understand their action.

5 Using two NAND gates, construct a basic SR flip-flop and understand its action.

6 Compare the action of the SR, D, T and JK flip-flops.

7 Describe the use of T flip-flops to construct an asynchronous 4-bit counter.

8 Describe the construction of a modular 10 counter.

Study questions and references

Basic references

Duncan (SIE) Chapter 15
Gregory   Chapters 2 and 3
Hartley   Chapters 16
Sparkes   Chapter 5

1 Write out the truth tables for each of the following logic gates: NOT, AND, NAND, OR, NOR.

2 Make notes on binary adders. In your answer, explain the binary representation of decimal numbers, the disadvantages of the simple adder and the difference between a half- and full-adder.

3 Explain the action of SR flip-flop. Include the truth table in your account.

4 Explain the differences in action between the SR, D, T and JK flip-flops.

5 Describe how four T flip-flops can be connected together to produce a four bit binary counter. Include the timing diagram in your account.

6 Describe what additions need to be made to convert the four bit counter into a modular-10 counter.

Experimental work

You will need apparatus similar to that used in *Electronic systems*, experiments 11 and 12. With the counting circuits in experiments 6 to 8 the wiring becomes very complicated using a breadboard. If you have a suitable logic teaching aid you are advised to use this. Either CMOS or TTL chips can be used but the correct power supply must be used. For CMOS this is easier as any smoothed d.c. supply between 3 and 18 V is suitable. TTL chips require a SV regulated supply.

Chips required	CMOS	TTL
quad 2 input AND	4081	7408
quad 2 input NAND	4011	7400
quad 2 input exclusive OR	4070	7486
quad 2 input NOR	4077	74266
4 bit full adder	4008	7483
dual D-type flip-flop	4013	7474

1 Checking truth tables of gate combinations

Note. The pin layouts for CMOS and TTL logic gates are slightly different - see figure E12.

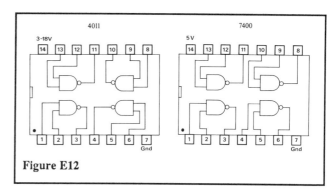

Figure E12

(a) Two NAND gates connected as shown in figure E13(a) should act as an AND gate. Set up the combination and check that this is correct. Do not forget the power lines to the chip: pin 14 (-V) and pin 7 (0V).

(b) Three NAND gates connected as shown in figure E13(b) should act as an OR gate. Set up the combination and check this is correct.

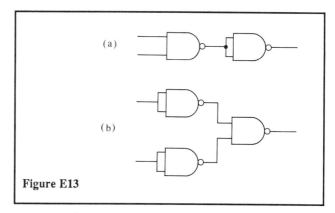

(a)

(b)

Figure E13

2 The exclusive OR and exclusive NOR gates

(a) With the exclusive OR gate, the output is high only when *one* input is high. Check that this is correct.

(b) With the exclusive NOR gate, the output is low only when *one* input is high. Check that this is correct.

(c) Build the NAND gate combination shown in figure E14 and check its truth table. What gate does the combination function as?

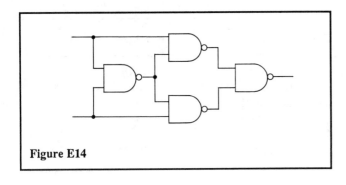

Figure E14

3 The binary half-adder

(a) This device adds two binary digits (represented by inputs A and B). Figure E15(a) shows how this can be done using just NAND gates. Check that it functions as a binary adder.

(b) Figure E15(b) shows a simpler way of constructing the half-adder. If an AND gate is not available, it can be replaced by two NAND gates.

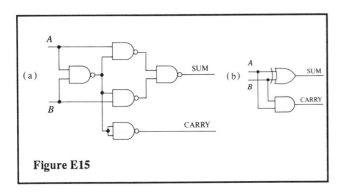

Figure E15

4 The binary full-adder

(a) Figure E16(a) shows a diagrammatic representation of a full-adder. A and B represent the binary digits but there is the facility for a 'carry' from the previous column of the addition. This is usually called the 'carry in' (C_{in}).

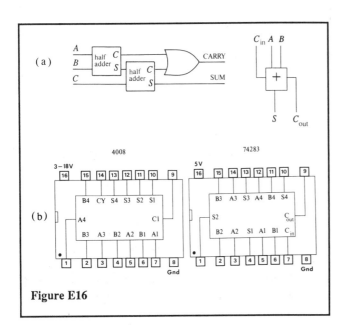

Figure E16

If the full-adder produces a carry, this is then called the carry out (C_{out}) and is passed to the next full-adder.

(b) Even a single full-adder is complicated to build but Figure E16(b) shows the CMOS and TTL chips that allow two four digit binary numbers to be added (with carry in and carry out facilities).

(c) The two numbers are A4A3A2A1 and B4B3B2B1. The sum is S4S3S2S1. The carry in is C_1 or (C_{in}) and the carry out is C_y (or C_{out}). All unused inputs must be connected to 0 V. Try adding some binary numbers.

5 The bistable latch or SR flip-flop

(a) Figure E17 shows a basic form of the circuit. Although little used in practice, it forms the basis of digital counting circuits. Build the circuit as shown. Q and $\bar{Q}$ are the outputs. Connect each output separately to 0 V with 680 Ω resistors and LED.

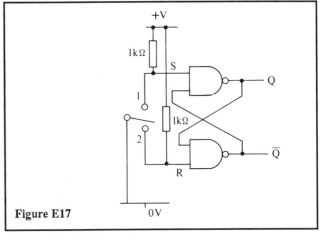

Figure E17

(b) Connect S to 0 V. Explain the state of the outputs.

(c) Connect R to 0 V. Explain the state of the outputs.

(d) Why must S and R not both be taken to 0 V at the same time?

(e) With S = R = 1, explain why the state of the outputs depends on the step before both were made 1.

6 Construction of a binary-3 counter

(a) It is as simple to use D-type flip-flops as T-type flip-flops. Both the CMOS and TTL D-type flip-flops trigger on the rising edge of the clock pulse. The pin arrangements are shown in figure E18(a). Note that the S(set) and R(reset) pins on each D-type in the CMOS chip must be tied low for counting. They are unconnected on the TTL and 'float' high.

(b) Set up the arrangement shown in figure E18(b). Using a slow clock (the SR flip-flop could be used), check that the binary counter goes to binary before resetting to 0 (note that Q_A is the least significant digit).

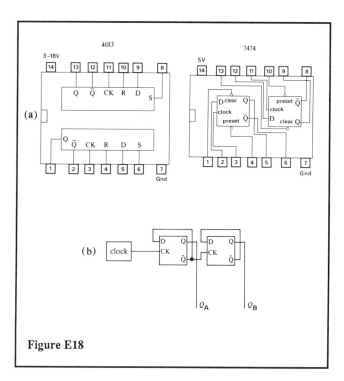

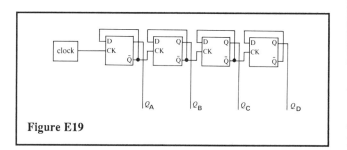

Figure E18

(c) It is possible with a few changes to make the counter count downwards from binary 3 to 0. See if you can work out how this is done.

7 Construction of binary-15 counter

(a) This requires two chips, i.e. four D-type flip-flops. The layout shown in figure E19 is an extension of the binary-3 counter used in the previous experiment. It is laborious to produce this circuit using a breadboard especially when there is a single chip that will do the complete job (CMOS: 4516; TTL: 7493).

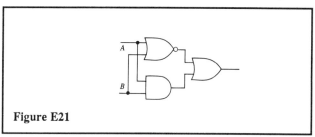

Figure E19

(b) Check that the completed circuit counts to 1111 before resetting to 0.

8 Construction of a modular-10 counter

(a) Figure E20 shows the layout for the CMOS counter that resets at 1010 (i.e. decimal 10). The AND gate is replaced by

a NAND gate if using TTL chips.

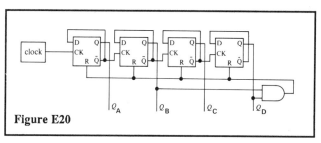

Figure E20

(b) Check that your circuit works and then re-design it so that it becomes (i) a modular-5, and (ii) a modular-12 counter.

Self-assessment questions

1 (a) Draw the truth table for the following combination of logic gates shown in figure E21.

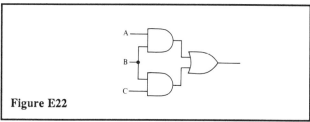

Figure E21

(b) Draw the truth table for the combination of logic gates shown in figure E22. Note that for three inputs there are eight possible values: 000 to 111.

A - B - C -

Figure E22

Write out in words the conditions for the output to be high.

(c) For the four NAND gates shown in figure E23a , which line in the truth table, figure E23b, gives the correct intermediate variables R, S, T and output variable U for given input variables P and Q ?

2 (a) (i) Draw a diagram to show how two NAND gates, each having two inputs, can be interconnected to make a simple bistable latch circuit.

(ii) Show with the aid of a truth table that the circuit must be in one of two stable states when both the unconnected inputs are held high (logic 1).

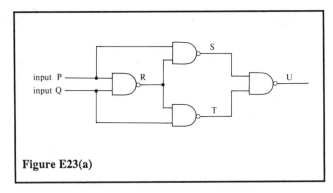

Figure E23(a)

	P	Q	R	S	T	U
A	0	0	1	1	1	1
B	0	1	1	1	0	0
C	0	1	0	0	1	1
D	1	0	1	0	1	1
E	1	1	0	1	0	0

Figure E23(b)

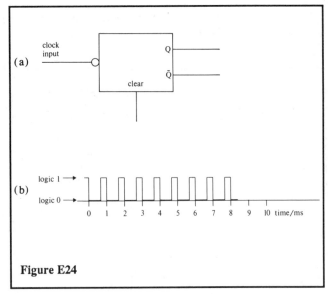

Figure E24

(iii) Explain in detail how the circuit can be forced to change from one stable state to the other.

(b) Show how a four stage binary counter can be converted to a denary (decimal) counter by the addition of a two input NAND gate. Assume that the counter can be cleared to zero (0000) by applying a low (logic 0) input to a single reset terminal.

3 (a) A light emitting diode (LED) which is connected to the output of a logic gate is required to light when the output is logic 1 (+5 V). For this to be achieved a forward current of 10 mA together with a forward p.d. of 2.0 V is required. Draw a circuit diagram to show how the LED is connected and calculate the value of any additional component required.

(b) The symbol shown in figure E24(a) represents a T or toggle flip-flop circuit. The small circle on the clock input indicates that toggling occurs when an input pulse goes from logic 1 to logic 0. The output Q can be set to logic 0, i.e. cleared, by momentarily connecting the clear input to a zero voltage line.

With the aid of a truth table for input and outputs, explain what is meant by the toggling action of this circuit.

(c) The clock pulses shown in figure E24(b) are applied to the flip-flop circuit. Using the same time scale as figure E24(a), sketch the outputs from Q and $\bar{Q}$.

(d) Draw a diagram to show how four of the circuits shown in figure E24(a) can connect together to make a four-bit binary counter to count upwards from zero. Show on your diagram where you would connect four LEDs to indicate the binary count, labelling them A to D with A being the least significant bit.

The clock pulses shown in figure E24(b) are fed into the input of the four-bit counter after its outputs have been cleared. Using a common time scale, show by means of graphs how the output signal from each of the four flip-flops varies between logic 0 and logic 1 for nine input pulses.

Theme 3 Devices and applications

Study time 1.5 weeks

Objectives

When you have completed the work in this theme you should be able to:

1 Understand the function of the following components: light-dependent resistor, thermistor, zener diode, light-emitting diode, relay, microphone, loudspeaker.

2 Describe how each component could be used in electronic circuits.

3 Have experience of designing circuits using these components.

4 Have experience of building a circuit involving one or

more of these components that includes a transistor, op-amp or logic gates as the processing parts of the system.

5 Understand the conditions for maximum voltage, current or power transfer in an electronics system.

Study questions and references

Basic references

Duncan SIE   (Reference to these books is
Gregory   needed throughout the following
Hartley   questions.)

1 Write notes on the use of each of the components in objective 1 in electronic circuits.

2 As the variety of work that could be undertaken in this area is so great, it is difficult to prescribe study questions. Also, you may be constructing and testing a practical circuit. Your teacher will probably suggest some ideas to you.

3 Explain the conditions needed for

(a) maximising voltage transfer in an electronics system
(b) maximising current transfer in an electronics system
(c) maximising power transfer in an electronics system

Self-assessment questions

1 (a) Describe with a labelled diagram the construction and operation of an electromagnetic relay.
(b) Explain the behaviour of the circuit shown in figure E25, as the intensity of the light incident on the LDR increases from a very low value. Discuss the purpose of the diode.

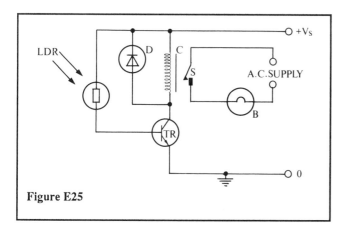

Figure E25

LDR = light dependent resistor
  C = relay coil
  D = diode
 TR = npn transistor
  S = normally closed relay contacts
  B = light bulb.

(c) In the above circuit which is powered by a 9 V battery the transistor has a current gain of 200. The relay is activated when a current of 90 mA flows through it and is de-energised when this current falls to 60 mA.
(i) Estimate the values of resistance of the LDR between which the relay will remain activated. (Assume that the base-emitter voltage is zero.)
(ii) Estimate the range of light intensity over which the remain activated, given that the LDR has a resistance of 10 kΩ when the light intensity is 10 lux. (Assume that the resistance of the LDR is inversely proprotional to the light intensity.)

2 Suitably chosen semiconductor diodes are required for each of the following purposes:

(a) as an indicator of high and low logic states,

(b) to protect a transistor from the induced e.m.f. generated across a relay coil during switching when the relay is controlled by the collector current of the transistor,

(c) explain the operating principles of each circuit, referring to the properties of the selected diode.

In each case

(i) state the name of a suitable type of diode,
(ii) draw a diagram of a circuit showing how the diode could be used for the intended purpose,
(iii) explain the operating principles of each circuit, referring to the properties of the selected diode,
(iv) explain the purpose of any additional components included in your circuit.*

In case (c) reference should also be made to a sketch of the diode's characteristics.

3 (a) Thermistors are variable resistors which usually have a *negative temperature coefficient of resistance*.
(i) Explain the meaning of the phrase in italics.
(ii) Above a particular value, the current in a circuit containing a thermistor may be observed to rise while all external factors remain constant. Explain how the properties of the thermistor alone could account for this observation.

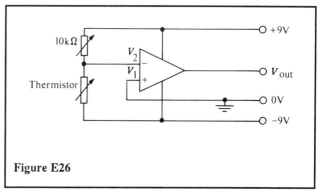

Figure E26

(b) The circuit in figure E26 shows a negative temperature coefficient thermistor used to control an operational amplifier, the output of which is intended to switch on a heater when the temperature in the vicinity of the thermistor falls below a certain value called the switching temperature.

(i) Describe what happens as the temperature of the thermistor falls to the switching temperature, and indicate how this switching temperature can be altered.

(ii) Show, by means of a labelled circuit diagram, how the output of the operational amplifier in the above circuit can, with the aid of a transistor, a relay and any other necessary components, switch on a heater which has an independent power supply. Indicate how a change in the value of V_{out} will switch the transistor and hence operate the relay, and explain whether the heater is switched on or off.

Answers to self-assessment questions

Theme 1 Operational amplifier

2 (c) 1.35 V
3 (c) 2.21 V

Theme 2 Logic circuits

1 (c) D
3 (a) 3 000 Ω resistor

Theme 3 Devices and applications

1 (c) (i) $2 \times 10^4 \ \Omega$ and $3 \times 10^4 \ \Omega$
       (ii) 3.3 lux and 5 lux

5.2 Energy and its uses

Theme 1 Energy resources

Objectives

When you have completed the work in this theme you should be able to:

1 Make a list of primary energy resources and make a brief statement for each of its

(a) importance and use in Britain
(b) origin
(c) likelihood of being 'finite'
(d) advantages and disadvantages

2 Give two examples of countries whose demand on primary energy resources is different from Britain's. Describe the differences and say something of the ways in which their demands are likely to change with time.

3 Understand and describe the technologies which are used in making an energy resource of wind, tides, waves and sunshine.

4 Understand what is meant by the term 'solar constant' and know its approximate local value in summer.

5 Give examples of conditions when the solar constant will change and relate these to the problems encountered in harnessing solar power.

6 Use the terms energy and power correctly.

7 Recognise that a variety of units are used to measure energy and appreciate the need to know suitable conversions from one to another.

8 Use expressions for potential and kinetic energy correctly when calculating energy changes in wind, wave and related situations.

Study questions and references

Basic reference:

Ramage, J. *Energy: A guide book*, chapters 1-3

1 Construct a suitable table and use it to fulfil objective 1 from part A.

2 Read the comprehension exercises on waves and answer the questions.

3 Think about a country that you know only a little about, Greenland, Peru or Taiwan perhaps. What sort of energy programme will it adopt? If you find this difficult to answer, which is understandable, then write a list of features which you would need to know about the country, its people, geography and climate before you could realistically assess its energy prospects.

4 Find a graph or table of values which give information about Britain's use of fossil fuels, coal and oil. Use this information to predict how long it will be before fossil fuels run so low that they become insignificant. (Try Ramage, p.23.)

5 Have you read about or can you find a reference to a source of energy using wind, wave or solar energy which is commercially viable, i.e. is not still a university project. What is its output? What are its prospects?

6 Do you have a pen-friend, a school-friend or relative who has experience of life in a country other than Britain? Ask them about the techniques for supplying energy that they have seen adopted in their country.

Self-assessment questions

For questions 1 and 2 use the grid on the right to answer A,B,C,D or E.

A	1 5 4 2 3
B	1 5 2 4 3
C	5 4 3 1 2
D	2 1 3 4 5
E	5 4 1 3 2

1 Here is a list of units in which energy is measured. Arrange them in increasing order, smallest first.

1 Kilocalorie.
2 Barrel of oil.
3 Kilowatt hour.
4 Joule.
5 Electronvolt.

2 Arrange the following energies in order of increasing energy, smallest first.

1 The kinetic energy of a 4 kg rock moving at 2 m s^{-1}.
2 The energy needed to warm up 1 kg of water by 1 °C.
3 The energy falling on the roof of a two-person tent in one minute on a sunny day.
4 The kinetic energy of 5 m^3 of air moving at 20 m s^{-1}.
5 The energy consumed by a 40 W lamp in one second.

3 Which of the following groupings is false?

	Finite	Infinite
A	Coal	Solar
B	Oil	Wind
C	Gas	Uranium
D	Coal	Tidal
E	Uranium	Solar

4 The graph in figure U1 shows how North Sea oil production has changed compared with total UK demand. As Britain was producing energy mainly from coal and oil during this period, what implications do you see for the economy and coal industry in the periods A to B, B to C, C to D?

5 Consider the following statement. 'The world demand for primary energy stands at 1.5×10^{20} J yr^{-1} and is increasing at a rate estimated to be between 3% and 5%. An estimate of the total supply of attainable resources on the planet is 60×10^{20} J.

(a) If these figures are accurate, when will the demand outgrow the supply if you assume (i) the greatest growth rate, (ii) the lower growth rate.

(b) Is there any evidence to suggest whether future patterns of demand will be greater than or less than those indicated?

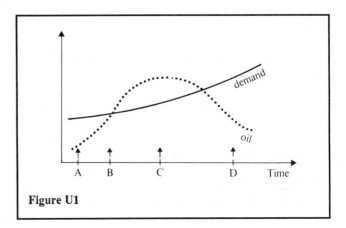

Figure U1

Theme 2 Energy conversion

Study time: 1 week approx.

Objectives

When you have completed the work in this theme you should be able to:

1 Describe the energy changes involved in the production of electricity from hydroelectric power indicating those changes which are least efficient.

2 Explain why it is desirable to store some of the energy produced by an HEP station and outline one way of doing this.

3 Sketch a graph to show the expected variation in demand of a small town over a 24 hour period.

4 State the ways in which *all* power stations which give an electrical output are the same.

5 Regard 'thermal' power stations as heat engines with an automatic consequential inefficiency and relate this inefficiency to the second law of thermodynamics.

6 State the ways in which 'thermal' power stations convert their raw fuel into internal energies, in particular the new technologies of fission stations.

7 Give an outline account of the techniques underlying the conversion of wind, wave and sunshine into electrical energy.

8 Explain why energy supplied from winds, waves or sunshine may show variations in output which are (i) predictable, and (ii) unpredictable.

Study questions and references

Basic reference:

Ramage, J. , chapters 4, 8, 9 and 10.

1 Study the graph in figure U2. It shows the variation in demand for power of a small town during a year.

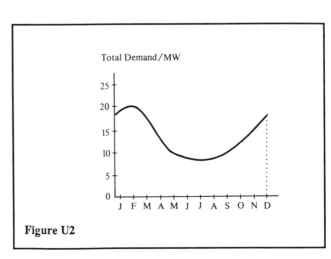

Figure U2

(a) What is significance of the area under the curve?

(b) Peak demand is 21 MW. Why should the local HEP station not be designed to give a total continuous output of 21 MW if needed?

(c) Designers claimed that an HEP station capable of a continuous output of about 13 MW would be suitable. How do you think they justify this value?

2 CHP (combined heating and power) is not a new idea. Waste steam from Battersea Power Station in London was used to provide heating for a local riverside housing estate soon after the Second World War.

Explain why the second law of thermodynamics makes CHP such an attractive proposition.

3 Explain the role of (i) the control rods, (ii) the graphite moderator, and (iii) the primary coolant fluid in a nuclear power reactor.

4 Wind-mills and watermills have long been a feature of alternative energy supplies in rural areas of Europe.

(a) What reasons can you give for the fact that they have remained a local, small-time, energy source?

(b) Recent designs look like producing 2.5 MW wind-mills in off-shore positions. What problems would arise in using such a scheme to replace the HEP station in Q1 above?

Self-assessment questions

1 The efficiency of a nuclear power station must reach an upper limit because

A the fuel used is impure

B the need to dipose of high-level waste causes concern

C all heat engines have a maximum efficiency

D a considerable amount of neutron flux passes out of the reactor

E melt-down has to be avoided.

2 Frictional forces make a particular wave turbine 50% efficient when producing rotation from water movement. The dynamo system is 60% efficient in turning this rotational energy into electricity. To produce a steady 20 kW output, such a wave generator system needs to be supplied with wave energy at the rate of

A 66 kW B 40 kW C 6 kW D 6.6 kW E 100 kW

3 The average camper requires 10 litres (10^{-2} m³) of hot water each day. A camp site at Henley-on-Thames holds, on average, 120 campers in summer when the solar constant is 1500 W m⁻². It provides the campers with hot water by running cold water through black hosepipes arranged in a spiral fashion facing south. The last time I visited the site, I stood in the morning wash queue and estimated a collecting area of black tubing to be approximately 6 m².

Use this information together with any other quantitative assumptions to find out if my shower was cold or warm.

Theme 3   Energy consumption

Study time: 1 week approx.

Objectives

When you have completed the work in this theme you should be able to:

1 Draw block diagrams to identify the main energy transformations taking place in a typical motor car.

2 Identify ways in which the efficiency of a motor car has been improved over the last 30 years or so.

3 Describe the cycle of events which enable liquid fuel to be converted to rotational motion by an internal combustion engine.

4 Apply your knowledge of conduction, convection, and radiation to the energy balances required to keep a simple building warm.

5 Extend your understanding of ways of heating buildings to enable you to perform quantitative calculations involving (i) the specific heat capacity of moving air, and (ii) U-values of wall and floor structures.

6 Be familiar with the use of the terms 'kilowatt hour', 'unit cost', 'therm', 'BTU' as they appear in literature concerning domestic energy consumption, e.g. bills.

7 Apply ideas of energy conservation, flow rates and water efficiency to electric showers, central heating systems and heaters.

Study questions and references

Basic reference:
Ramage, J. chapter 3.

1 The graph figure U3 shows how the velocity of a 1400 kg vehicle changed with time as a constant force was applied by the engine.

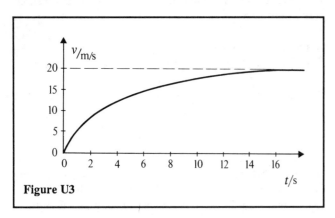

Figure U3

(a) Account for the general shape of the graph.
(b) By considering the initial acceleration, calculate a value for the steady force on the vehicle.
(c) Use your answer to (b) to find a value for the work done per second to overcome the drag forces at 20 m s⁻¹.
(d) How would an improved grade of engine lubrication oil influence the vehicle's behaviour?
(e) How would the graph change if the vehicle was driven, just as hard but in reverse?

2 To raise the temperature of the air in a living-room from 0 °C to 18 °C requires about half-a-million joules and costs approximately 0.9 p. To raise the temperature from 0 °C to 20 °C costs approximately 1.0 p. The annual heating bill for the warmer room is about £100 more than for the cooler room. Can you explain why?

3 Take a look at the room you are in. Where does its heating energy come from? Try to identify some of the ways in which that energy is being 'lost'. Consider conduction, convection and radiation.

4 Go to your local Electricity and Gas Showrooms. You will be able to obtain a number of free leaflets on heating. Select a few, especially those which refer to the following: 'therms' 'BTU', 'KW hr', 'units' and calculating bills. Try to find out how these terms are related to joules.

Self-assessment questions

1 A person drags a heavy block across the ground. A force of 200 N is needed to pull the load at a steady speed of 0.5 m s⁻¹ for 10 metres (figure U4).

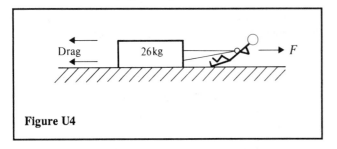

Figure U4

Which of the statements below *incorrectly* describes an aspect of this situation?

A The work done by the person is 2 000 J.
B The acceleration was zero.
C The power developed by the person was 100 W.
D The drag forces totalled 200 N.
E The total work done was 4 000 J, that is 2 000 J by the person plus 2 000 J by friction.

2 Which of the following energy changes *does not* play a part in determining the overall energy efficiency of a motor car?

A Compression of the fuel mixture warms up the engine.
B Oil reduces friction between pistons and cylinders.
C Wind resistance causes drag on the body.
D Kinetic energy is transformed to internal energy via the brakes.
E Friction between tyre and road transforms energy.

3 A model house was constructed with linear dimensions 1/10th of those of a real house. When deciding at which rate the model be supplied with energy in order to maintain the same temperature as the real house, the following statements were made:

(a) 'The volumes of the rooms are 1/1000th of those of the real house. This should be a major factor for consideration'.
(b) 'The wall areas will be 1/100th of those of the real house. This is an important consideration'.
(c) 'The walls in the model are 1/10th as thick as those in real house. This is important'.

All three statements may be used to determine an answer. How would you see their priorities and which would you use? If the real house needed a 12 kW heating system, what do you think might be suitable for the model?

4 (a) A 2 m² single-glazed window has a U-value of approximately 5.0 W m⁻². A similar double-glazed unit, costing £400 more, has a U-value approximately 2.0 W m⁻². If each were used for a year in a room in which the inside temperature was an average of 10 °C above the outside temperature, then how much energy would the double-glazed unit save?
(b) At a cost of about 6p per kW hr, what is the total financial saving?
(c) How long would it take to recoup the cost of fitting the double-glazed unit?

Answers to self-assessment questions

Theme 1 Energy resources

1 E
2 A
3 C
4 A to B ... Either import energy or develop coal industry. B to C ... Either sell oil and develop coal, or rundown coal and use oil. C to D ... Redevelop coal? Import energy or use other alternatives.
5 47 years, 28 years.

Theme 2 Energy conversion

1 C
2 A
3 It depends on how long it takes 120 campers to wash. If we assume that all can wash in, say, 1 hour, then a 100% efficient calculation gives a rise in temperature of about 2 °C - a cold shower!

To enable campers to have a warm shower they'll have to wait 10 hours approximately. But, the energy is collected from sunrise until sundown at Henley and most often the water is warm!

Theme 3 Energy consumption

1 E
2 D
3 The air changes would require volumes but their contributions would be minimal. The rate of conduction depends on area divided by thickness and so would imply that the model loses energy at 1/10th of the real house. Therefore, a heating system of 1.2 kW would do the job.

4 (a) About 2×10^9 J.
  (b) About £32.
  (c) About 12 years.

5.3 Fluids and waves

Theme 1   Real gases

Objectives

When you have completed the work in this theme you should be able to:

1 Describe Andrews' experiment and the results be obtained.

2 Define the terms critical temperature and critical pressure.

3 Draw graphs of pV against p for real gases and explain the significance of the Boyle temperature.

4 Explain the deviations from ideal gas behaviour in terms of intermolecular forces and finite molecular volumes.

5 Explain the terms in Van der Waals' equation.

Study questions and references

Basic references

An introduction to this theme is given in the unit *Thermal properties*, topic 4. This can be supplemented by the following recommended A-level texts.

Nelkon   Chapter 12
Muncaster   Chapter 14
Whelan   Chapter 28

1 Draw a sketch of Andrews' experiment and the graph of pressure against volume he obtained for carbon dioxide. Indicate on the graph where the carbon dioxide was (a) gas, (b) vapour, (c) liquid, (d) a mixture of vapour and liquid, and draw the critical isothermal. Define the terms critical temperature and critical pressure.

2 Draw sketch graphs of pV against p for (a) an ideal gas, and (b) real gases at a particular temperature.

3 Draw sketch graphs of pV against p for a real gas at a number of temperatures and hence define the Boyle temperature.

4 State Van der Waals' equation and write brief notes explaining how the terms in the equation take account of intermolecular forces and finite volumes of molecules.

Self-assessment questions

Complete the self-assessment questions in topic 4.6 of the unit *Thermal properties*.

1-5 Choose all the correct responses.

1-2 These questions refer to figure F1 which is a graph of pressure gainst volume for carbon dioxide. Three isothermals are given.

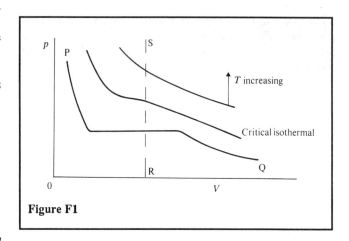

Figure F1

1 For the isothermal PQ it can be deduced that

A saturated vapours obey Boyle's law
B unsaturated vapours are easily compressed
C liquids do not compress easily
D liquids obey Boyle's law.

2 The changes that take place in the carbon dioxide when proceeding along the line RS are

A unsaturated vapour to liquid
B saturated vapour to gas
C unsaturated vapour to saturated vapour
D unsaturated vapour to gas

3-4 These questions refer to figure F2 on the next page which is a graph of pV against V for nitrogen. Four isothermals are given.

3 The Boyle temperature for nitrogen, according to the graph, is

A 126 K
B 177 K
C 252 K
D 323 K

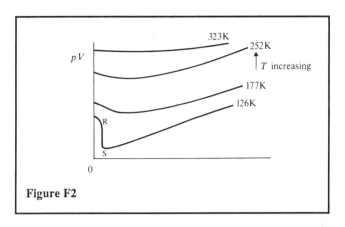

Figure F2

4 Part RS of the 126 K isothermal refers to the nitrogen in

A the gaseous state
B the saturated vapour state
C the unsaturated vapour state
D the liquid state.

5 The equation below can be used to describe the variation of pV with p for a real gas.

$$pV = A + B_p + C_p{}^2$$

A For an ideal gas B and C are zero.
B For a real gas at the Boyle temperature, B is zero and C negligible.
C For one mole of a real gas $A = RT$.
D For a real gas B and C depend on the temperature.

6 The critical temperature of oxygen is 155 K and its Boyle temperature is 423 K. Is it possible to liquefy oxygen at room temperature by compressing it?

7 The following is van der Waals' equation. What do the terms a/V^2 and b take account of?

$$\left(p + \frac{a}{V^2}\right)(V - b) = RT$$

Theme 2 Non-viscous fluids

Study time: 0.5 week

Objectives

When you have completed the work in this theme you should be able to:

1 Explain what is meant by streamline or laminar flow.

2 Derive and use the equation of continuity.

3 Derive and use Bernoulli's equation.

4 Explain the terms static pressure and dynamic pressure.

5 Explain the principles behind the Pitot-static tube and the Venturi meter.

Study questions and references

Basic references
This theme is covered by topic 4 of the unit *Behaviour of matter*. It may be supplemented by the following recommended A-level texts.

Duncan   Chapter 10
Nelkon   Chapter 4
Muncaster   Chapter 12
Wenham   Chapter 11
Whelan   Chapter 9

1 Write a brief note explaining what is meant by streamline or laminar flow.

2 Derive the equation of continuity, i.e.

$$A_1\rho_1v_1 = A_2\rho_2v_2$$

3 Derive Bernoulli's equation, i.e.

$$\rho + \tfrac{1}{2}v^2 + h\rho g = \text{a constant}$$

and define the terms static pressure and dynamic pressure.

4 Sketch the Pitot-static tube and the Venturi meter and explain how each operates.

5 Work through the questions given in topic 4 of *Behaviour of matter*.

Self-assessment questions

1-2 Choose all the correct responses.

1 For a non-viscous fluid flowing in an orderly manner through a horizontal tube

A successive particles of fluid pass a point with the same velocity

B if the cross-sectional area of the tube decreases, the velocity decreases
C if the velocity of the fluid decreases due to a change in cross-sectional tube area, the pressure increases
D the velocity of the fluid at a point is the tangent to the streamline at that point.

2 For a non-viscous fluid flowing in an orderly manner through the tube shown in figure F3, ingoing from P to Q

A the fluid velocity increases
B the total pressure increases
C the dynamic pressure increases
D the static pressure increases

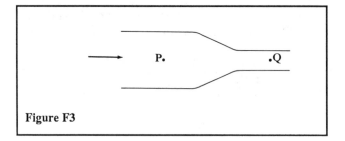

Figure F3

3 A fluid flows along a horizontal pipe of cross-sectional area 20 cm² in an orderly manner with a velocity of 6.0 m s⁻¹. What will be its velocity when the cross-sectional area of the pipe reduces to 10 cm²?

4 For a fluid flowing in an orderly manner through a horizontal pipe of cross-sectional area 16 cm² the static pressure is 4.0×10^4 Pa and the total pressure 4.5×10^4 Pa. Calculate the velocity of the fluid and the volume flowing through the tube per second if it has a density of 1000 kg m⁻³.

5 A horizontal pipe tapers from a diameter of 100 mm to a diameter of 60 mm and carries oil of density 850 kg m⁻³. The pressure difference between the two sections is measured as 30 kPa. Calculate the velocity of the oil in the wider pipe.

Theme 3   Viscous fluids

Study time: 0.5 week

Objectives

When you have completed the work in this theme you should be able to:

1 State and use Newton's law of viscosity.

2 Derive Poiseuille's equation from dimensional considerations and use the equation to solve problems involving orderly flow through tubes.

3 Explain what is meant by terminal velocity for an object falling in a fluid.

4 Use Stokes' law to solve problems involving falling spheres.

Study questions and references

Basic references

Bolton   Chapter 16
Duncan   Chapter 10
Nelkon   Chapter 7

Muncaster   Chapter 12
Wenham   Chapter 11
Whelan   Chapter 19

1 Explain and define the terms (a) tangential stress, (b) velocity gradient.

2 Describe the relationship between tangential stress and velocity gradient for a Newtonian fluid and hence define the coefficient of viscosity. State the type of behaviour that occurs with non-Newtonian fluids.

3 Derive Poiseuille's equation, for orderly flow through a pipe, using dimensional methods.

4 Describe how the coefficient of viscosity of water can be determined using Poiseuille's equation.

5 State the forces acting on a sphere falling freely in a fluid and hence explain how its velocity varies after it has fallen from rest, explaining the term terminal velocity.

6 State Stokes' law and explain how it can be used in the determination of the coefficient of viscosity of a fluid such as glycerine.

Self-assessment questions

1-2 Choose all the correct responses.

1 For a Newtonian fluid

A the tangential stress is proportional to the velocity gradient
B the coefficient of viscosity is independent of the size of the tangential stress
C the coefficient of viscosity does not change with temperature
D when a fluid flows over a plate the force acting on the plate depends on its area

2 Which of the graphs in figure F4 could describe how the distance fallen by a sphere from rest in a viscous fluid varies with time?

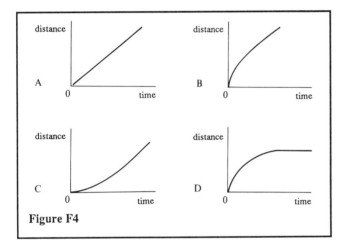

Figure F4

3-5 For each numbered quantity select from the list below its dimensions

A LT^{-1}
B $ML^{-1}T^{-1}$
C MLT^{-2}
D $ML^{-1}T^{-2}$

3 Velocity.

4 Pressure.

5 Coefficient of viscosity.

6-7 Choose the correct answer.

6 Two solid spheres X and Y of the material fall from rest in a viscous fluid. If X has twice the diameter of Y it will have a terminal velocity which is

A a quarter that of Y
B a half that of Y
C twice that of Y
D four times that of Y.

7 Water flows steadily under the same pressure head through two tubes X and Y of the same length. If X has a diameter twice that of Y then the volume rate of flow of the water through X will be

A twice that of Y
B four times that of Y
C eight times that of Y
D sixteen times that of Y.

Theme 4   The Doppler effect

Study time: 0.5 week

Objectives

When you have completed the work in this theme you should be able to:

1 Explain what is meant by the Doppler effect.

2 Derive and use expressions for the change in frequency of a wave motion when (a) the source is moving relative to a fixed observer, and (b) the observer is moving relative to a fixed source.

3 Derive and use expressions for the Doppler effect with light.

4 Use the above expressions in problems involving sound and light, including the red shift and high temperature measurements.

Study questions and references

Basic references

With the exception of the Doppler effect with light, the above objectives are covered in topic 2.3 of the unit *Waves and vibrations*. The following references can be used to complement the unit and some extend it to a consideration of light waves. (See also the topic guide to the Physics of Astronomy in this book.)

1 Write notes explaining what the Doppler effect is and deriving the expressions specified in objective 2.

2 If v_s is considerably less than the wave speed, show that for electromagnetic waves travelling at speed c from a moving source, a fixed observer will detect a frequency change approximately given by

$$\frac{\Delta f}{f} - \frac{v_s}{c}$$

3 Write notes explaining the principles involved in radar traps, the red shift, and the broadening of spectral lines at high temperature.

Self-assessment questions

Complete the self-assessment questions given on the Doppler effect in topic 2 of the unit *Waves and vibrations*.

1-3 Choose all correct responses.

1 When a source of sound is moving with a constant velocity towards a stationary observer, to the observer

A the frequency of the sound increases
B the wavelength of the sound increases
C the speed of the sound increases

2 When a source of sound is stationary and being approached at a constant velocity by an observer, according to the observer

A the frequency of the sound increases
B the wavelength of the sound increases
C the speed of the sound increases

3 The light from a distant star shows a shift towards the red end of the spectrum in the spectral lines it emits. This is because

A it is moving away from us
B it is at a high temperature
C we are moving towards the star
D it is a dying star

4 The breadth of the spectrum lines produced by a hot gas depends on

A the wavelength of the line concerned
B the speed of the gas molecules
C the temperature of the gas
D the velocity of the gas

Theme 5 Diffraction and interference

Study time: 1 week

Objectives

When you have completed the work in this theme you should be able to:

1 Describe briefly the diffraction patterns formed by a straight edge and a circular obstacle.

2 Describe and explain the diffraction pattern of a single slit, deriving the equation $d \sin \theta = n \lambda$ for minima.

3 Describe the patterns produced by double and multiple slits, varying in number, and give a qualitative explanation of them.

4 Describe and explain the main features of the pattern obtained when light passes through a diffraction grating.

5 Derive and use an equation relating the wavelength to the angular separation of the diffracted spectra and the coarseness of a diffraction grating.

6 Describe and explain the formation of fringes in an optical wedge illuminated normally, both in transmission and reflection.

7 Describe and explain Newton's rings, deriving the equation relating the wavelength, ring radius and radius of curvature of the lens.

8 Give a simple account of the formation of colours by thin films.

9 Outline experiments to determine the wavelength of light using (a) a diffraction grating, (b) Newton's rings and to measure the angle of small-angle wedges.

Study questions and references

Basic references

The unit *Waves and vibrations*, topic 5, covers virtually all aspects of this theme. This can be complemented by references to any of the recommended A-level course texts.

Bolton   Chapter 9
Duncan   Chapter 18
Nelkon   Chapters 23 and 24
Muncaster   Chapters 25 and 26
Wenham   Chapter 21
Whelan   Chapters 38 and 39

1 Work through topic 5 of the unit *Waves and vibrations*. In doing this, you could usefully study the following and make notes or sketches.

2 Sketch the intensity-angle (or $\sin \theta$) graphs for (a) a single slit, (b) a double slit, (c) many slits, when illuminated by monochromatic light.

3 Derive the relationships (a) $d \sin \theta = n \lambda$ for a single slit and (b) $d \sin \theta = n\lambda$ for a diffraction grating.

4 Explain how fringes are formed when a small angle wedge of air or liquid film is illuminated normally by monochromatic light and derive the equation by which the wedge angle can be obtained from fringe measurements.

5 Describe and explain Newton's rings, deriving the relationship between wavelength, ring radius and radius of curvature of the lens.

6 Explain how colours are formed by thin films when they are illuminated by white light.

7 Outline the experiments described by objective 9.

Self-assessment questions

Complete the questions given with topic 5 of the unit *Waves and vibrations*.

1-8 Choose all the correct responses.

1 Figure F5(a) shows the fringe pattern produced on a screen

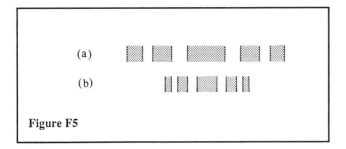

Figure F5

when blue light passes through a narrow adjustable slit. This pattern could be changed to that in figure F5(b) by

A changing to red light
B making the slit wider
C increasing the slit to screen distance
D making the slit narrower.

2 Figure F6 represents the relative intensity distribution produced on a screen by

A monochromatic light passing through a single slit
B a number of wavelengths passing through a single slit
C monochromatic light passing through multiple slits
D a number of wavelengths passing through multiple slits.

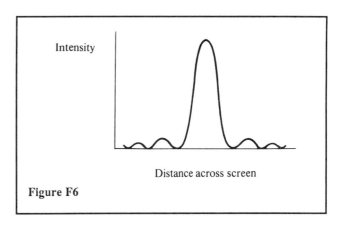

Figure F6

3 Light from a hot gas is incident normally on a diffraction grating. If the grating is replaced by one with twice as many rulings per millimetre

A the angles of diffraction for spectral lines in the first-order are doubled
B the angle between the first-order and the second-order lines is doubled
C the width of the zero order is increased
D the width of the first-order spectrum is increased.

4 In the two -slit interference experiment shown by figure F7 a pattern of equally-spaced parallel fringes is produced on the screen. The separation of the fringes will be increased if

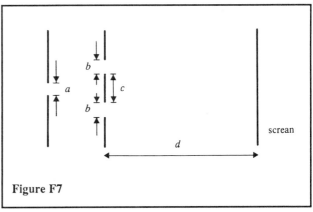

Figure F7

A a is increased
B b is increased
C c is increased
D d is increased

5-6

When Newton's rings are produced as a result of monochromatic light incident normally on a convex lens resting on a plane glass surface, which of the diagrams in figure F8 could illustrate the observed pattern of dark fringes?

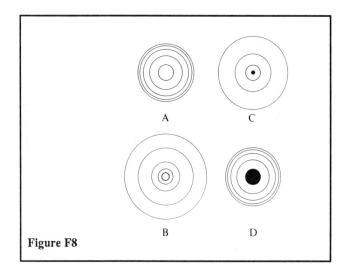

A

C

B

D

Figure F8

5 When the fringes are viewed by reflection?

6 When the fringes are viewed by transmission?

7 When light is reflected from an optically denser medium

A its frequency increases
B its wavelength increases
C its speed increases
D it changes phase

8 Monochromatic light is incident normally on a thin wedge-shaped air film and the fringes so produced observed. The separation of the fringes

A increases when the angle of the wedge decreases
B is the same along the length of the wedge
C increases when the wavelength increases
D is the same when the wedge is viewed by reflection or transmission

Answers to self-assessment questions

Theme 1 Real gases

1 B,C
2 B
3 D
4 B
5 A,B,C,D
6 No
7 a/V^2 intermolecular forces, b the volume of molecules.

Theme 2 Non-viscous fluids

1 A,D
2 A,C
3 $A_1v_1 = A_2v_2$, hence $v_2 = 12.0$ m s^{-1}
4 Dynamic pressure $= \frac{1}{2}\rho v^2 = 0.5 \times 10^4$ Pa, hence
     $v = 3.2$ m s^{-1}
   Volume(s) $= Av = 5.1 \times 10^{-3}$ m^3 s^{-1}
5 $p_1 + \frac{1}{2}\rho v_1^2 = p_2 + \frac{1}{2}\rho v_2^2$ and $A_1v_1 = A_2v_2$ or $d_1^2 v_1 = d_2^2 v_2$.
   Hence $p_1 + \frac{1}{2}\rho v_1^2 = p_2 + \frac{1}{2}\rho(d_1^2 v_1/d_2^2)^2$ and $v_1 = 3.2$ m s^{-1}

Theme 3 Viscous fluids

1 A,B,D
2 B
3 A
4 D
5 B
6 D
7 D

Theme 4 The Doppler Effect

1 A
2 A,C
3 A
4 A,B,C

Theme 5 Diffraction and interference

1 B
2 A
3 C,D
4 D
5 D
6 A
7 D
8 A,B,D

5.4 Medical physics

Theme 1 Ultrasonics

Objectives

When you have completed the work in this theme you should be able to:

1 Use the following terms correctly: sonar, intensity, reflection coefficient (α), specific acoustic impedance (Z), absorption coefficient (k), coupling medium, artifact .

2 Describe the operation of a piezoelectric transducer as a generator and detector of ultrasound.

3 Recall the properties of ultrasound waves and the nature of their reflection in body tissue.

4 Describe, with the aid of block diagrams, the methods of ultrasonic scanning for diagnostic purposes.

5 Give examples of the use of ultrasonic scanning.

6 Explain how Doppler Shift Δf, in the frequency of ultrasound can be used to measure movement within the body.

7 Describe, with the aid of block diagrams, the use of the Doppler effect to measure blood flow and foetal heart movement.

8 Compare the advantages of ultrasound diagnostic techniques with alternative methods.

Study questions and references

Basic reference: Pope, J.A. *Medical physics* , chapter 10.

1 Make notes from this reference on objectives 2, 4, 7 and 8.

2 Write a brief account of the nature and properties of ultrasound and their interaction with body tissue, including the terms in objective 1. (See also unit *Waves and vibrations*, topic 2.)

3 Study and make notes on the derivation of the Doppler Shift formulae (see also unit *Waves and vibrations*, topic 2).

Self-assessment questions

1-3 Choose all correct responses.

1 Ultrasound can be used

A for detecting cancer
B to detect twins in early pregnancy
C to measure the position of the mid-line of the brain
D to study the lungs
E to measure thickening of the arteries (atheroma).

2 In an ultrasound scanner the echo signal is detected by applying it to

A the Y plates of a CRO
B the X plates of a CRO
C a loudspeaker
D The brightness control of a CRO.

3 Ultrasound as used in medical diagnosis

A has a wavelength of about 1 mm
B is more penetrating at higher frequencies
C is reflected from tissue interfaces
D has a better resolution than X-ray diagnosis
E has no proven harmful effect on the patient

4 (a) What is meant by the resolution of an ultrasound image, and on what factors will it depend?
(b) What is the wavelength of an ultrasound signal of frequency 2 MHz in muscle? (Velocity of sound in muscle is 1580 m s^{-1}.)

5 An ultrasound beam of frequency 2 MHz travels at 1.5 km s^{-1} in soft tissue. What is the speed of a surface which it strikes when a Doppler shift of 279 Hz is recorded.

Theme 2 X-rays

Objectives

When you have completed the work in this theme you should be able to:

1 Use the following terms correctly: photon energy, hardness, total linear attenuation coefficient (μ).

2 Recall the nature of X-radiation.

3 Describe the principle of production of X-rays by a rotating anode tube.

4 Recall the intensity-wavelength spectra produced by a tungsten target and their dependence on tube voltage and current and on filtration.

5 Use the relationships
(i) intensity in vacuum $I = I_0/x^2$ (inverse square law)
(ii) intensity in a medium $I = I_0 e^{-\mu x}$
(iii) half value thickness $x_{\frac{1}{2}} = \dfrac{\ln 2}{\mu}$

6 Explain the four mechanisms of attenuation of X-rays in soft tissue and account for their relative importance, depending on incident energy and proton number of irradiated tissue.

7 Describe the factors affecting the quality of a radiographic image, and a method of fluoroscopically intensifying the image.

8 Give examples of the use of X-rays in diagnosis and therapy.

Study questions and references

Basic reference: Pope,J.A. *Medical physics,* chapter 11.

An introduction to X-ray spectra is given in *Electronics and the nucleus,* topic 7.3.

1 Write a brief account of the nature and properties of X-rays including the terms listed in objective 1.

2 Make notes with sketch diagrams on objectives 3, 4, 6 and 7.

3 Record and learn the relationships in objective 5.

4 Read some of the background or similar resources and make brief notes on the applications of X-rays in medicine, their benefits and hazards (see also theme 3).

Self-assessment questions

1-3 Choose all correct responses.

1 X-rays

A are photons of very high energy
B are electromagnetic radiation of very short wavelength
C are completely absorbed by a few millimetres of lead
D can be diffracted, reflected and refracted
E are scattered in all directions by an material through which they pass

2 X-ray contrast media

A are used to overcome the problem of scatter
B are usually based on barium when applied to the digestive tract
C enable the X-ray dose to the patient to be reduced
D depend for their operation on the photoelectric effect
E can be either very transparent or very opaque to X-rays

3 The following factors affect the amount of scatter on a radioagraph

A tube voltage
B use of grid
C the size of the beam
D film-focus distance
E exposure time

4 A beam of X-rays from a point source emerges through a circular aperture of diameter 2.5 cm, placed at a distance of 10 cm from the source. Calculate the area covered by the beam when it strikes the surface of a patient at a distance of 80 cm from the source.

5 Successive equally thick sheets of a material placed in a narrow photo beam reduce its intensity respectively to 40%, 16%, 6.4% and 2.5% of its initial value. State and explain the law which applies in this case. If each sheet is of thickness 2 mm, determine (a) the half-value thickness of the material, (b) the percentage transmission through a sheet 5 mm thick.

6 What will be the intensity I of an X-ray beam of incident intensity I_0 at a distance r, if it has to pass through an absorber of thickness d, and absorption coefficient μ.

Theme 3   Nuclear medicine

Study time: 1 week

Pre-requisites for this option are topics 3, 4 and 5 of *Electrons and the nucleus* on ionising radiations and decay and use of radioisotopes.

Objectives

1 When you have completed the work in this theme you should be able to use the following terms correctly: metastable radio-nuclide, tracer.

2 State the properties of an ideal radiopharmaceutical.

3 Give examples of the production of radionuclides by neutron capture and fission in a nuclear reactor, and by proton capture in a cyclotron.

4 Describe the production and use of Technetium 99 and Iodine 131 as radiopharmaceutical tracers.

5 Use symbolic representation of nuclear reactions.

6 Describe in general terms the range of damage caused to humans by ionising radiations, from the molecular to the systemic levels.

7 Define, know the units of, and use the following terms in radiation dosimetry: activity, exposure, absorbed dose, relative biological effectiveness, dose equivalent, physical and biological half-life.

8 Recall the background level of radiation and examples of some common medical dose rates (e.g. chest X-ray).

9 Recall the general requirements for the use of radioisotopes (of the ICRP) and the specific precautions you should take in using radioisotopes in the laboratory.

10 Explain the principle of the ionisation chamber, and describe how this is used in the thimble, capacitor and pocket types.

11 Explain the principle of the scintillation counter and describe how this is used in the photomultiplier.

12 **Extension** Describe the structure and operation of the Geiger counter.

13 Describe the structure and operation of the film badge and thermoluminescent dosimeter.

14 Describe the structure and operation of the rectilinear scanner and gamma camera.

15 Give an example of gamma radiotherapy.

Study questions and references

Basic reference: J. Pope, J.A. *Medical physics*, chapters 12-15.

1 Refer to *Electrons and the nucleus*, topic 4 for a summary of objective 2.

2 Use the references and background resources to write notes on objectives 3, 4, 6, 8, 10, 11, 13, 14 and 15.

3 Record and explain the following nuclear reaction which summarises the generation and use of technitium 99m as a radiopharmaceutical:

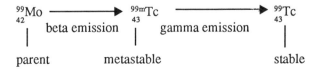

4 Write the definitions, names and relationships between the units of radiation dosimetry in objective 7. Solve problems from the reference on these.

5 The ICRP principles for the use of radioisotopes are:

(i) all uses of radioisotopes must show a positive net benefit;
(ii) all exposures due to these uses must be as low as reasonably achievable;
(iii) maximum exposure limits are set for different groups of people, i.e. for the general population this is 0.2 sieverts up to the age of 30 years.

Precautions for laboratory use of sealed sources used in this physics course are given in part 2 of this resource book. For the additional precautions required for open sources (solutions and powders) refer to J.B. Dance, *Radioisotopes Experiments in Physics, Chemistry and Biology*.

6 **Extension** If you have not already done so, carry out experiment EN 4 on the use of the Geiger-Muller tube.

Self-assessment questions

1-3 Choose all correct responses

1 The following statements concerning organ imaging are true.

A It is ideally performed with beta emitters
B Technetium-99m is used for radionuclide brain imaging.
C Gamma emitting radionuclides are more useful for therapy than diagnosis. The heart takes up Iodine-131 and may be used as a function study.
D Technetium-99m and Iodine-123 accumulate in the thyroid gland

2 The total genetic dose from diagnostic radiology in the UK is higher than that from

A television sets
B radiotherapy
C the natural background radiation
D atomic energy establishments 'background' radiation.

3 The following detectors are used for radiation dosimetry

A film badge
B scintillation counter
C Geiger counter
D rectilinear scanner
E gamma camera.

5 (a) Explain the meaning of the terms in italics in the following sentence:

A radioactive source containing material whose *activity* is 3×10^9 Bq (8×10^{-2} Ci), emits only gamma-rays whose energy is such that the *half-value thickness* in lead is 9×10^{-3} m and produces at 1 m from the source an *absorbed dose* in tissue of 5×10^{-3} Gy (0.5 rad) every hour.

(b) A source such as that described in (a) falls from the container onto the floor. It has to be replaced by a technician who has available a pair of long-handled tongs and a lead shield 18 mm thick, behind which he can work. Tests made previously have shown that it takes 36 s to replace the source if the lead shield is used, but only 8 s if no shield is used.

In each case, the body is the same distance from the source. Neglecting other factors which might affect the problem, state your reasons whether or not you would recommend the technician to use the lead shield.

(c) Suppose another longer, pair of tongs became available, enabling the body to be kept twice the distance away from the source that was possible in (b), but with which no shields can be used. State, with reasons, whether you would recommend the use of the longer tongs if it takes 27 s to complete the operation.

Theme 4 Biomedical measurement

Study time: 0.5 week

Objectives

1 When you have completed the work in this theme, you should be able to use the following terms correctly: biopotentials, membrane potentials, axon, neuron, axoplasm, action potential, polarisation, de-polarisation, repolarisation, reverse polarisation, electrocardiogram (ECG), P-wave, T-wave, QRS pulse artifacts.

2 Describe the biological generation and conduction of electrical signals, and their detection at the skin surface.

3 Describe the basic structure of the heart, with appropriate diagrams.

4 Describe the heart's response to the typical action potentials.

5 Explain the principles of operation of ECG machines in obtaining diagnostic information.

6 Draw typical ECG waveforms and identify the important parts.

7 Describe blood pressure measurement techniques to include

(a) the sphygmomanometer,
(b) invasive techniques - (i) variable inductive methods,
(ii) variable capacitive methods, (iii) variable resistance pressure transducers.

Study questions and references

Basic reference :

Pope, J.A. *Medical physics*, chapters 5 and 7.

1 Make illustrated notes from this reference on objectives 2, 3, 4, 5, 6 and 7.

2 Read the following article and answer the questions on it.

C Comprehension
Measuring blood flow
(From an article in *Physics in Technology* by C.A. Greatorex, March 1982)

The body depends on blood for the distribution of oxygen and nutrients and for the collection and disposal of carbon dioxide and other waste products. Thus, there is a continuous network of vessels through which blood flows from the heart through arteries, returning at lower pressure via the veins. A similar circuit forces blood through the lungs and back to the heart.

Invasive methods

Invasive methods permit surgical exposure without cutting into the blood vessels, and use flow probes into which the intact blood vessel - vein or artery - is inserted. The probes are electromagnetic devices which use the laws of electromagnetic induction and the fact that blood is an electrical conductor. Thus, if a magnetic field is applied across a blood vessel the induced electric field is given by $E = Bv$, where B is the magnetic field strength and v is the mean blood velocity. If two pickup electrodes are positioned to contact the blood vessel on either side, a distance w apart, the inter-electrode p.d. V is given by $V = Ew = Bvw$.

Thus, if the flow probe keeps the cross-section of the blood vessel constant then the flow F is given by $F = \pi Vw/4B$.

In practice, the intact blood vessel is inserted into a cuff-type probe by means of a slot. A selection of probes allows for differing diameters of blood vessels. The current through the electromagnet is alternating and the resulting signal detected at the electrodes is amplified and rectified. This produces a good signal-to-noise ratio and eliminates electrolytic effects.

Unfortunately, this method also produces extra (spurious) signals due to the magnetic field also interacting with the electrode circuit. Thus, when the flow is F the detected p.d. V will be

$$V = \frac{4BF}{\pi w} + k\frac{\mathrm{d}B}{\mathrm{d}t}$$

where k is a constant for a particular arrangement.

This spurious p.d. $k\,\mathrm{d}B/\mathrm{d}t$ may be ten times the wanted flow signal, but its effect can be nullified by adding an externally generated p.d. of value

$$-k'\frac{\mathrm{d}B}{\mathrm{d}t}$$

where $k' = k$.

Electromagnetic flowmeters have good linearity, can indicate the direction of flow and can produce a pulsatile flow record. However, surgery is necessary and this may not be acceptable.

Non-invasive methods

These use electrical impedance techniques and ultrasound.

Impedance methods

Electrical impedance methods may be used in a number of sites in the body. They can measure the 'stroke volume' of the heart and also determine blood flow in the limbs, giving us a particularly simple, continuous and non-invasive technique for the investigation of deep vein thrombosis.

The technique measures change in tissue impedance (resistance) by 'injecting', between one pair of electrodes, a high-frequency signal of about 100 kHz from a constant-current generator and measuring the resultant potential difference between a second pair of electrodes at the site of interest. The impedance between the detecting electrodes is proportional to the p.d. between them. As the tissue volume changes with pulses of blood flow, the resulting p.d. changes give a measure of the impedance variations. A knowledge of the basal (normal) impedance, the changes of the impedance and the associated time intervals, together with the electrode position and the resistivity of the blood, allows calculation of flow to be made.

Ultrasound methods

Ultrasound in the 2-10 MHz range is used and depends on the fact that the moving red blood corpuscles reflect the sound with a change in its frequency (a 'Doppler shift'), given by

$$\Delta f = 2\frac{uf}{c}\cos\theta$$

where f is the transmitted frequency, u is the velocity of the reflector along the direction of flow, c is the speed of sound in the tissue and θ is the angle between the direction of movement and the axis of the ultrasonic beam.

The best frequency (in MHz) to use is $f = 90/D$, where D is the thickness (in mm) of interposed tissue between the blood vessel and the probe. The results from a simple Doppler shift meter are qualitative only, and to extract all the information present in the reflected signals sophisticated spectrum analysers have been developed. It is even possible to produce 'images' of blood vessels.

These are just a few of the ways in which physics has impinged upon the measurement of blood flow, enabling clinicians to reach a greater understanding of the human circulatory system.

Questions

1 The electromagnetic flow probe uses 'the fact that blood is an electrical conductor' (second paragraph).
(a) Suggest a physical reason why blood conducts electricity.
(b) What problem might occur if a steady magnetic field were to be used in the probe rather than an alternating field?
(c) Blood does not flow at a constant speed through the blood vessels, but pulses with the beat of the heart. Sketch how you would expect the blood flow in an artery, say, to vary with time over a period of about 5 seconds.
(d) The probe uses an alternating magnetic field to produce the induced voltage output. Now sketch, on the diagram you have drawn in answer to (c) above, how you would expect the output of the device to vary with time.

2 (a) Why is it important to keep 'the cross-section of the blood vessel constant' (third paragraph)?
(b) Draw a labelled diagram showing how an electromagnet, its coils and pickup electrodes might be arranged around a blood vessel.
(c) Calculate a value for the inter-electrode potential difference likely to be produced by a such a device across a blood vessel in the arm in which the blood flow is about 1 cm³ s⁻¹. Assume a magnetic field (B-field) of 0.01 T and make sensible estimates of any other quantities you may need.

3 The passage states that 'Unfortunately, this method also produces extra (spurious) signals...' (fourth paragraph).
(a) Explain the 'interaction' which produces these spurious signals.
(b) Give one physical factor that is involved in determining the size of the constant 'k' (fourth paragraph).
(c) What are the characteristics of the signal used for 'nullifying' the spurious signal described in the fourth paragraph?
(d) What is meant, in the context of this passage, by the terms (i) *noise*, (ii) *a good signal-to-noise ratio* (fourth paragraph)?

4 (a) Explain the distinction between 'invasive' and 'noninvasive' methods.
(b) 'Impedance techniques' use a constant-current generator (ninth paragraph) whereas ordinary supplies, like batteries, are constant-e.m.f. devices. (*Note.* 'Impedance' in this case is purely resistive.)

(i) Explain why the 'impedance between the detecting electrodes is proportional to the p.d. between them' (ninth paragraph).

(ii) What would be needed to give the same information if a constant-e.m.f source were used instead of a constant-current source?

(iii) Explain how changes in the tissues might cause the impedance between the two electrodes to vary.

5 Another system that measures blood flow noninvasively uses a beam of 'ultrasound in the 2-10 MHz range (tenth paragraph).

(a) What is meant by 'ultrasound'?

(b) Flesh is mostly water, and the speed of sound in water is 1440 m s^{-1}. Using this information, estimate the upper limit of the wavelength of the sound used in this technique.

(c) Assuming a velocity of blood flow of about 0.3 m s^{-1}, calculate a likely maximum change in frequency that an ultrasound device might be called upon to detect.

Self-assessment questions

1-6 Write down the letter (A-I) of the correct word(s) to substitute in the numbered spaces in the following paragraphs.

A   action potential
B   axon
C   axoplasm
D   biopotentials
E.   depolarisation

G.   neuron
F.   membrane potential
H.   polarisation
I.   reverse polarisation

Messages are passed by nerves changing their (1). When a nerve cell or (2) is stimulated, sodium ions move into the (3) which increases the positive charge in the cell. The (4) changes from about -70 mV to 0 mV, called (5) and these to about +40 mV, called (6).

7-9 Match the following parts of an ECG trace with the action of the heart it represents.

7 P-wave

8 QRS pulse

9 T-wave

A atrial contraction
B atrial relaxation
C ventricular contraction
D ventricular relaxation

Theme 5 The physics of seeing and hearing

Study time: 1 week

Objectives

When you have completed the work in this theme, you should be able to:

1 Use the following words correctly: sensitivity (of eye), spectral response, spatial resolution, persistence of vision, depth of focus, depth of field, sensitivity (of ear), frequency of response, dB, dBA.

2 Draw a clear labelled diagram of the eye as an optical system and describe the function of the constituent parts.

3 Draw a clear labelled diagram of the retina and explain the function of each part.

4 Understand the following defects of vision and how to correct them by the use of lenses:

(a) myopia
(b) hypermetropia
(c) presbyopia
(d) astigmatism

5 Solve problems for lenses by using ray diagrams and using the lens formula for the lenses.

6 Draw a clear labelled diagram of the ear and explain the function of each part.

7 Draw clear labelled diagrams of the cochlea and explain their function.

8 Describe

(a) sensitivity of the ear
(b) frequency response of the ear

9 Use dB, dBA scales to calculate relative intensity levels of sound and sound exposure.

10 Describe how hearing can become defective as a result of

(a) exposure to excessive noise
(b) deterioration with age.

Study questions and references

Basic references:

Pope, J.A. *Medical physics,* chapters 3 and 4.
For hearing: Hobson's Science Support Series *Noise* and the Question Booklet.

1 Make illustrated notes on objectives 2, 3, and 4 using Pope, chapter 3.

2 Answer the self-assessment questions in the unit *Waves and vibrations*, section 3.4, to cover objective 5.

3 Make illustrated notes on objectives 6 and 7 using Pope, chapter 4.

4 Answer the questions in Hobson's Question Booklet on the *Noise* booklet to cover objectives 8, 9 and 10.

Self-assessment questions

1 The far point of a short-sighted or myopic eye is 2.00 m.

(a) What power of lens is required to correct this?
(b) What is the focal length of this lens?

2 The near point of a long-sighted or hyperopic eye is 1.00 m. A lens of power +2.00 D is placed directly in front of the eye. What is the near point of the eye-lens combination?

3 A bat produces a sonar pulse with an intensity of 2×10^{-2} W m^{-2}.

(a) Express this in dB.
(b) This is equivalent to the loudness of a shotgun blast. Why is it not damaging to humans?

4 In musical terms a very soft sound is described as triple piano (ppp) and has an intensity of about 10^{-8} W m^{-2}, and a very loud sound as triple forte (fff) and has an intensity of about 10^{-2} W m^{-2}. Express these in dB.

5 The external auditory canal acts like a tube closed at one end by the ear drum. For a young person this is about 2.8 cm long.

(a) Calculate the wavelength of the fundamental vibration mode.
(b) Calculate the frequency, assuming the speed of sound = 340 m s^{-1}.
(c) What connection does this have with the sensitivity of the ear?

Answers to self-assessment questions

Theme 1 Ultrasonics

1 A,B,C,E
2 D
3 C,D,E
4 0.8 mm
5 0.1 m s^{-1}

Theme 2 X-rays

1 A,B,E
2 B,D,E
3 A,B,C
4 312 cm^2
5 (a) 1.5 mm
  (b) 10%
6 $I = I_0 e^{-\mu d}/r^2$

Theme 3 Nuclear medicine

1 B,C,D,E
2 A,B,C,D
3 A,B,C
4 A,C,D
5 (b) no shield (c) use longer tongs.

Theme 4 Biomedical measurement

1 D
2 G
3 C
4 F
5 E
6 I
7 A
8 C (B also occurs at this stage but is not normally observed.)
9 D

Theme 5 The physics of seeing and hearing

1 (a) -0.50 dioptre, (b) diverging -2.00 m
2 0.33 m
3 (a) 103 dB
(b) It is at a frequency of over 30 kHz so beyond human range.
4 40 dB, 100 dB
5 (a) 11.2×10^{-2} m
(b) 3036 Hz
(c) Maximum sensitivity expected at around 3 kHz.

5.5 Nuclear physics

Theme 1 Gross nuclear properties

Objectives

When you have completed the work in this theme you should be able to:

1 Estimate from the scattering of alpha particles the size of the nucleus.

2 Describe the diffraction patterns obtained by electrons incident on nuclei and hence estimate the nuclear size.

3 Derive from given data the relationship between nuclear radius and mass number.

4 Identify from the atomic number and mass number of a nuclide the numbers of protons and neutrons in the nucleus and the effect on these numbers of alpha, beta and gamma emissions.

5 Identify the forms of the force-distance curves for the attractive and repulsive forces needed to hold nuclei together.

6 Calculate the density of nuclear material.

7 Describe the liquid drop model for the nucleus.

Study questions and references

Basic references

APPIL unit *Electrons and the nucleus*, topics 3, 4 and 5 and *Waves and vibrations*, topic 5.

Caro, D.E., McDonell, B.M. and Spicer, B.M. *Modern physics*, chapters 8, 12, 14 and 15, gives a reasonable coverage of objectives 1, 4 and partially 5.

For coverage of the other objectives, reference will need to be made to university level physics texts.

1 Work through topic 3 of the unit *Electrons and the nucleus*.

2 Remind yourself of the diffraction effects that occur when waves are diffracted by looking through topics 5.2 and 5.3 of the unit *Waves and vibrations*. Then study the paragraph on a compact nucleus and its extension question in topic 5.1 in the unit *Electrons and the nucleus*.

3 Derive the relationship $R = r_0 A^{1/3}$.

4 Work through topic 4.1 of the unit *Electrons and the nucleus*.

5 Read Caro *et al* chapter 15.7 on nuclear forces and argue for the forms that the force-distance curves must take for the attractive and repulsive nuclear forces.

6 Calculate the density of nuclear matter and show that it is approximately constant regardless of nucleus (see the extension to topic 5.1 in the unit *Electrons and the nucleus*).

7 Look up the Bohr liquid drop model for the nucleus in texts, e.g. Littlefield and Thorley, chapter 19.3, and make notes in which you compare the liquid properties of latent heat, surface tension and constant density with equivalent properties for nuclei. This model will be used in later themes to explain binding energy and nuclear fission.

Self-assessment questions

1-5 Choose all the correct responses to each question.

1 Alpha particles of energy 5 MeV are directed at a thin gold foil.

A Most of the alpha particles will pass straight through the foil with little change in their direction.
B In a head-on collision with a nucleus, the alpha particle loses all its kinetic energy.
C The distance of closest approach to a nucleus is when the height of the potential hill round the nucleus is 5 MW.
D The electric potential energy of an alpha particle a distance r from the centre of a gold nucleus is $2Ve$, where V is the potential at distance r from the nucleus.

2 Figure N1 shows how the intensity, on a logarithmic scale, varies with angle θ of scattering for high-speed electrons of energy E incident on oxygen nuclei.

A The electrons have a wavelength given by $\lambda = hc/E$ where h is the Planck constant and c the speed of light in a vacuum.
B The nuclei can be considered to be behaving like circular discs of diameter D and diffracting the electrons so that the first minimum occurs when $\sin \theta = 1.22 \lambda / D$.
C Increasing the energy of the electrons gives a first minimum at a bigger angle θ.
D For the same energy electrons, nuclei of another element with a smaller nuclear diameter will give a first minimum at a smaller angle θ.

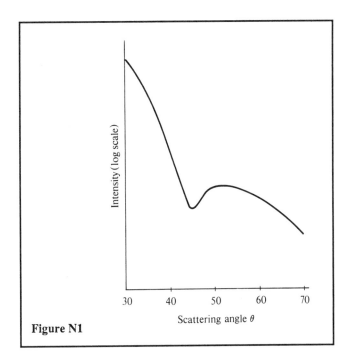

Figure N1

5 The correspondence between drops of liquid and nuclei is

A both have a density independent of size
B energy is needed to remove a molecule from a drop or a nucleon from a nucleus
C molecules in the surface of a drop and nucleons in the surface of a nucleus are less tightly bound than those in the interior
D unstable drops and unstable nuclei fragment into smaller drops or nuclei

6 For the electron scattering results for oxygen nuclei given by figure N1 the electrons had an energy of 420 MeV. Estimate the radii of the oxygen nuclei.

7 The following table shows the nucleon number A and radii R for a number of nucleons. Show that the relationship $R = r_0 A^{1/3}$ fits the data and obtain a value for r_0.

A	$R/10^{-15}$ m
1	1.00
4	2.08
12	3.04
16	3.41
28	3.92

8 The mass of a nucleus is approximately AM, where A is the nucleon number and M the mass of a nucleon. Using the relationship $R = r_0 A^{1/3}$ for the radii of nuclei, determine a value for the density of nuclear material given that r_0 has a value of about 1.3×10^{-15} m and M about 1.7×10^{-27} kg.

3 $^{232}_{90}$Th decays through a series of nuclides to $^{208}_{82}$Pb. In the series of decays:

A six alpha particles and eight beta particles are emitted
B six alpha particles and four beta particles are emitted
C twelve alpha particles and eight beta particles are emitted
D twelve alpha particles and four beta particles are emitted.

4 The nuclear force between nucleons is:

A strongly attractive at distances between nucleons of about 1 to 2×10^{-15} m
B strongly repulsive at distance between nucleons of less than 1×10^{-15} m
C becomes insignificant at distances greater than about 3×10^{-15} m
D independent of whether the nucleons are protons or neutrons.

Theme 2 Nuclear stability

Study time: 1 week

Objectives

When you have completed the work in this theme you should be able to:

1 Use a graph of the number of neutrons against proton number for stable nuclei to make predictions of whether a nuclide will be radioactive and whether the emission will be of positive or negative beta particles or alpha particles.

2 Explain the terms mass defect and binding energy.

3 Carry out calculations on the mass balance in alpha or beta active decays and determine the energy released.

4 Explain the terms in the equation for the binding energy derived from the liquid drop model.

5 Calculate the energy and hence wavelength of gamma radiation emitted in a radioactive decay from the mass balance.

6 State the evidence for energy levels in the nucleus.

Study questions and references

Basic references

APPIL unit *Electrons and the nucleus*, topic 5.1 covers objectives 1, 2, and 3 and in the extension objectives 5 and 6. These objectives are also covered in many standard A-level texts (see the list given in Part 4 of this book.)

Caro, D.E., McDonell, B.M. and Spicer, B.M. *Modern physics*, chapter 15.

For coverage of objective 4, reference will need to be made to university level physics texts.

1 Work through topic 5.1 of the unit *Electrons and the nucleus*, including the extension for gamma emission.

2 Look up the equation given on the basis of the liquid drop model for the binding energy (see self-assessment question 4) and write notes explaining the significance of the terms in the equation (e.g. Littlefield and Thorley, chapter 19.3).

3 From a consideration of gamma emission from a radioactive nuclei explain the evidence for energy levels within nuclei.

Self-assessment questions

1-6 Choose all the correct responses to each question.

1 Figure 5.2 in the unit *Electrons and the nucleus* shows how the neutron number varies with proton number (or atomic number). Which of the following are correct statements about the graph?

A All the isotopes which do not fall on the line $N = Z$ are radioactive.
B Up to $Z = 18$ positive beta emitters have more protons than neutrons.
C Up to $Z = 83$ negative beta emitters have more neutrons than protons.
D For proton numbers greater than $Z = 83$ all isotopes are radioactive.

2 $^{220}_{86}$Rn decays by alpha emission. Which of the following are correct statements about this decay?

A The atomic number of the decay product will be 82.
B The atomic mass of the decay product will be 216.
C The difference between the masses of the radon and its decay product will be the mass of the alpha particle.
D Energy is released in the decay because the mass of the radon is greater than the masses of the products.

3 $^{42}_{19}$K decays by negative beta emission to give a positive ion daughter nuclide. Which of the following are correct statements about this decay given the following data:

Element	Proton number	Nucleon number	Atomic mass/u
potassium	19	39	38.96371
	19	41	40.96183
	19	42	41.96240
calcium	20	40	39.96259
	20	42	41.95863
	20	43	42.95878

1 u is equivalent to 931.3 MeV. The mass of an electron is 0.00055 u.

A The difference in mass between the $^{42}_{19}$K and its decay product must be 0.00055 u.
B The maximum energy of the beta particle will be 4.29 MeV.
C The decay product must be another isotope of potassium.
D The effect of the decay is to give a decay product which has fewer neutrons than $^{42}_{19}$K.

4-6 One form of the binding energy equation derived from the liquid drop model for a nucleus of nucleon number A, proton number Z and neutron number N is:

$$\text{binding energy} = aA - bA^{2/3} - \frac{cZ^2}{A^{1/3}} - d\left(\frac{N-Z}{A}\right)^2$$

where a, b, c and d are constants.

4 Which of the terms represents the stability of the nuclei due to the neutron-proton ratio and is zero when $A = 2Z$?

5 Which of the terms arises from a consideration of surface tension effects?

6 Which of the terms arises from a consideration of the repulsive forces between protons in the nucleus?

A The term involving the constant a.
B The term involving the constant b.
C The term involving the constant c.
D The term involving the constant d.

7 Use the equation given for the binding energy above to explain why

(a) light nuclei have equal numbers of protons and neutrons,
(b) nuclei with large nucleon numbers contain more neutrons than protons.

8 $^{226}_{88}$Ra emits alpha particles with energies of 7.65×10^{-13}J and 7.36×10^{-13} J together with gamma radiation of just one wavelength.

What is the wavelength of the gamma radiation? $h = 6.63 \times 10^{-34}$ J s, $c = 3.00 \times 10^8$ m s^{-1}.

Objectives

When you have completed the work in this theme you should be able to:

1 Explain gamma emissions as the means by which excited nuclei lose energy.

2 Explain electron and positron emission and electron capture in terms of changes to neutrons and protons.

3 Describe the beta energy spectrum and explain it in terms of the emission of neutrinos.

4 Explain alpha particle emission in terms of alpha particles, unlike beta and gamma, having a pre-existence in nuclei and 'tunnelling' out through the Coulomb barrier.

5 Explain why the half-life of an alpha emitter is related to the energy of the alpha particle emitted.

Study questions and references

Basic references

Caro, D.E., McDonell, B.M. and Spicer, B.M., *Modern Physics*, chapter 15.

This book covers objectives 1-5 to some extent.

1 Following on from the previous theme, write notes explaining gamma emissions as being the means by which excited nuclei lose energy, the concept of nuclear energy levels (comparing these and gamma photon emission with atomic energy levels and photon emission) and the fact that the gamma photons are not thought to exist within the nucleus prior to the decay but only to occur at the instant of decay when there is a jump between energy levels.

2 Write notes explaining the following processes:

$n \longrightarrow p + \beta^- + \gamma$ (negative beta emission)

$p \longrightarrow n + \beta^+ + \gamma$ (positive beta, or positron emission)

$p + e^- \longrightarrow n + \gamma$ (electron capture)

3 Explain what is meant by the beta energy spectrum and explain why this spectrum means there must be another particle emitted in beta decay, the particle being called the neutrino.

4 Write a note explaining that electrons, i.e. beta particles, are not thought to exist within the nucleus prior to the decay but are produced at the instant of decay.

5 Write notes explaining alpha particle emission from nuclei in the following terms. Alpha particles exist as discrete entities within nuclei prior to decay occurring, a simple model of such a nucleus consisting of an alpha particle moving around within a potential well. A calculation of the height of the potential barrier that an alpha particle would appear to have enough energy to overcome to escape from the nucleus.

(Using $V = Q/4\pi\varepsilon_0 R$, where $R = r_0 A^{1/3}$ and $Q = Ze$) gives a height of the order of 30 to 100 MeV. Alpha particles have energies of the order of 4 to 9 MeV and so apparently should not escape from the nucleus. The explanation has to be in terms of wave mechanics and a finite small chance that the alpha particle can appear outside the nucleus - apparently going through the barrier in what is termed 'tunnelling'.

6 High-energy alpha particles are given off when the decay has a short half-life, lower energy alpha particles being given off when the half-life is longer (this is sometimes referred to as the Geiger-Nuttall rule). Examine data to confirm this. Write a note giving an explanation for it in terms of the higher energy alpha particles within a nucleus having a smaller 'thickness' of potential barrier to tunnel through and so more readily, more quickly, escape and so give a shorter half-life.

Self-assessment questions

1-6 Choose all the correct responses.

1 When gamma radiation occurs, there is :

A a change in the number of protons in the nucleus
B a change in the number of neutrons in the nucleus
C a change in the excited state of a nucleus
D a change in the number of photons in the nucleus.

2 When negative beta radiation occurs there is:

A a change in the number of protons in the nucleus
B a change in the number of neutrons in the nucleus
C a change in the number of electrons in the nucleus
D a change in the atomic mass

3 When alpha radiation occurs there is:

A a change in the number of protons in the nucleus
B a change in the number of neutrons in the nucleus
C a change in the atomic mass
D a change in the proton number.

4 When negative or positive beta emission occurs:

A the beta particles have discrete energies
B a neutrino is also emitted
C the number of nucleons changes
D there is a change in the proton-neutron ratio.

5 Electron capture involves:

A the emission of beta radiation
B the emission of a neutrino
C a change in the number of nucleons
D a change in the proton-neutron ratio.

6 $^{216}_{86}$Rn emits alpha particles with an energy of 8.04 MeV.
$^{232}_{9}$Th emits alpha particles with an energy of 4.01 MeV.

Which of the following could be valid deductions from this data?

A ^{216}Rn has a smaller half-life than ^{232}Th.
B ^{216}Rn has a smaller nuclear potential barrier than ^{232}Th.
C The chance of an alpha particle tunnelling through the potential barrier is smaller for ^{216}Rn than ^{232}Th.
D Alpha particles within the ^{216}Rn nuclei are at a higher energy level than those in ^{232}Th.

Theme 4 Nuclear power sources

Study time: 0.5-1 week

Objectives

When you have completed the work in this theme you should be able to:

1 Describe the form of the graph of binding energy per nucleon with nucleon number and explain how fission of heavy nuclei could liberate energy, giving an estimate of the amount.

2 Using the binding energy equation for the liquid drop model of the nucleus, explain the effect of fission on the various terms in the equation.

3 State that spontaneous fission is rather rare but that fission can be induced in some cases by striking nuclei with neutrons.

4 Balance and explain a fission equation of the form

$$^{235}U + n \longrightarrow {}^{236}U \text{ (excited)} \longrightarrow X + Y + xn + Q$$

5 State that the probability of ^{235}U fission is greatest for very low energy neutrons, so-called thermal neutrons.

6 Explain what is meant by a chain reaction and critical size.

7 For controlled chain reactions, explain the functions of the moderator and the importance of the neutron absorption cross-section.

8 Explain the function of control rods and the importance of the neutron absorption cross-section and delayed neutron emission.

9 Distinguish between thermal reactors and fast-breeder reactors.

10 Discuss the safety factors involved with nuclear reactors.

11 Describe how reactors can produce useful radioactive isotopes and explain the technique of activation analysis.

12 Using the graph of binding energy per nucleon against nucleon number, explain how fusion of light nuclei can liberate energy.

13 For a given fusion reaction, calculate the energy released.

14 Explain why a very high temperature is necessary for a fusion reaction.

Study questions and references

Basic references

APPIL unit *Electrons and the nucleus*, topics 5.1 and 5.2 partially cover objectives 1, 4, 6, 7 and 8. Topic 5.3 covers objectives 13 and 14.

For a complete coverage of objectives and greater depth, reference will need to be made to university level texts.

1 Sketch the basic form of the graph of binding energy per nucleon with mass number and use it to explain how the fission of heavy nuclei can lead to a release of energy. Estimate the energy released if ^{235}U splits into two roughly equal parts (about 200 MeV).

2 State the effects on the terms in the binding energy equation for the liquid drop model of the nucleus (see earlier themes) of increasing Z, i.e. moving from lighter to heavier nuclei. Note that for light nuclei, N equals Z and both A and Z are low. Increasing Z will considerably increase the Z^2 term. Hence, explain the effects of fission on the various terms in the binding energy equation.

3 Distinguish between spontaneous fission and induced fission as a result of a neutron being absorbed by a nucleus in terms of the need, according to the liquid drop model, to produce a distortion of the drop.

4 Write down a typical equation for the fission of ^{235}U when bombarded by neutrons and, using atomic mass data, calculate the energy released.

5 Write notes explaining the terms chain reaction, critical size, the need for low energy neutrons for fission with ^{235}U, and the functions of the moderator and control rods. In explaining the moderator and control rods, use the term neutron absorption cross-section and give examples of materials with low and with high cross-sections, indicating which would be used as the moderator and which for control.

6 Write a brief note explaining the difference between a thermal rector based on natural uranium and a fast-breeder based on plutonium.

7 Write notes on both the short-term and long-term safety considerations for nuclear reactors, covering such aspects as shielding, the pressure vessel, control rods, and the storage and disposal of radioactive wastes.

8 Explain how energy is generated in fusion reactions and why a high temperature is necessary for such reactions.

Self-assessment questions

1-4 Choose all the correct responses to each question.

1 When a nucleus such as ^{235}U undergoes fission into two roughly equal parts:

A about 0.9 MeV per nucleon is released
B the parts have greater binding energies than ^{235}U
C fission can be induced by neutrons bombarding ^{235}U nuclei
D fission frequently occurs spontaneously

2 When $^{235}_{92}$U is bombarded by neutrons a possible reaction is the production of two products $^{87}_{35}$Br and $^{146}_{57}$La. Atomic mass of $^{235}_{92}$U = 235.04 u; atomic mass of $^{87}_{35}$Br = 86.92; atomic mass of $^{146}_{57}$La = 145.90 u; mass of $^{1}_{0}$n = 1.01 u; 1 u is equivalent to 931 MeV.

A Three neutrons are produced in the fission.
B There is an energy release of 186 MeV.
C Most of the energy released occurs as kinetic energy for the Br and La fragments.
D The probability of the fission occurring depends on the energy of the bombarding neutrons.

3 A material for use as a moderator must:
A absorb neutrons
B slow down neutrons
C have a high neutron absorption cross-section
D have a nuclear mass as close to that of a neutron as possible.

4 The reaction rate of a reactor can be controlled:

A by increasing the amount of moderator material in the reactor
B by increasing the amount of material with high neutron absorption coefficients in the reactor
C because there is some delayed neutron emission
D by extracting energy from the reactor .

5 Calculate the energy released in the following fusion reaction

$$^{2}_{1}H + ^{3}_{1}H \longrightarrow ^{4}_{2}He + ^{1}_{0}n + Q$$

Atomic mass of ^{2}H = 2.01410 u; atomic mass of ^{3}H = 3.01605 u; mass of ^{1}n = 1.00867 u; 1 u is equivalent to 931.3 MeV.

Answers to self-assessment questions

Theme 1 Gross nuclear properties

1 A,B,C,D
2 A,B
3 B
4 A,B,C,D
5 A,B,C,D
6 sin 45° = 0.61 hc/VeR, hence R = 2.5 × 10^{-15} m
7 r_0 = 1.3 × 10^{-15} m
8 0.1 × 10^{17} kg m^{-3}

Theme 2 Nuclear stability

1 B,C,D
2 B,D
3 B,D
4 D
5 B
6 C
7 (a) d term becomes zero.
(b) This decreases the c term.
8 $E = hc/\lambda$, hence λ = 6.86 × 10^{-12} m

Theme 3 The mechanism of α, β and γ decay

1 C
2 B
3 A,B,C,D
4 B,D
5 B,D
6 A,B,D

Theme 4 Nuclear power sources

1 A,B,C
2 A,B,C,D
3 B,D
4 B,C
5 17.58 MeV

5.6 Optical instruments

Theme 1 Optical instruments

Study time: 1.5 weeks

Objectives

When you have completed the work in this theme you should be able to:

1 Describe the optical system and action of the camera, explaining the terms *f*-number and its relationship to image brightness, depth of focus and depth of field and their dependence on lens aperture.

2 Describe the optical system and action of the projector and photographic enlarger.

3 Describe the optical system and action of a compound microscope, and draw diagrams of the paths of rays from a non-axial point which produce an image

(a) at the near point
(b) at infinity.

4 Describe the optical system and action of a refracting astronomical telescope in normal adjustment, including diagrams of the paths of rays of light through the telescope from a distant non-axial point.

5 Derive and recall an expression for the angular magnification of a refracting astronomical telescope in

(a) normal adjustment
(b) near point adjustment.

6 Explain the term eye-ring and the relationship of its diameter with the diameter of the objective, focal length of the lenses and the angular magnification when the telescope is in normal adjustment.

7 Explain the relationship between the focal lengths of the lenses in an astronomical telescope and the diameters of the objective and pupil of the eye.

8 Compare the Galilean (terrestrial) telescope with the astronomical telescope.

9 Describe the optical system of prism binoculars.

10 Describe the optical system and action of the Newtonian reflecting telescope and compare it with the refracting telescope.

11 Describe the construction of a simple spectrometer, explaining how it is adjusted and used to determine the refractive index of a prism.

Study questions and references

Basic references

The unit *Waves and vibrations*, topic 3, gives both a basic introduction to this theme and covers objectives 1,3,4,5,6,7,8,9,10 and 11. This can be complemented by reference to any of the recommended A-level Physics course texts. The following are chapter references in such texts.

Bolton   Chapter 10
Duncan   Chapter 5
Nelkon   Chapter 20
Muncaster   Chapter 21
Whelan   Chapter 36

1 Work through topic 3 of the unit *Waves and vibrations* including the syllabus extensions.

2 Sketch the optical system of a projector and describe the functions of the illumination and projection lens systems.

Self-assessment questions

1-6 Choose all the correct responses.

1 When the *f*-number on a camera is increased:

A the size of the aperture is increased
B the amount of light entering the camera is increased
C the depth of field is increased
D the depth of focus is increased.

2 A compound microscope in normal adjustment:

A has an objective lens of short focal length
B has the final image located at the least distance of distinct vision
C has the distance between the objective and eyepiece lenses equal to the sum of their focal lengths
D has a magnifying power equal to the product of the linear magnifications produced by the two lenses.

3 The eye-ring in an astronomical telescope used in normal adjustment is

A at the least distance of distinct vision from the eyepiece
B at the focus of the objective lens
C at the position where the eyepiece forms an image of the objective lens

D at the position between the lenses where the intermediate image is formed.

4 A refracting telescope consists of an objective lens of focal length 1000 mm and an eyepiece of focal length 50 mm. In normal adjustment:

A the distance between the lenses is 1050 mm
B the final image is 50 mm from the eyepiece lens
C the magnifying power is 20
D the magnifying power is increased by increasing the focal length of the eyepiece lens.

5 The main purpose of the collimator in a simple spectrometer is to:

A provide a parallel beam of light
B focus the light from the source onto the prism or grating
C produce a narrow beam of light
D focus the light from the source onto the cross-wires.

6 The Galilean telescope

A has a convex objective lens
B has a concave eyepiece lens
C produces an inverted image
D is longer than an astronomical telescope.

Theme 2 Resolving power

Study time: 0.5 week

Objectives

When you have completed the work in this theme you should be able to:

1 Describe the diffraction pattern produced by a circular aperture.

2 Define resolving power and use it in discussing images formed by refracting and reflecting telescopes.

3 Explain Rayleigh's criterion and the use of an equation for the minimum angle of resolution of the form $\theta = \lambda/D$.

4 Compare the operation of a radio-telescope with an optical telescope.

Study questions and references

Basic references

The unit *Waves and vibrations*, topic 5, gives a basic introduction to the diffraction of waves passing through apertures and covers the above objectives. This can be complemented by references to any of the recommended A-level Physics course texts.

Bolton	Chapter 9
Duncan	Chapter 18
Nelkon	Chapter 24
Whelan	Chapter 39

1 Work through sections 5.2 and 5.3 of the unit *Waves and vibrations*.

2 Make notes on the construction and operation of a radio-telescope. How is the resolution of the image made acceptable?

Self-assessment questions

1-2 Choose all the correct responses.

1 When a circular aperture is illuminated normally by parallel monochromatic light the angular width of the central maximum is:

A increased if the wavelength is increased
B increased if the diameter of the aperture is increased
C increased if the intensity of the light is increased
D increased if the distance of the screen on which the light falls from the aperture is increased.

2 The resolving power of an astronomical telescope is increased if:

A the diameter of the objective lens is increased
B the diameter of the eyepiece lens is increased
C the magnifying power of the telescope is increased
D the wavelength of light viewed is increased.

Theme 3   Aberrations

Objectives

When you have completed the work in this theme you should be able to:

1 Explain the terms spherical aberration and chromatic aberration.

2 Explain how two different glasses can be used to produce an achromatic doublet.

3 Compare the merits of lenses and curved mirrors as telescope objectives.

Study questions and references

Bolton	Chapter 10
Duncan	Chapter 5
Nelkon	Chapters 19 and 20
Whelan	Chapter 34

1 Make notes explaining what spherical aberration is ,with (a) lenses, (b) mirrors, and how it can be reduced.

2 Make notes explaining what chromatic aberrration is with lenses and how it can be eliminated for two colours by combining lenses of two different glasses in an achromatic doublet.

3 Write notes on the benefits of using curved mirrors as objectives for large telescopes in terms of chromatic aberration, suspension of the objective and difficulty maintaining uniform refractive index through the glass of a large lens.

Self-assessment questions

1-2 Choose all the correct responses.

1 Spherical aberration with lenses

A occurs because the focal length for rays close to the axis differs from that for rays from far the axis
B is reduced by reducing the diameter of an aperture in front of the lens
C is reduced by arranging for the deviation produced by the lens to be divided equally between the two lens surfaces
D is reduced by reducing the wavelength of the light.

2 Chromatic aberration with lenses

A   occurs because the refractive index depends on the wavelength
B occurs because the focal length of a lens depends on the wavelength
C can be reduced by reducing the diameter of an aperture in front of the lens
D can be reduced by changing the curvature of the lens surface.

3 Explain how chromatic aberration can be eliminated for two colours for the objective lens of a telescope.

4 Explain the advantages of using a curved mirror instead of a lens for the objective of an astronomical telescope.

Theme 4   Optical fibres

Objectives

When you have completed the work in this theme you should be able to:

1 Explain the role of internal reflection in the transmission of light by optical fibres.

2 Calculate the critical angle given the refractive indices of the core and the cladding.

3 Explain the terms dispersion and multimode transmission.

4 Explain how the dispersion can be reduced by reducing the core diameter or using a graded index fibre.

5 Describe the advantages of optical fibre systems over copper cable systems for telecommunications.

Study question and references

Bolton, chapter 15.
Ed. Nicholl, B. and Selfe,J.   *Telecommunications in practice*, chapters 4, 9 and 12.

1 Write notes explaining how, for light to be transmitted along a fibre, rays must be   reflected from the core-cladding interface at angles equal to or greater than the

critical angle, explaining the relationship between the critical angle and the refractive indices of the core and the cladding.

2 Write notes explaining how there can be a range of angles greater than the criticial angle and so there will be a range of paths that can be followed by rays within the fibre, hence the terms multimode transmission and dispersion.

3 Write notes explaining how multimode dispersion can be reduced by reducing the core diameter and by a graded index fibre.

4 Write notes listing the advantages of optical fibre systems over copper cable systems for telecommunications.

Self-assessment questions

1-3 Choose all the correct responses.

1 When light is transmitted along an optical fibre

A the refractive index of the core is less than that of the cladding

B the refractive index of the core is very close to that of the cladding

C rays meet the core-cladding interface at angles greater than the critical angle for transmission over any significant distance

D the critical angle C for transmitted rays is given by $n_1 \sin C = n_2$ where n_1 is the refractive index of the cladding and n_2 that of the core.

2 Multimode transmission

A occurs when transmission over a number of paths is possible
B can occur with light of just one wavelength
C can be reduced by reducing the core diameter
D gives rise to dispersion

3 A graded index fibre

A has an abrupt difference in refractive index at the core-cladding interface
B has a refractive index which varies gradually from the centre of the core outwards and into the cladding
C gives higher dispersion than a step index fibre
D gives single mode transmission

Answers to self-assessment questions

Theme 1 Optical instruments

1 C,D
2 A,B,D
3 C
4 A,C
5 A
6 A,B

Theme 2 Resolving power

1 A
2 A

Theme 3 Aberrations

1 A,B,C
2 A,B
3 A converging lens is produced by combining a converging lens with a diverging lens, the two lens being made of different types of glass with different dispersive powers .The dispersion produced by one lens is cancelled by that produced by the other.
4 No chromatic aberration. Only one surface to be constructed to the right curvature. Difficult to maintain uniform refractive index throughout the glass of a large lens. It is easier to support a mirror than a lens.

Theme 4 Optical fibres

1 B,C
2 A,B,C,D
3 B

5.7 Physics of Astronomy

This option is divided into four THEMES which follow roughly the historical development of astronomy, often called the first science. It seems that all cultures of the world develop astronomy when they reach the agricultural stage of society.

Why do you think this is?

Your main reference text for this option is McGillivray, *Physics and Astronomy*, but Waxman's *Workbook for Astronomy* would also be useful if available.

Pre-requisite knowledge

(a) Area of a circle
(b) Surface area of a sphere
(c) Volume of a sphere
(d) Cartesian co-ordinates of arc i.e. degrees, minutes and seconds
(e) Polar co-ordinates - radians.

Theme 1 Optical detection

Study time: 1 week

Objectives

When you have completed the work in this theme you should be able to:

1 Describe the structure of the human eye and its function as an optical detector, including

(a) resolving power
(b) frequency response.

2 Explain the mechanism of photon detection by a photographic film emulsion and use the term 'image density'. Describe

(a) the effect of long exposure on the image density
(b) the frequency response of a fast panchromatic film.

3 Describe two methods of photoelectric detection i.e.

(a) the photoemissive cell
(b) the photodiode

and their frequency response.

4 Describe the use of a photomultiplier for image enhancement.

5 Describe the structure and function of an optical telescope, including

(a) light gathering power
(b) resolving power
(c) magnifying power .

Study questions and activities

1 Write notes on objective 1. These should include the function of the cornea and lens as refractive components, and the function of the rods and cones. Include a diagram, and a graph of frequency response.

2 PRACTICAL - Resolution of the eye

The resolution of an optical instrument depends on the diffraction pattern produced when the light (or other electromagnetic radiation) passes through an aperture (e.g. pupil) or lens.

Two sources are said to be resolved when the central maximum of one diffraction pattern is not closer than the first minimum of the other. (See figure P1.)

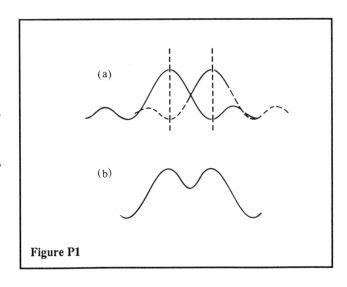

Figure P1

This experiment measures the angular resolution of your eye and investigates the effect of colour .

(a) Move the source with the two holes (figure P2) away from the eye until you decide that the two holes no longer appear distinctly separate. Measure the distance from your eye, remembering to include an error range.

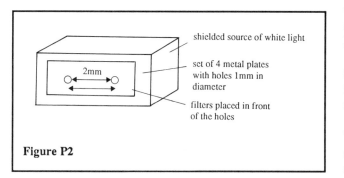

shielded source of white light

set of 4 metal plates with holes 1mm in diameter

filters placed in front of the holes

2mm

Figure P2

Repeat with red, green and blue filters.

(b) The resolving power θ of the eye is given by the ratio

$$\frac{a}{D}$$

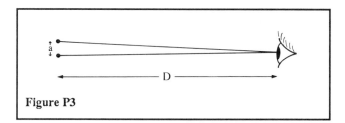

a

D

Figure P3

where *a* is the separation of the holes and *D* is the distance from the holes to the eye (see figure P3).
Compute the resolution of your eye from your results.

(c) Does the resolution depend on the colour of the light? Comment on your results.

(d) If possible, conduct an investigation to find out if resolution of the eye is linked to eye colour.

(e) 'African astronomers of the ancient civilisation of the Dogons could resolve objects (e.g. double stars) by sight, even though this feat cannot be reproduced today'.

Comment on this statement in the light of your results and any other relevant points.

3 Using star charts, find two stars which would be suitable for a 'test' of eye resolution. This kind of test was used on prospective sailors before the advent of other eye testing techniques.

(*Note.* This activity requires an understanding of stellar co-ordinates)

4 Write notes on objective 2, which should include a graph of frequency response for the emulsion. You should compare this with that for the eye.

5 PRACTICAL - Frequency response for a photographic emulsion

If facilities allow it, you could devise an experiment to test this, using a prism to produce a spectrum from sunlight. (Some detail is available in the JMB Teacher's Guide to the Physics of Astronomy Option.)

6 Write notes on objective 3 - these should include graphs of frequency response, and why these detection methods are useful compared with photographic detection.

7 You need to recall the structure of the photomultiplier in detail. Write notes on objective 4, including a circuit diagram of the photomultiplier.

8 Write notes on objective 5. The emphasis should be on the function of each component, rather than the varying design of optical telescopes.
(Work through *Waves and vibrations* section 3.6.)

9 (a) Compare the resolving power and the light gathering power of the human eye with those of a
(i) 10 cm telescope
(ii) 4 m telescope
(b) Why, for practical purposes, is there a minimum value on the focal length of the eyepiece?

Self-assessment questions

Choose one correct response from A to E.

1 The part of the eye which refracts incident light the most is

A the pupil
B the cornea
C the aqueous humour
D the lens
E the retina

2 The rod cells in the eye have a frequency response which peaks at

A 400 nm
B 450 nm
C 510 nm
D 560 nm
E 640 nm

3 A photomultiplier has six dynode stages, each of which has a secondary emission coefficient of four. Starlight incident on the photocathode releases a current of 7.5×10^{-10} A. The resulting current passing out of the photomultiplier is

A 9.7×10^{-7} A
B 4.5×10^{-9} A
C 3.07×10^{-6} A
D 3.0×10^{-9} A
E 3.07×10^{6} A

4 A refracting telescope has an objective lens of diameter 50 cm. At a wavelength of 500 nm the (theoretical) minimum resolvable angle would be

A 1.22×10^{-6} rads
B 1.22×10^{6} rads
C 3.05×10^{-7} rads
D 1×10^{-6} rads
E 1×10^{6} rads

5 A refracting telescope has an objective mirror of focal length $F = 800$ cm and an eyepiece of focal length $f = 6$ cm. What would be the relative size of the new magnifying power if the objective lens was replaced by a lens of $F = 900$ cm and the eyepiece by one of $f = 4$ cm?

A 0.59
B 0.66
C 1.5

Theme 2   Astronomical sources

Objectives

1 Recall the full electromagnetic spectrum.

2 (a) Describe the emission spectrum of a black body radiator.
(b) Use the relationships

(i) $\lambda_{max} T = $ constant (Wien's displacement law)
(ii) $E = \sigma T^4$ (Stefan's law)

3 Understand and recall the system for describing stellar magnitudes, and define the terms

(a) apparent magnitude
(b) absolute magnitude
(c) photographic magnitude
(d) luminosity

4 Understand and recall the system of stellar classification. Recall the classification of our local star (the sun).

5 Understand the mechanism which produces the varying magnitude observed for a binary star system.

6 Describe the construction of the Hertzsprung-Russell (H-R) diagram to classify stars. Use the terms

(a) main sequence
(b) dwarf star
(c) giant star

with reference to the diagram.

7 Describe the way in which emission spectra are produced by excited atoms, and the way in which absorption lines are produced. Extend this to an understanding of the nature of a stellar spectrum.

Study questions and activities

1 Write notes on objective 1 if this topic is not entirely familiar to you. It would be useful to become familiar with the wavelength units 'microns' and 'Angstroms' which you may encounter in Astrophysics texts.

(*Note.* The Angstrom is not an S.I. unit.)

2 Write notes on objective 2 - these should include graphical representations. (Ref. A-Level Physics course text)

3 Write notes on objectives 3 and 4. Part 3b includes the use of the term 'parsec' which you will define in Theme 3 Objective 3. Part 3d should include the relation $L = 4\pi R^2 \sigma T^4$. You should appreciate the 'average star' description of the sun.

4 Write notes on objective 5. Include a graphical representation of how the magnitude of a system varies with time (a light curve), and (briefly) the difference between eclipsing and non-eclipsing binaries.

5 Write notes on objective 6. You should be able to place the sun on the H-R diagram.

6 Write notes on objective 7. This develops core work on spectra. See unit *Electrons and the nucleus*, topic 7.

Self-assessment questions

1 The star Sirius has an apparent magnitude of approximately -1.47 at a distance of 2.65 parsec from the earth. The sun has an absolute magnitude of +4.9 and is at a distance of 4.81×10^{-6} parsec. At what distance would Sirius appear at the same magnitude as the sun?

A 1.4 pc
B 4×10^4 pc
C 2.4×10^{-5} pc
D 2.4×10^5 pc
E   26.7 pc

2 The sun's surface temperature $T = 5800$ K and its radius $R = 7 \times 10^5$ km. The radius of the earth $r = 6.38 \times 10^3$ km and its distance from the sun $d = 1.5 \times 10^8$ km. What is the power (energy per second) of the sunlight incident on the earth's daytime hemisphere?

A 1.8×10^{-17} W
B 1.8×10^{17} W
C 3.94×10^{26} W
D 8.9×10^{35} W
E 2.2×10^9 W

3 The spectral classification of the sun is

A F 0
B O 5
C A 2
D G 2
E G 9

4 Which letter correctly indicates the position of the sun on the Hertzsprung-Russell diagram (Figure P4)?

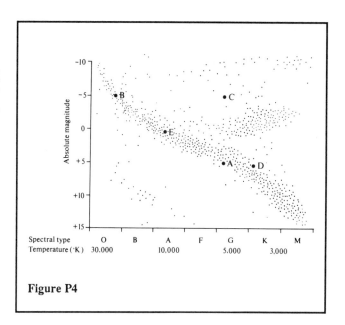

Figure P4

5 The spectrum of a star is seen to contain dark lines at wavelengths which correspond to the emission spectrum of Ca II ions. This is because

A the star does not contain the element calcium
B Ca II ions in the outer layers of the star have absorbed these wavelengths
C Ca II ions in the outer layers are emitting these wavelengths
D the star's temperature is too low to excite these wavelengths
E Ca II ions in the core of the star are emitting these wavelengths.

Theme 3   Analytical techniques

Study time: 0.5 week

Objectives

1 Understand and describe the Doppler effect on electromagnetic waves.
Use the equation $\Delta\lambda / \lambda = v/c$.

2 Describe the effect of the Doppler shift on stellar and planetary spectra, and deductions from this i.e.

(a) rotation of the source
(b) motion of the source

and be familiar with the use of the Hubble constant.

3 Describe parallax and its effect on

(a) the apparent position of an astronomical object
(b) the emission spectrum.

Recall the definition of the parsec.

4 Recall the definition of a light year, and relate this to the parsec.

5 Describe the importance of Cepheid variables as distance indicators.

Study questions and activities

1 Write notes on objectives 1 and 2. See unit *Waves and vibrations* topic 2.3.

2 If available, use the practical activity on p.44 of Waxman on the *Rotational velocity of Saturn* using Spectroscopy data. You should do PART A ONLY unless you wish to extend the work beyond the syllabus.

3 Write notes on objectives 3 and 4.

4 Write notes on objective 5. You are not required to recall details of stellar evolution, but it is very interesting.

Self-assessment questions

1 The spectrum of the planet Venus shows absorption lines which are tilted, and the spectrum as a whole is shifted toward the red. This would indicate that

A the planet is rotating and approaching the earth
B the planet is re-radiating sunlight
C the planet is rotating faster than the earth
D the planet is rotating and receding from the earth
E the planet is rotating more slowly than the earth.

2 Barnard's Star is at a distance of 5.97 light years from the earth. What is the maximum apparent angular displacement of the star due to the parallax effect of the earth's motion over one year?

A 0.36"
B 0.55"
C 1.83"
D 0.16"
E 1.09"

3 An absorption line in the spectrum of Arcturus is shifted by 0.026 nm (toward the blue end of the spectrum) from its normal position at 425 nm. What is the relative velocity of Arcturus to the earth.

A + 18 m s^{-1}
B -18 m s^{-1}
C +18 km s^{-1}
D +2.6 km s^{-1}
E -18 km s^{-1}

Theme 4   Extending the observation window

Study time: 2 weeks

Objectives

1 Describe the function of a radio telescope.

2 Describe the nature of astronomical radio sources, specifically

(a) the sun
(b) the Milky Way
(c) other galaxies.

3 Describe the application of radio spectroscopy to astronomical observation, especially the significance of the 21 cm hydrogen line.

4 Describe the application of radar to the observation of

(a) meteors
(b) planetary surfaces.

5 Appreciate the necessity for extraterrestrial detectors, arising from the absorption properties of the earth's atmosphere. Use the term 'observation window'.

6 Recall the main factors which affect the observation window i.e.

(a) CO_2
(b) O_3
(c) water vapour
(d) dust.

7 Describe the kinds of astronomical sources which are observed in the

(a) infra-red
(b) ultraviolet
(c) X-ray
(d) gamma-ray

regions of the electromagnetic spectrum.

8 Describe the main contrbutions made to observation from the following platforms:

(a) high-altitude balloons
(b) Voyager
(c) Skylab
(d) satellites.

Study questions and activities

1 Write notes on objective 1. These should include a block diagram of the components of a radio telescope, rather than a detailed description of each one. Do not include any details of interferometric techniques.

2 Write notes on objectives 2 and 3.

3 Figure P5 shows three traces taken from a scan of the Milky Way on the 21 cm wavelength.

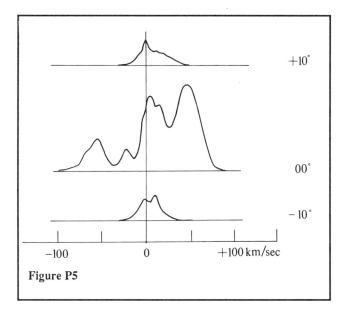

Figure P5

The top trace is the signal from the 'top' of the galaxy, the middle trace is from the centre of the galaxy, and the bottom trace is from the 'bottom'. The horizontal axis represents velocity.

Use this radio spectroscopic data to answer the following questions.

(a) What has caused the splitting of the signal into three main peaks in the centre trace?
(b) What is the velocity difference represented by the centre trace?
(c) Explain how the three traces indicate the general structure of the galaxy.

4 Write notes on objective 4, including a brief description of planetary surfaces.

5 In figure P6, the fraction labelling the profile lines represents the amount of incident energy transmitted by the atmosphere at that altitude and wavelength.

(a) What is the frequency range of the main atmospheric window? What electromagnetic radiation does this include?
(b) What range of frequency is least well transmitted by the atmosphere?
(c) Explain why it is advantageous to observe from a balloon platform at an altitude of 30 km. Over which wavelengths is this advantage lost?
(d) What kind of observation (infra-red, X-ray, etc.) is most likely to be carried out by satellite-borne telescopes?
(e) The Infra-Red Astronomical Satellite (IRAS) is crucial to infra-red observation. What other factor, besides atmospheric transmission, makes ground-based observation extremely difficult in this waveband?

6 Write notes on objective 6, referring to the graph from figure P6.

7 Write summary notes on objective 7 and 8. You should realise that many of the initiatives which extend the observation window have resulted from international scientific collaboration.

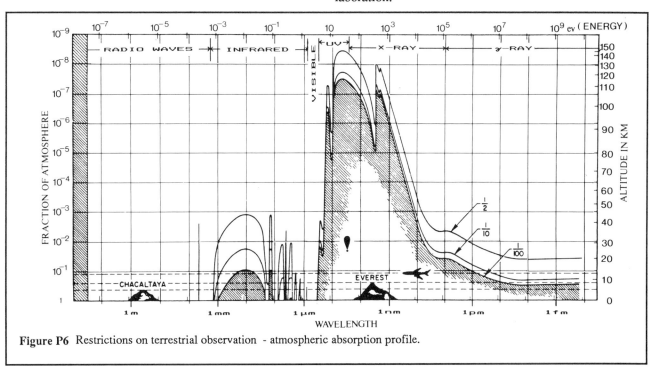

Figure P6 Restrictions on terrestrial observation - atmospheric absorption profile.

Self-assessment questions

1 A radio telescope operates at a wavelength of 10 cm. How large would its dish have to be in order to have a resolving power of 2.5×10^{-3} rad^{-1}, i.e. that of the human eye?

A 3.2×10^{-3} m
B 3.05×10^{2} m
C 4.88×10^{-5} m
D 3.05 m
E 4.88 m

2 Strong radio signals at a wavelength of 21 cm are detected from the Galaxy because of emission from

A neutral hydrogen atoms
B intersellar dust particles
C ionised hydrogen atoms
D Cepheid variables
E distant planets.

3 'Radar measurements of the surface on the planet Mars have shown that the height difference between the highest mountains and deepest valleys is about 12 km'. (McGil-livray).

Presuming these measurements were taken using a radar pulse directed at the planet from earth, what would be the time difference between the received pulse reflected from the highest mountain to one reflected from the deepest valley?

A 2×10^{-5} s
B 4×10^{-5} s
C 6×10^{-5} s
D 8×10^{-5} s
E 10^{-5} s

4 A radar beam of wavelength 1 cm is directed at the planet Venus which has a radius of 6.1×10^{6} m. The reflected beam contains a spread of wavelengths covering a range of 1.2×10^{-10} m either side of the original wavelength. Assuming that this effect is due entirely to the rotation of the planet, the period of this rotation is

A 1.8 days
B 6.9×10^{7} days
C 2.1×10^{7} days
D 243 days
E 0.02 days

Answers to self-assessment questions

Theme 1 Optical detection

1 B
2 C
3 C
4 A
5 D

Theme 2 Astronomical sources

1 C
2 B
3 D
4 A
5 B

Theme 3 Analytical techniques

1 D
2 E
3 C

Theme 4 Extending the observation window

1 B
2 A
3 D
4 D

5.8 Rotational dynamics

Theme 1 Rotating bodies

Objectives

When you have completed the work in this theme you should be able to:

1 Define and use the terms torque, moment, couple, centre of gravity, moment of inertia, radius of gyration, angular velocity, angular acceleration.

2 Explain the term centre of mass.

3 State the equilibrium conditions for a body acted on by coplanar forces.

4 Apply the equation $T = I\alpha$ to the solution of problems.

5 Derive moments of inertia using, where appropriate, the theorems of parallel and perpendicular axes.

6 Define angular momentum and angular impulse and solve problems involving them.

7 State and apply the law of conservation of angular momentum.

8 Derive and use the equation for the work done by a torque equation $W = T\theta$.

9 Derive and use the equation for rotational kinetic energy.

Study questions and references

Basic references

Topic 5 of the unit *Forces and motion*.
McGillivray, D. *Rotational dynamics,* chapters 1-7.

Akrill	Chapters 11, 12 and 13
Bolton	Chapter 5
Duncan	Chapter 7
Nelkon	Chapter 3
Muncaster	Chapter 6
Whelan	Chapter 6

1 Work through topic 5 of the unit *Forces and motion*.

2 Define the terms torque and moment.

3 State the conditions for the equilibrium of a rigid body acted on by coplanar forces and work through examples involving these conditions.

4 Define the term 'centre of gravity'.

5 Define the term couple and give examples of common situations where couples occur.

6 Define the term centre of mass and describe the motion of the centre of mass of a system of connected particles when no external forces act on the system.

7 Define the terms angular velocity and angular acceleration and derive the equations relating these to translational velocities and accelerations, i.e. $v = r\omega$ and $a = r\alpha$.

8 State the effect of an unbalanced torque on a rigid body.

9 Explain how the application of Newton's second law of motion to a body acted on by an unbalanced torque leads to the equation $T = I\alpha$ and work through examples involving this equation.

10 Define moment of inertia and derive it for a ring, a circular disc, a rod of rectangular or circular cross-section, a rectangular plate, a hollow cylinder, a spherical shell and a solid sphere.

11 State the theorems of parallel and perpendicular axes and explain their use in the calculation of moments of inertia.

12 Define radius of gyration.

13 Define angular momentum and angular impulse and state their relationship. State the relationship between torque and rate of change of angular momentum, also the law of conservation of angular momentum.

14 Work through examples involving the conservation of angular momentum, including a consideration of the spinning of a skater and the motion of planets and satellites.

15 Derive the equation for the work done by a constant torque, i.e. $W = T\theta$.

16 State the equation for the rotational kinetic energy of a body and work through examples involving it and $W = T\theta$, e.g. energy stored in flywheels.

Self-assessment questions

1-12 Choose all the correct answers.

1-3 Each of the following represents a quantity associated with rotational motion.

A rotational kinetic energy
B angular acceleration
C angular impulse
D angular momentum

Which of these quantities is

1 zero when a rigid body is rotating with a constant angular velocity
2 zero when there is no change in angular momentum
3 constant when there is a constant net torque?

4 A rigid body is in equilibrium when acted on by a set of coplanar forces if

A the resultant force is zero
B the resultant force acts through the centre of mass
C there is no angular acceleration
D the resultant force and the resultant couple are both zero.

5 Figure R1 shows a rigid beam resting on two supports. In (a) the supports are at the ends of the beam. If one of the supports is moved to the middle of the beam, as in (b), then

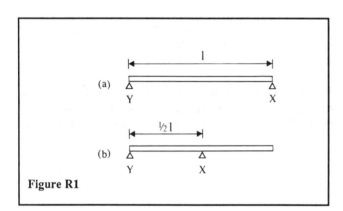

Figure R1

A the reaction at support X is increased
B the reaction at support Y is increased
C the beam is still in equilibrium
D there is a net clockwise moment.

6 A disc rotating about an axis through its centre has an angular acceleration if

A the angle swept out by a radius per second increases
B the linear speed of a point on the rim is constant
C the frequency of rotation is constant
D the centripetal acceleration is constant.

7 A disc can turn freely about an axis through its centre. If the disc is at rest an angular acceleration about this axis can be produced by

A a resultant force applied to the centre of the disc
B a torque
C a couple
D a resultant force applied tangentially to the rim of the disc .

8 A constant torque T acts on a rigid body and causes its angular velocity to change from ω_1 to ω_2 in a time t. If the body has a moment of inertia of I about the axis of rotation then the change in angular momentum will be

A $I(\omega_2 - \omega_1)$
B $I(\omega_2 - \omega_1)$
C T/t
D Tt

9 An ice-skater spinning with arms outstretched increases the speed of rotation by pulling the arms in to the sides. This is because

A the moment of inertia is decreased
B angular momentum is conserved
C the angular momentum is increased
D friction is reduced.

10 A flywheel of mass m and radius r has a moment of inertia I about its central axis. If it is rotating at n revolutions per second, the amount of work done by it coming to rest is

A $In^2/2$
B $mr^2n^2/2$
C $2\pi In^2$
D $2\pi In^2$

11 A cylindrical solid object rotates about a central axis running its length. Its moment of inertia will be changed if

A the angular velocity increases
B a fly hits and sticks to the outer surface of the cylinder
C the axis of rotation is changed
D the temperature rises and the cylinder expands.

12 A satellite orbits a planet with a constant speed along a circular path centred on the planet. Which of the following will be constant for the satellite?

A linear momentum
B angular momentum
C rotational kinetic energy
D linear kinetic energy

13 A dumb-bell consists of a slender rod of length 1.00 m and mass 5.0 kg with a uniform sphere of mass 40 kg and radius 0.10 m at each end. What is the moment of inertia of (a) a sphere about an axis through its centre, (b) a sphere about an axis through the centre of the dumb-bell rod, (c) the slender rod about an axis through its centre, and (d) the dumb-bell about an axis through its centre.

14 A bicycle wheel has a mass of 2.0 kg, a radius of 0.30 m and a radius of gyration of 0.25 m. What is its total kinetic energy when the wheel moves across the ground at a linear speed of 2.0 m s^{-1}?

15 What torque is exerted by a car engine working at a power of 50 kW when it is rotating at 60 revolutions per second ?

16 What is the energy stored in a flywheel of mass 300 kg and radius of gyration 1.2 m when it is rotating at 30 revolutions per minute?

17 An electric motor has a rotor of mass 200 kg and radius of gyration 0.14 m. What is the torque required to give the rotor an angular acceleration of 0.5 rad s⁻².

Theme 2 Oscillatory rotational motion

Study time: 0.5-1 week

Objectives

When you have completed the work in this theme you should be able to:

1 State the conditions for simple harmonic motion of rigid bodies.

2 Solve problems involving simple harmonic motion of rigid bodies, including the compound pendulum and torsional oscillations.

3 Describe how such oscillations can be used to determine moments of inertia.

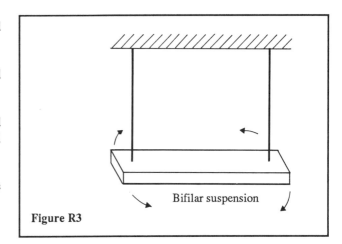

Figure R3

Study questions and references

Basic references
McGillivray, D. *Rotational dynamics*, chapter 8.

Akrill	Chapter 15
Nelkon	Chapter 3
Whelan	Chapter 6

1 Write a note comparing the equations for simple harmonic motion of particles with those for rigid bodies, in particular
$a = - \omega^2 x$
$\alpha = - \omega^2 \theta$.

2 Derive the equation for the periodic time of oscillation of a compound pendulum when the amplitude of oscillation is small.

3 Derive the equation for the periodic time of oscillation of a rigid disc rigidly connected to the end of a thin torsion wire (figure R2) and which oscillates by twisting and untwisting the wire.

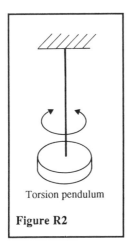

Torsion pendulum

Figure R2

4 Derive the equation for the periodic time of oscillation of a rigid body supported by a bifilar suspension (figure R3) and subject to small amplitude oscillations in the horizontal plane.

5 Describe how moments of inertia can be determined experimentally using measurements of the periodic time of rotational oscillations.

Self-assessment questions

1-3 Choose all the correct responses.

1 For a torsion pendulum the periodic time is doubled by

A doubling the radius of the disc, its mass remaining constant
B doubling the mass of the disc, its radius remaining constant
C doubling the radius of the disc and doubling its mass
D halving the torsional rigidity of the supporting wire.

2 For a rigid object performing rotational simple harmonic motion

A the angular acceleration is proportional to the angular displacement
B the periodic time is proportional to the square of the moment of inertia
C the frequency of rotation is proportional to the restoring couple per unit displacement
D the periodic time depends on the angular displacement

3 The period of oscillation T of a compound pendulum consisting of a long, rigid, metal bar is given by

$$T = 2\pi\sqrt{\left(\frac{h^2 + k^2}{hg}\right)}$$

where h is the distance of the knife edge about which the oscillation occurs from the centre of mass, k is the radius of gyration about an axis through the centre of mass and g is the acceleration due to gravity. Measurements of the periodic time are made for different values of h. A straight line graph can be obtained by plotting

A T against h
B T^2 against h^2
C T^2 against h
D T^2h against h^2

4 A circular disc of mass 0.80 kg and radius 100 mm is suspended by a wire through its centre, as in figure R3, and makes 100 oscillations in 118 s. What is the torsional rigidity of the supporting wire?

Answers to self-assessment questions

Theme 1 Rotating bodies

1 B,C
2 B,C
3 C
4 D
5 A,C
6 A
7 B,C,D
8 A,D
9 A,B
10 D
11 B,C,D
12 B,C,D

13 (a) $I = \frac{2}{5}mr^2 = 0.16 \text{ kg m}^2$.
(b) $I = 0.16 + 40 \times 0.60^2 = 14.56 \text{kg m}^2$
(c) $I = \frac{1}{12}mL^2 = 5.0 \times 1.0^2/12 = 0.42 \text{ kg m}^2$
14 $\omega = v/r = 2.0/0.30 = 0.67 \text{ rad s}^{-1}$
$\quad I = mk^2 = 2.0 \times 0.25^2 = 0.125 \text{ kg m}^2$
Total K.E. $= \frac{1}{2}I\omega^2 = 5.1 \text{ J}$
15 $P = T\omega$, hence $T = 133 \text{ N m}$
16 $I = mk^2 = 432 \text{ kg m}^2$
$\quad \omega = 2\pi f = \pi \text{ rad s}^{-1}$
K.E. $= \frac{1}{2}I\omega^2 = 680 \text{ J}$
17 $I = mk^2$
$\quad T = I\alpha = 2.0 \text{ N m}$

Theme 2 Oscillatory rotational motion

1 A
2 A,B
3 D
4 $I = \frac{1}{2}mr^2 = 2.0 \times 10^{-5} \text{ kg m}^2$
$\quad T = 2\pi\sqrt{(I/c)}$, hence $c = 1.1 \times 10^{-8} \text{ N m rad}^{-1}$

5.9 Solid materials

Theme 1 Microscopic properties

Objectives

When you have completed the work in this theme you should be able to:

1 Use force-separation and potential energy-separation graphs for two atoms to explain Hooke law behaviour and thermal expansion.

2 Recall how crystalline structures can be ascribed to the orderly packing together of particles.

3 Explain what is meant by describing metals as poly-crystalline and the term grain.

4 Describe the microscopic behaviour occurring during elastic and plastic deformations of ideal metals, explaining the term slip plane and hence distinguishing microscopically between brittle and ductile behaviour.

5 Explain how bubble rafts can be used as a model for a metal and the significance of dislocations.

6 Describe polymers as composed of long-chain molecules which can be linear chains, branched chains or cross-linked chains and explain the significance of the chains on the macroscopic properties.

7 Explain how some polymers can be amorphous or crystal-line and the significance of the glass transition temperature.

Study questions and references

Basic references

Topics 2 and 3 in the unit *Behaviour of matter*.
This can be supplemented by reference to the following A-level texts.

Gordon, J.E., *The new science of strong materials*, chapter 4 for objectives 4 and 5.

Bolton	Chapter 16
Duncan	Chapters 2 and 4
Muncaster	Chapters 9 and 11
Nelkon	Chapter 5
Wenham	Chapters 13, 14 and 15
Whelan	Chapters 16, 17 and 22

1 Make sketches of the force-separation and potential en-ergy-separation graphs for two atoms, indicating clearly on each graph the equilibrium separation of the atoms.

On the force-separation graph also indicate when the forces are attractive and when repulsive.

2 Write a note explaining how the shape of the force-sepa-ration graph near the equilibrium separation can be used to explain Hooke's law.

3 Write a note explaining how the shape of the potential en-ergy-separation graph near the equilibrium separation can be used to explain thermal expansion.

4 Make a brief note to remind yourself how crystal structures can be simulated by the orderly packing together of spheres.

5 Write notes explaining what is meant by the terms poly crystalline and grain and describe in outline one piece of evidence for the polycrystalline nature of a metal.

6 Write a brief note or use simple sketches to describe the microscopic behaviour occurring during elastic and plastic deformations of ideal metals (ideal meaning perfectly packed atoms). Then use your note or sketches to explain the term slip plane.

7 Write a brief note about the effect of cracks on the strength of a metal.

8 By examining pictures of, or carrying out experiments with, bubble rafts, make simple sketches to show grain boundaries and dislocations. Write a note explaining the effects of these on the properties of the material.

9 Draw simple sketches to give idealised pictures of the forms of polymer chains that can occur, i.e. linear, branched and cross-linked.

10 Write notes on the relationship between structure and properties, including:

(a) the difference between an amorphous and a crystalline structure,
(b) how a linear chain polymer can more easily have a crys-talline structure,
(c) how the degree of crystallinity of a polymer affects its stiffness,
(d) how cross-linking between chains increases stiffness.

11 Write a note explaining the term glass transition tempera-ture and its effect on the properties of a polymer.

12 Write a note explaining how structure changes in rubber can account for its changes in properties when stretched only a little to when considerably stretched.

Self-assessment questions

1-6 Multiple choice - choose all correct responses.

1 For the force-separation graph for two atoms:

A the forces are repulsive at separations less than the equilibrium separation and attractive at greater separations
B stretching a solid results in the net interatomic forces becoming attractive
C squashing a solid results in the net interatomic forces becoming repulsive
D when a solid obeys Hooke's law the slope of the graph at about the equilibrium separation is a straight line.

2 For the potential energy-separation graph for two atoms:

A the potential energy is a minimum at the equilibrium separation
B the potential energy is zero at the equilibrium separation
C increasing the temperature means the separation of the atoms just increases
D thermal expansion occurs because the graph is not symmetrical about the equilibrium separation.

3 A solid metal is

A an amorphous material
B a crystalline material
C a disorderly arrangement of atoms
D composed of regions where atoms are orderly packed.

4 Plastic deformation of a metal:

A is when forces applied to the metal cause permanent deformation
B occurs when planes of atoms within a grain slide over one another to new equilibrium positions
C is greatest in brittle materials
D is greatest when the grains are large.

5 Which of the following statements is correct ?

A linear chain polymer can have a crystalline structure
B A cross-linked polymer tends to be more rigid than a linear chain polymer.
C Below the glass transition temperature a polymer is less stiff than above it.
D Rubber becomes more crystalline when stretched than unstretched.

6 Poly(e)thene is a linear chain polymer, hence

A it can have a range of values of density
B it can have a range of values of Young modulus
C it can be crystalline
D it is always completely amorphous.

7 Figure S1 shows a graph of how the resultant force F between a pair of atoms in a solid varies with their separation

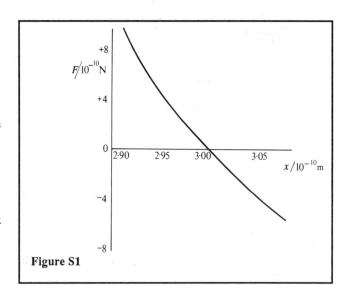

Figure S1

x. Positive values of F indicate repulsion, negative values attraction.

(a) Use the graph to determine:

(i) the equilibrium separation,
(ii) the separation at which the attractive force is 4.0×10^{-10} N.

(b) Use the graph to explain:

(i) why solids resist being stretched or compressed,
(ii) why Hooke's law is obeyed for small extensions or compressions.

For small displacements from the equilibrium separation the force F is related to the displacement Δx by the relationship $F = k\Delta x$.
(iii) Find the value of k.

(c) Use the graph to determine:

(i) the separation at which the potential energy will be a minimum,
(ii) the energy needed to decrease the separation of the atoms from 3.00×10^{-10} m to 2.95×10^{-10} m.

8 (a) Explain the terms grain boundary and slip plane.
(b) Explain how grain size affects the amount of slip and hence the ductility of a metal.
(c) Explain how cracks affect the strength of a material.

9 Explain the term dislocation and how dislocations affect the properties of a material.

10 Describe the structural and property changes that occur for a polymer at its glass transition temperature.

11 A plastic teaspoon at room temperature is fairly rigid and brittle. However, if it is put into boiling water it becomes very flexible. When the spoon is then cooled it again becomes rigid and brittle. Explain this behaviour in structural terms for the polymer.

Theme 2 Macroscopic properties

Objectives

When you have completed the work in this theme you should be able to:

1 Use and explain the terms stress, strain, limit of proportionality, Young modulus, elastic limit, elastic and plastic behaviour, tensile strength.

2 Use stress-strain graphs to determine Young modulus and tensile strength.

3 Describe and recognise force-extension and stress-strain graphs for brittle and ductile materials.

4 Describe fracture with brittle and ductile materials.

5 Explain the terms energy density and specific energy and determine the energy per volume from the area under a stress-strain graph.

6 Describe the property and structure changes that occur in work hardening and annealing.

7 Explain the terms creep, fatigue and hysteresis.

8 Describe force-extension and stress-strain graphs for polymers and relate the graphs to polymer microstructure.

9 Distinguish between thermoplastic and thermosetting polymers on the basis of their properties and microstructure.

10 Describe the principle of photoelastic stress analysis.

Study questions and references

Basic references

Topic 3 in the unit *Behaviour of matter*, sections 3.2 and 3.3.

The following are alternative sources of reference:

Gordon, J.E. *The new science of strong materials*, chapter 2.

Bolton	Chapter 16
Duncan	Chapters 1 and 2
Muncaster	Chapters 9 and 11
Nelkon	Chapters 5 and 25
Wenham	Chapter 13
Whelan	Chapter 17

1 Make a note of the definitions of stress, strain, limit of

proportionality, Young modulus, elastic limit and tensile strength.

2 Sketch a force-extension graph and identify on it the regions of elastic and plastic behaviour.

3 Solve problems involving forces, extensions, cross-sectional area or dimensions, length and Young modulus for materials stretched within the limit of proportionality.

4 Sketch force-extension or stress-strain graphs for brittle and ductile materials and explain the differences between them.

5 Write a note describing fracture with brittle and ductile materials, relating it to the force-extension or stress-strain graphs in 4.

6 Write a note describing the relationship between the energy in a stretched wire and the area under the force-extension graph and derive the relationship energy per unit volume = $\frac{1}{2}$ stress × strain.

7 Define the terms energy density and specific energy.

8 Write notes explaining what happens to the properties of a material, and its grain structure, when it is work hardened.

9 Write notes explaining what happens to the properties of a material, and its grain structure, when it is annealed.

10 Sketch a force-extension graph showing a material exhibiting hysteresis.

11 Write notes explaining the terms creep and fatigue.

12 Sketch a typical force-extension or stress-strain graph to breaking point for a polymer such as polyethene (polythene). Add notes explaining what is happening to the polymer chains at each stage of the graph .

13 Write a note distinguishing between the properties and microstructure of thermosetting and thermoplastic polymers.

14 Write a note explaining the principle of photoelastic stress analysis.

Self-assessment questions

1-3 Figure S2 shows a stress-strain graph. Which of the

labels A, B, C, D or E indicate the following quantities?

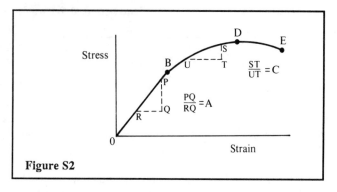

Figure S2

1 Tensile strength.
2 Young modulus.
3 Limit of proportionality.

4-7 Which of these units applies to the following quantities?

A Pa **B** N **C** J **D** m **E** no unit

4 Stress.
5 Strain.
6 Young modulus.
7 Tensile strength.

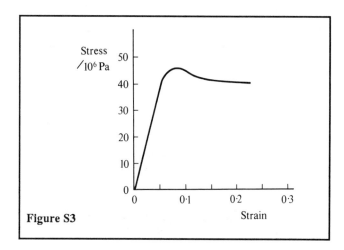

Figure S3

8 Figure S3 shows a stress-strain graph. From the graph, estimate
(a) the Young modulus, (b) the limit of proportionality, (c) the tensile strength.

9 A uniform wire of length 2.0 m and cross-sectional area 1.0×10^{-6} m^2 is suspended vertically and a mass of 10 kg hung from it.
(a) What is the stress produced in the wire?
(b) What is the strain if the Young modulus for the wire is 200 GPa and the limit of proportionality is not exceeded?
(c) What will be the extension produced?

10 A rod of mild steel is steadily stretched in a tensile testing machine. At first, it stretches uniformly by relatively small amounts, then it yields and necks before finally breaking. Figure S4 shows the initial and the unbroken rods.

Sketch a force-extension graph to represent the behaviour of the material.

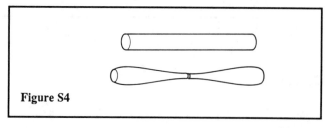

Figure S4

11-13 Figure S5 shows stress-strain graphs, all to the same scale, for materials A, B, C and D. Which of these describes:

11 The most brittle material?
12 The most ductile material?
13 The stiffest material?

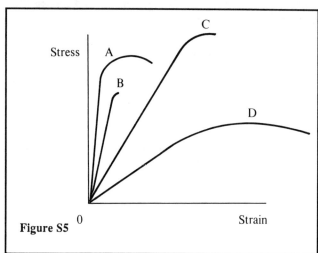

Figure S5

14 For the material described by the force-extension graph in figure S6, estimate the energy stored in the material when it is stretched by (a) 0.5 mm, (b) 1.0 mm.

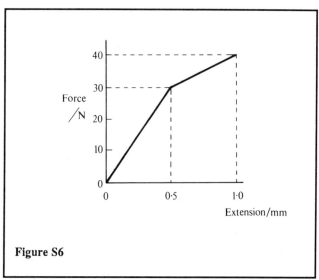

Figure S6

15 Complete the following table:

Process	Change in ductility/ brittleness	Change in grains
Work hardening		
Annealing		

16 Figure S7 shows a graph of a material exhibiting elastic hysteresis. What is represented by the shaded area on the graph?

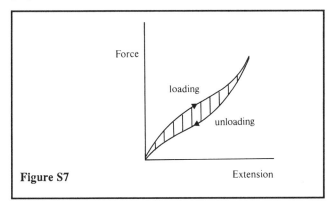

Figure S7

17 Explain the terms creep and fatigue.

18 Which of the following statements describes (a) a thermoplastic polymer, (b) a thermosetting polymer?

A When heated it softens and becomes more flexible.
B When heated its mechanical properties do not noticeably change.
C It has a structure of cross-linked polymer chains.
D It has a structure of polymer chains without any cross links.

19 Figure S8 shows a stress-strain graph for a thermoplastic at different temperatures. How do the tensile strength and Young modulus change when the temperature is increased?

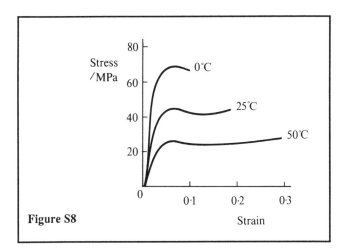

Figure S8

20 Figure S9 shows a stress-strain graph for a polymer at two different temperatures, one being below the glass transition temperature and one above. Which graph refers to which temperature?

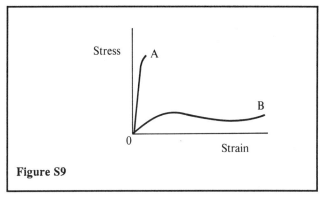

Figure S9

21 A strip of a thermoplastic polymer is held by a student between his two hands and slowly pulled. At first, the polymer slightly increases in length but then it suddenly develops a neck, as shown in figure S10. A further slight pull results in the necked region spreading rapidly along almost the entire length of the strip. Further pulling produces no further necking but the strip extends more easily than it did initially. Sketch a possible stress-strain graph for this polymer. (Note, you can do this as an experiment with a strip cut from a polyethene (polythene) bag. The effect will probably depend on the direction you cut the strip from the bag.)

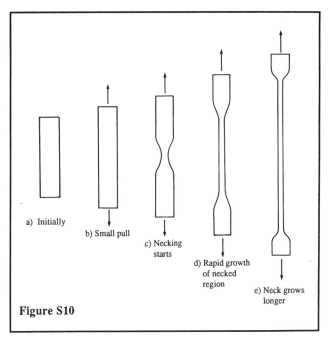

Figure S10

22 Suggest an explanation for the behaviour described in question 21 in terms of polymer chains. You may assume that the chains are linear ones and initially they are coiled in random directions.

Theme 3 Materials technology

Objectives

When you have completed the work in this theme you should be able to:

1 Describe how the materials used by humans have changed over the years.

2 Explain how the fact that some materials are strong in tension and others in compression has affected their use, i.e. in structures such as bridges or buildings.

3 Explain why the properties of particular materials make them suitable for particular applications, the range of materials being considered including metals, polymers, ceramics, concrete, timber and composites.

4 Explain what is meant by a structure and the problems of bridging a space with beams.

Study questions and references

Basic references
Gordon, J.E. *The new science of strong materials*, chapters 2, 6, 7 and 8.
Gordon, J.E. *Structures*, chapters 9, 10 and 11.
Bolton, W. *Patterns in physics*, chapter 16.

1 Read one or both of the following and make notes on how materials have changed over the years and affected their use:

Bolton, W. chapter 16, Supplementary material, Bridges.
Gordon, J.E. chapter 10.

2 Write notes, with simple sketches, describing how structures can, in some cases, require materials strong in tension and others strong in compression.

3 List structural materials which are particularly useful in (a) tension, and (b) compression structures.

4 Write notes, with sketches, explaining how reinforcing or pre-stressing concrete improves its properties and give examples of other composites.

5 Draw up a table comparing the general properties, i.e. density, melting-point, thermal conductivity, thermal expansion, electrical conductivity, tensile strength, Young modulus, hardness, of metals, polymers, ceramics and wood. Values for the properties are not necessary if you can describe the comparative values in words such as high, low, etc. You might find it useful to consult tables of properties or make judgements based on your own experience.

6 Examine objects and identify the types of materials involved in them and why such materials have been chosen. For example, you could list the types of materials used in a mains electrical plug and explain why the different materials are used.

7 Read Gordon, J.E. *Structures*, chapter 11 and write brief notes, with sketches, describing the ways beams can be used to bridge gaps.

8 Read Gordon, J.E. *Structures*, page 192 and make notes on scaling.

Self-assessment questions

1 When used in structures subject to tension, which of the following materials are sources of weakness?

A Stone B Cast iron C Mild steel D Concrete E Wood

2-5 The following are categories of materials:

A Metals B Polymers C Ceramics

2 Which category has the highest melting-points?
3 Which category has the highest thermal conductivities?
4 Which category has the highest electrical conductivities?
5 Which category is likely to have the softest materials?

6 Explain why bridges made from stone tend to be arches rather than simple beams resting across the gap.

7 Explain how using reinforcing bars with concrete enables it to be used in structures involving tension.

8 Are the main cables of a suspension bridge in tension or compression and how does this affect the choice of material for them?

9 If all the linear dimensions of a steel wire were scaled up by a factor of four, by what factors do the following change:

(a) volume, (b) mass, (c) surface area, (d) stress for a given load?

Answers to self-assessment questions

Theme 1 Microscopic properties

1 A, B, C and D are all correct.

2 A and D are correct.

3 B and D. The regions of order referred to in D are grains.

4 A, B and D. Plastic deformation is greatest in ductile materials. A material is made more ductile by increasing grain size. This is because slip within a grain does not cross over from one grain to another and thus the largest amount of slip occurs with the largest grains.

5 A, B and D are correct. Below the glass transition temperature a polymer is more rigid.

6 A, B, C. It is because polythene can be crystalline that a range of properties occur, depending on the degree of crystallinity.

7 (a) (i) 3.00×10^{-10} m. (ii) 3.05×10^{-10} m.

(b) (i) Stretching results in an opposing attractive force, compressing results in an opposing repulsive force. (ii) The graph is a straight line in that region. (iii) k = slope of graph at equilibrium separation = 80 N m^{-1}.

(c) 3.00×10^{-10} m. (ii) The potential energy is the area between the graph and the zero force axis. From 3.00×10^{-10} to 2.95×10^{-10} m energy is approximately $\frac{1}{2} \times 4 \times 10^{-10} \times 0.05 \times 10^{-10} = 0.10 \times 10^{-20}$ J.

8 (a) The grain boundary is the boundary between regions of orderly arrangements of atoms. Slip planes are planes within grains along which slip occurs.

(b) The larger the size of the grain the greater the amount of slip that can occur and hence the greater the amount of plastic deformation that is possible. This means a more ductile material. A brittle material is one which suffers little plastic deformation before breaking. The term plastic deformation is used for deformations which are not elastic and result in permanent deformation.

(c) Cracks result in stress concentrations when forces are applied to a cracked material (see Gordon, *The new science of strong materials*, chapter 4).

9 Dislocations are imperfections in the way atoms are packed together. The term edge dislocation is used for the line in a solid where there is an imperfection due to an extra layer of atoms occurring in the solid on one side of the line when compared with the other side. When the solid is subject to stress, the dislocations can move and, in doing so, give rise to plastic deformations. However, if there are many dislocations they interact, become 'tangled', and inhibit further movement. Thus, the material becomes more brittle.

10 At the glass transition temperature a polymer changes from a fairly rigid material to one with a lower Young modulus, i.e. it becomes more flexible. Below the glass transition temperature, the polymer chains cannot easily move. Above it, they are reasonably free to slide past each other and uncoil.

11 The glass transition temperature is somewhere between room temperature and that of boiling water.

Theme 2 Macroscopic properties

1 D

2 A

3 B

4 A

5 E

6 A

7 A

8 (a) $40 \times 10^6/0.05 = 8.0 \times 10^{-8}$ Pa

(b) 40×10^6 Pa

(c) 45×10^6 Pa

9 (a) $10 \times 9.8/1.0 \times 10^{-6} = 9.8 \times 10^7$ Pa

(b) E = stress/strain, hence strain = $9.8 \times 10^7/200 \times 10^{11}$ = 4.9×10^{-4}

(c) Extension = $4.9 \times 10^{-4} \times 2.0 = 9.8 \times 10^{-4}$ m

10 The material is ductile and shows a considerable amount of plastic deformation, hence the graph would be like figure S3 .

11 B

12 D

13 A

14 Energy/volume = area under force-extension graph.

(a) 15 J (b) 32.5 J

15 Work hardening causes a material to become more brittle as a result of deformation of the grains and a consequential hindering of slip and dislocation movement. Annealing increases ductility as a result of causing grains to grow.

16 Energy is used to extend the material and not all this energy is recovered when the material contracts back to its original length, the shaded area representing the energy 'lost' (a rise in temperature occurring).

17 Creep can be defined as the continuing deformation of a material with the passage of time when the material is subject to a constant stress. Repeated stressing and unstressing, or alternating stresses of compression and tension, can cause a material to fail even though the stresses applied were less than the stress normally needed to cause fracture. Such a type of failure is called fatigue failure.

18 Thermoplastic A, D. Thermosetting B, C.

19 Both decrease.

20 A above the glass transition temperature when the materials brittle and stiff.

B below it when it is ductile and more flexible.

21 See figure S11.

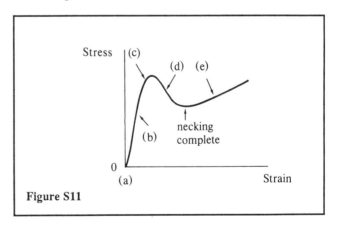

Figure S11

22 With reference to figure S11: at (b) the initially randomly orientated coiled chains become more orientated but still coiled. At (c) the onset of necking marks the stress at which that part of the sample has molecular chains all orientated in the same direction. As the necking spreads so the orientated region grows. When necking is complete the coiled chains are all orientated in the same direction. Further force (e)

causes the chains to uncoil and eventually they begin to slip past each other.

Theme 3 Materials technology

1 A, B, D
Concrete can be used in tension if reinforced or pre-stressed.
2 C
3 A
4 A
5 B
The following table outlines the properties of materials and has been used as the basis of the replies to questions 2-5.

Property	Metals	Polymers	Ceramics
Density/10^3 kg m^{-3}	2-16	1-2	2-17
Melting point/°C	200-3500	70-200	2000-4000
Thermal conductivity	High	Low	Medium
Thermal expansion	Medium	High	Low
Electrical conductivity	High	Low	Low
Tensile strength/mPa	100-2500	30-300	10-400
Young modulus/GPa	40-100	0.7-3.5	150-450
Hardness	Medium	Low	High

6 Stone is weak in tension but strong in compression. A stone beam bridge when subjected to a load bends in such a way that the bottom part has tension forces which stretch. If the stone forms part of an arch structure the forces act so as to put the stone in compression.

7 The bottom edge of a loaded beam is in tension. Since concrete is weak in tension it will have a tendency to crack at the lower edge. A reinforcing steel rod at the bottom of the beam will prevent the beam from cracking as the steel rod takes most of the tensile force.

8 In tension. Thus, a material strong in tension has to be used, this being steel.

9 (a) Volume is proportional to the cube of length, hence the volume is increased by $4^3 = 64$. (b) Mass is proportional to volume and so increased by a factor of 64. (c) Area is proportional to the square of length and so there is an increase of $4^2 = 16$. (d) Stress = force/area so increasing the area by a factor of 16 decreases the stress by a factor of 1/16.

5.10 Telecommunications

Theme 1 Principles

Objectives

When you have completed the work in this theme you should be able to:

1 State the methods used for telecommunication.

2 Explain the significance of the term bandwidth in relation to telecommunication methods.

3 Describe amplitude modulation and state the bandwidth required.

4 Explain the problem of noise with amplitude modulated signals and how digital transmission overcomes it.

5 Describe pulse coded modulation.

6 Describe electromagnetic waves as plane polarised travelling E- and B-fields with the speed being given by

$$c = \frac{1}{\sqrt{(\mu_0 \varepsilon_0)}}$$

in a vacuum.

Study questions and references

Basic references

Ed. Nicholl, B. and Selfe, J. *Telecommunications in practice*, chapters 4 and 13.

Bolton Chapters 9 and 15.

1 List the methods currently used and in development for long-distance transmission of information.

2 Make notes of the range of frequencies encountered in speech and in music, i.e. the bandwidth required for communicating them. Hence, state the bandwidth requirements of a system used to communicate them and the problems that occur if the bandwidth is inadequate.

3 Describe amplitude modulation and note the bandwidth required for amplitude modulated transmissions, $f_c \pm f_m$.

4 Make notes on the effect of noise on amplitude modulated transmissions and how digital transmissions overcome the problem.

5 Write notes explaining pulse coded modulation.

6 Sketch an electromagnetic wave in the form of travelling

plane polarised electric and magnetic fields , noting the relationship for the speed in a vacuum as

$$c = \frac{1}{\sqrt{(\mu_0 \varepsilon_0)}}$$

Self-assessment questions

1-3 Choose all the correct responses.

1 Music has frequencies ranging from 50 to 15 000 Hz. The bandwidth needed for optimum transmission is thus

A 50 Hz
B 14 950 Hz
C 15 000 Hz
D 15 050 Hz

2 Transmission of music through a system having a bandwidth less than that of the music

A is not possible
B results in a lot of noise
C results in a drop in quality
D has no effect on the sound.

3 An amplitude modulated radio transmission occurs at a carrier frequency of 500 kHz for an audio wave of bandwidth 10 kHz. The required bandwidth for the amplitude modulated wave will be

A 10 kHz
B 20 kHz
C 490 kHz
D 510 kHz

4 Explain how noise is a problem with amplitude modulated transmissions but can be overcome with digital transmissions.

5 Explain the operations of pulse amplitude modulation, quantisation and encoding that occur with pulse coded modulation.

6 Choose all the correct responses. A plane polarised electromagnetic wave travelling in a vacuum

A has its electric and magnetic fields at right angles to each other
B has its electric field in just one plane
C has its magnetic field in just one polane
D is either just an electric field or a magnetic field

Theme 2 Radio systems

Objectives

When you have completed the work in this theme you should be able to:

1 Using block diagrams, describe a simple amplitude modulated radio transmitter and receiver.

2 Explain the function and action of the parallel tuned LC circuit.

3 Describe the half-wave dipole aerial and explain how it can be modified by the use of directors and a reflector.

4 Describe the parabolic dish aerial.

5 Describe the directional characteristics of aerials in the form of polar diagrams, relating these to the diffraction pattern for a slit or circular hole.

6 Using a block diagram, describe the sending of a message via a satellite.

7 Explain what is meant by geostationary satellites and calculate orbits.

8 Explain how satellites receive their power.

Study questions and references

Basic references

Ed. Nicholl, B. and Selfe, J. *Telecommunications in practice*, chapters 1, 2 and 7.

Bolton   Chapters 9 and 15.

1 Draw a block diagram for a simple amplitude modulated radio receiver, and describe what happens at each block in the sequence.

2 Write notes explaining what happens to the current in and the potential difference across a parallel LC circuit at resonance. Hence, explain the use of a such a circuit for tuning.

3 Make sketches of the half-wave dipole and its modifications using a reflector and directors, clearly indicating distances and sizes in terms of the wavelength of the radio waves. Explain the reason for the distance of the reflector from the dipole.

4 Sketch the parabolic dish aerial and indicate on your sketch the sub-reflector and feed.

5 Sketch a polar diagram for an aerial and explain the relation of such diagrams to diffraction patterns occurring from slits or circular holes, noting the equations which would enable the angular width of the central maximum to be calculated.

6 Draw a block diagram describing the stages involved in sending from a central exchange a telephone message via a satellite.

7 Write notes explaining the term geostationary satellite and the derivation of the equation for the orbit.

8 Write a note describing the provision of electrical and motive power to a satellite. What determines the life of a satellite?

Self-assessment questions

Questions 1-4. For each numbered question select the heading below which describes that part of an amplitude modulated radio receiver which carries out the required function.

A Tuner
B Aerial
C Demodulator
D Loudspeaker

1 Detects the radio signals.
2 Selects one radio frequency.
3 Separates the audio signal from the radio signal.
4 Converts the audio signal into sound.

Questions 5-8 Choose all the correct responses.

5 For a parallel LC circuit at resonance

A the current in L is out of phase with that in C
B the reactance of L is the same as that of C
C the current entering the LC arrangement is effectively zero
D the potential difference across the LC circuit is zero.

6 For a half-wave dipole aerial with reflector and directors

A the lengths of the two rods used for the dipole are each $\lambda/2$
B the reflector is $\lambda/4$ behind the dipole
C the waves reflected at the reflector suffer a phase change of $\lambda/2$
D the function of the directors is to enable radio waves to be detected from any angle.

7 A parabolic dish aerial can be made more directional by
A increasing the wavelength detected
B increasing the diameter of the dish.
C increasing the focal length of the dish
D increasing the radius of curvature of the dish

8 For a geostationary satellite the time taken to complete one orbit is

A 1 day
B 1 lunar month
C 1 year
D zero time since it is stationary.

9 Calculate the radius of the orbit of a geostationary satellite.

Universal constant of gravitation = 6.67×10^{-11} N m^2 kg^{-2}, mass of the earth = 6.0×10^{24} kg.

Theme 3 Optical fibre systems

Objectives

When you have completed the work in this theme you should be able to:

1 Explain the role of internal reflection with the transmission of light by optical fibres.

2 Calculate the critical angle given the refractive indices of the core and cladding.

3 Explain the terms dispersion and multimode transmission.

4 Explain how the dispersion can be reduced by reducing core diameter or using a graded index fibre.

5 Explain the operation of a helium-neon laser and light-emitting diodes.

6 Describe the characteristics of sources used with optical fibres.

7 Explain the operation of the p-i-n photodiode.

8 Explain the term attenuation and use the relationship for optical power decay $P = P_o e^{-\alpha x}$

9 Explain the need for repeater stations.

10 Explain the advantages of an optical fibre system compared to cable or radio systems.

Study questions and references

Ed. Nicholl, B. and Selfe, J. *Telecommunications in practice*, chapters 4, 9 and 12.

Bolton   Chapters 15 and 18.

1 Write notes explaining how for light to be transmitted along a fibre, rays must reflect from the core-cladding interface at angles equal to or greater than the critical angle, explaining the relationship between the critical angle and the refractive indices of the core and the cladding.

2 Write notes explaining how there can be a range of angles greater than the critical angle and so there will be a range of paths that can be followed by rays within the fibre, hence explain the terms multimode transmission and dispersion.

3 Write notes explaining how multimode dispersion can be reduced by reducing the core diameter and by a graded index fibre.

4 Write notes, with an energy level diagram, to explain the operation of a helium-neon laser. The term stimulated emission should be used and explained.

5 Briefly describe the principle of the photodiode and the p-i-n diode.

6 Write a note comparing light sources for use with optical fibres.

7 Write a brief note on the reasons for the output power from a fibre being less than the input power, describing the way the power decays with distance by the equation $P = P_o e^{-\alpha x}$. Hence, explain the need for repeater stations.

8 Compare the advantages and disadvantages of an optical fibre system of telecommunications between Britain and the mainland of Europe, with systems using cable, satellites or radio wave transmitters on towers.

Self-assessment questions

1-3 Choose all the correct responses.

1 When light is transmitted along an optical fibre
A the refractive index of the core is less than that of the cladding
B the refractive index of the core is very close to that of the cladding
C rays meet the core-cladding interface at angles greater than the critical angle for transmission over any significant distance
D the critical angle C for transmitted rays is given by $n_1 \sin C = n_2$ where n_1 is the refractive index of the cladding and n_2 that of the core.

2 Multimode transmission

A occurs when transmission over a number of paths is possible
B can occur with light of just one wavelength
C can be reduced by reducing the core diameter
D gives rise to dispersion.

3 A graded index fibre

A has an abrupt difference in refractive index at the core-cladding interface
B has a refractive index which varies gradually from the centre of the core outwards and into the cladding
C gives higher dispersion than a step index fibre
D gives single mode transmission.

4 Explain how population inversion is produced with a helium-neon laser and explain why such an inversion is necessary for the action of the laser.

5 Explain how photons impinging on a reverse biased p-n junction can increase the leakage current and how this effect is enhanced in the p-i-n diode.

6 State the factors that can produce pulse broadening when light is transmitted through an optical fibre.

Answers to self-assessment questions

Theme 1 Principles

1 B
2 C
3 B

4 With amplitude modulation noise affects the waveform and hence the sound when it is extracted from the waveform. With digital transmissions the start and end of a pulse is not affected by noise, only the height is affected.
The start and end of the pulse can then be used to regenerate the pulse without the noise.

5 Pulse amplitude modulation involves sampling the signal at regular time intervals. Each sample is then quantised, i.e. converted to a binary number related to the size of the signal. Then encoding occurs with a binary digit being added to indicate whether the signal was positive or negative.

6 A, B, C

Theme 2 Radio systems

1 B
2 A
3 C
4 D
5 A,B,C
6 B,C
7 B
8 A
9 $F = GMm/R^2 = mv^2/R$ with $v = 2\pi R/T$, hence $R^3 = GMT^2/4\pi^2$ and R is about 35 000 km.

Theme 3 Optical fibre systems

1 B, C
2 A, B, C, D
3 B

4 The helium atoms are excited to their first level. This level coincides with a higher level in neon and collisions between helium and neon atoms result in the neon having more atoms at the higher level than lower levels. This is a population inversion. This condition enables stimulated emission to occur.

5 Electron-hole pairs are produced in the depletion layer. The holes so produced give quite a large increase in the numbers of minority charge carriers and hence in the leakage current. P-i-n diodes have an intrinsic layer between the p and n materials and so a wider depletion layer in which photons can produce electron-hole pairs.

6 More than one path is possible, i.e. multimode transmission is possible. Also, the speed of light in the fibre depends on wavelength and so different wavelengths will take different times to pass through a fibre.

Part 6
Answers to questions on objectives

6.1 Unit BM

Topic 1

1 A mole of oxygen and a mole of carbon dioxide contain the same number of molecules.

2 (a) 27 g
(b) $1.5 \times 10^{-5} \, m^3$
(c) $4.5 \times 10^{-23} \, g$
(d) $4.0 \times 10^{28} \, m^{-3}$

3 The irregular motion of the smoke or carbon particles suggests that they are being hit by varing numbers of molecules travelling in different directions at different times.

4 The *laws* of symmetry summarise countless observations on, for example, reflection about a plane (related to the 'laws of reflection' used in optics). The particulate *theory* gives an explanation of the laws, such as those governing the shapes of crystals, in terms of ideas about atoms. The *model* of a cubic crystal is built using these theoretical ideas, and gives support to them if it fits the observations summarised in the laws.

5 (a) 29 electrons, 29 protons, 35 neutrons
(b) Copper
(c) The ease of movement through the material, facilitated by the sharing of electrons, leads to it being a good thermal and electrical conductor.

6 (a) 11%
(b) 1%
(c) 13%

Topic 2

1 Refer to section 2.2 and the answer to Q2.5.

2 Refer to your answer to Q2.4.

3 The very small compressibility of condensed phases of matter, such as solids.

4 $1/273 \, °C^{-1}$ or $0.0037 \, °C^{-1}$

5 (a) 273 K and $1.0 \times 10^5 \, Pa$
(b) $8.31 \, J \, mol^{-1} \, K^{-1}$

6 (a) If p is the atmospheric pressure in mm Hg and A is the cross-sectional area of the tube,

$(p - 758) \times 80A = $ constant
$(p - 755) \times 50A = $ constant

(b) Boyle's Law
(c) 763 mm Hg

7 (a) $U_f - U_i = W - Q$
(b) U
(c) Refer to section 2.3

8 $0.044 \, kg \, m^{-3}$

9 (a) $\approx 1.2 \times 10^{-5} \, K^{-1}$
(b) $\approx 6 \, mm$
(c) expansion joints, supported on rollers, etc.

Topic 3

1 (a) The limit of proportionality
(b) Hooke's law
(c) See figure 6.1

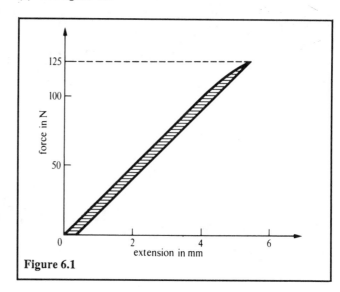

Figure 6.1

(d) 25 N
(e) $\approx 120 \, N$
(f) $2.5 \times 10^9 \, Pa$
(g) 1:4
(h) 0.3 J (shaded area on graph)

2 (a) and (c).

3 Refer to sections 3.1 and 3.2.

4 (a) The strain or the extension at the elastic limit is very much larger for rubber than for steel; several times the original length for rubber, compared with about one thousandth for steel. It is this very obvious feature of the deformation behaviour of rubber that gains it the elastic description, though since steel can withstand much higher stress with no permanent deformation, it could be described as more elastic than rubber.

(b) Permanent change in shape as the result of an applied stress. No, many such as polystyrene are brittle. Others such as poly(e)thene show considerable elastic deformation as well as plastic deformation.

5 $33.8 \, N \, m^{-1}$

6 Comparison should include elastic deformation, yield stress, yield point in steel but not in brass, ultimate tensile strength, fracture strength and strain at fracture.

7 Copper; face centred cubic polycrystalline material, metallic bonding: ductile and a good conductor. Glass fibre; layers of glass fibres that are strong but brittle in a low density matrix which prevents fractures from spreading through the material: light and strong. Diamond; tetrahedral crystal (preferably without fault) with covalent bonding: a hard material, which, because the structure is not layered, makes slip very hard.

8 There is no one right answer for this one!

Topic 4

1 The velocity gradient is the change in velocity with respect to the distance perpendicular to the direction of flow (figure 6.2).

$$\text{velocity gradient} = \frac{\Delta v}{\Delta x}$$

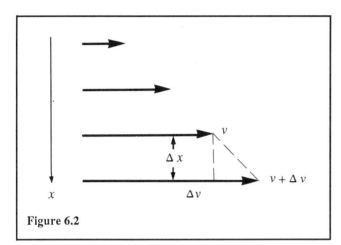

Figure 6.2

2 (a) Refer to section 4.1.
(b) (i) Increase steadily during streamline flow, owing to greater relative velocities between layers; sudden increase at critical velocity owing to onset of turbulence.
(ii) Decrease owing to increased kinetic energy of the molecules.
(c) The oil will be required to lubricate over a wide range of temperatures. If the viscosity varies, the oil will either be too viscous to allow movement when the machine is starting cold or insufficiently viscous to provide a lubricating layer when the machine is running hot.
3 (a) The train will cause the air around it, moving at a high speed, to have a lower pressure than that still air on the platform. There will, therefore, be a resultant force towards the train . . . on you!
(b) The water between them will have to move more quickly than that on the outside of each. Thus, there will be a resultant force pushing the two ships together.
4 The velocity v of a fluid of density ρ_f can be found by applying Bernoulli's equation

$$p + \tfrac{1}{2}\rho_f v^2 + h\rho_f g = \text{constant}$$

For horizontal flow h is zero so

$$p + \tfrac{1}{2}\rho_f v^2 = \text{constant}$$

The difference in pressure $h\rho g$ between the moving air and still air is equal to $\tfrac{1}{2}\rho_f v^2$. Hence

$$v = \sqrt{\frac{2h\rho g}{\rho_f}}$$

Topic 5

1 The resistivity ρ (in Ω m) of a material is defined by the equation

$$R = \rho l/A$$

where R (in Ω) is the resistance of a piece of the material which has a length l (in m) and a cross-sectional area A (in m^2).
2 (a) A s
(b) $kg\ m^2\ s^{-2}$
(c) $kg\ m^2\ s^{-3}\ A^{-1}$
(d) $kg\ m^2\ s^{-3}\ A^{-2}$
3 See section 5.3, particularly Q5.11 and Q5.13.
4 (a) See sections 5.1 and 1.4.
(b) The formula for the drift velocity of charge carriers is:

$$v = I/nAe$$

so the quantities needed are I, N, A and e.
5 Non-linear devices include thermistors, semiconductors such as silicon and germanium, thermionic (vacuum) diodes, junction diodes, electrolytes, etc. Suitable graphs of current against potential difference would be similar to those shown in the text.

6 $\dfrac{1}{R} = \dfrac{1}{R_1} + \dfrac{1}{R_2}$ see Q5.16.

7 Use the relationships $V = IR$, $P = IV$ (or $P = I^2R$). $R = \rho l/A$ and $A = \pi r^2$
8 (a) 4.5 V
(b) 3.0 Ω
If the current through the circuit is I, 3.0 V $= I \times 6\ \Omega$, so $I = 0.5$ A.
If the internal resistance is r, 4.5 V $= 0.5$ A(6 $\Omega + r$).
9 (a) 2.0 A through the 6.0 Ω resistor, 1.0 A through the 12.0 Ω resistor.
(b) 36 W
(c) 4.0 Ω
10 (a) 100 m
If the current through the element is I, and its resistance is R

$$1000\ W = 250\ V \times I, \text{ so } I = 4.0\ A$$
$$250\ V = 4.0\ A \times R, \text{ so } R = 62.5\ \Omega$$

Let the length of wire required be l, then

$$62.5\ \Omega = 5.0 \times 10^{-7}\ \Omega\ m \times l/0.8 \times 10^{-6}\ m^2$$

(b) 3.9×10^{-4} m s^{-1}

$$v = 4.0\ A/8.0 \times 10^{28}\ m^{-3} \times 0.80 \times 10^{-6}\ m^2$$
$$\times 1.6 \times 10^{-19}\ C$$

11 (a) and (b) See section 5.2.

(c) The resistivity of silicon decreases as the impurity concentration (i.e. the number density of impurity atoms) increases.

6.2 Unit FM

Topic 1

1 Average speed is the total distance travelled (measured along the paths taken) divided by the time taken. Average velocity is total displacement divided by time taken (total displacement is distance 'as the crow flies' the direction being given).

2 A stroboscopic method would be appropriate.

3 (a) Initial vertical velocity = 2 m s^{-1}
Initial horizontal velocity = $2\sqrt{3}$ m s^{-1}
(b) Time taken to fall 20 m = 1.8 s
(using $s = ut + \frac{1}{2}at^2$)
(c) Horizontal distance travelled = 6.3 m

4 (a) The object rises and slows down (the rate of retardation decreases as it rises); the object stops momentarily and begins to fall (with decreasing acceleration); it bounces up and its velocity is reversed and decreased at the rebound. The object is made of an elastic material, such as rubber.
(b) Height reached = 6 m (the area between curve AB and the time axis represents height).
(c) Area BCD = area OAB, and these represent the distances up and down respectively.
(d) -18 m s^{-2} at A, -10 m s^{-2} at B.
Note. The motion clearly indicates that there is an air resistance force opposing motion which is proportional to the velocity. This is not required in topic 1 but it may be a useful point to return to later. The maximum negative acceleration occurs when the ball is travelling up with maximum velocity v_A and there is a force ($mg + kv_A$) acting downwards. At C the force producing the downward acceleration is ($mg - kv_C$). At B, when the velocity is zero, the acceleration is $-g$.

5 40 km h^{-1} at 90° to direction of aircraft.

6 Volume of iron weight = $\dfrac{1}{7.8 \times 10^3}$ m^3

Upthrust = $\dfrac{1 \times 10^3}{7.8 \times 10^3}$ g N = 0.128 g N

Balance reading = 872 g

7 Mass of passengers = 800 kg
Mass of balloon + cabin + passengers = 2000 kg
Upthrust − weight of helium = 2000 g N
$(1.3 - 0.17)V$ g N = 2000 g N
$V = 1800$ m^3
Assume cylindrical shaped balloon of length 3 times diameter

$V = (3d)\left(\dfrac{\pi d^2}{4}\right) = \dfrac{3\pi d^3}{4}$

$d^3 \approx 800$ m^3

$d \approx 9$ m

Balloon could be 9 m diameter and 27 m long to carry the passengers.

Topic 2

1 [MLT^{-2}], derived from the dimensions of mass, [M], and acceleration, [LT^{-2}].

2 (a) The mass of an object can be measured by comparing it with a known mass. A beam balance can be used for comparing gravitational masses or an inertia balance (e.g. a loaded steel blade vibrating in a horizontal plane) can compare inertial masses.
(b) Weight is measured by a spring balance – a force meter.

3 (a) A force due to gravity and a force due to tension in the thread. These forces are equal and the resultant is zero.
(b) Gravitational force, which produces an acceleration.
(c) 1 kg, approximately. Gravitational force varies with location but is approximately 9.8 N kg^{-1} at all places on the Earth's surface.
(d) 1.00 N

4 330 N, 430 N

5 (a) If T is the tension in the string and a the acceleration
$$T = 4.0a$$
and
$$1.0g - T = 1.0a$$
(b) 2.0 m s^{-2}
(c) 8.0 N
(d) $\sqrt{8}$ m s^{-1} = 2.8 m s^{-1}

6 Acceleration = -1.9 m s^{-2}
Braking force = 1.9×10^3 N
Braking time = 8 s

7 (a) Mary is correct. Tom is wrong; these forces do not form a 'third-law pair' since they act on the same body.
(b) The three 'third-law pairs' are:
Force of the earth on the man, and force of the man on the earth.
Pull of the parachute on the man and pull of the man on the parachute.
Force of air acting on the parachute and force of parachute acting on the air.

Topic 3

1 See section 3.2.

2 Impulse is represented by the area under the force–time curve.
Impulse = 4.7 N s = change in momentum
Change of velocity of 1 kg truck = 4.7 m s^{-1}
The graph of the force on the 2 kg truck is a reflection of the first graph in the time axis.

3 (a) Accelerating force = 7.5 kN
(b) The weight of the golfer = 750 N. The accelerating force is ten times as large.

4 The sudden stopping of the hammer produces a large force acting over a small area where the brick breaks (hence a very high pressure is applied over this small area). The equal force of the brick on the hand holding it produces a small pressure and small compression of the tissue, since the force is acting over the large area of the whole hand. This is not the case when the blow is applied directly to the hand.

5 8.0 kN

6 $\frac{2}{3}$. Yes, but $\frac{1}{3}$ of the original energy is used to produce permanent deformation, sound and to do work against frictional forces.

7 (a) 1.8×10^7 m s^{-1}

(b) Mass of recoiling nucleus $= 3.4 \times 10^{-25}$ kg

If the speed of recoil is v

$3.4 \times 10^{-25} \times v$ kg m s^{-1} $= 6.4 \times 10^{-27}$
$\times 1.8 \times 10^7$ kg m s^{-1}

speed of recoil of nucleus $= 3.4 \times 10^5$ m s^{-1}

8 See figure 6.3.

F_1 is the frictional force on the tyre due to the road. This is the force which propels the car forward.

R is the normal contact force acting on the tyre due to the road.

T is the total force on the tyre due to the road.

F_2 is the frictional force from the tyre on the road. F_1 and F_2 form a 'third-law pair'. Forces R and W form a 'third-law pair'. (W is the weight of the car that cuts through this wheel.)

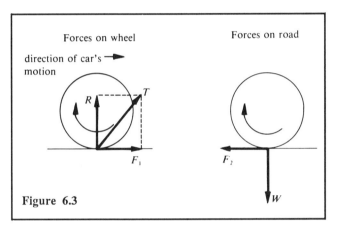

Figure 6.3

Topic 4

1 (a) B

(b) D

(c) C

(d) A

2 (a) 4 m s^{-2} towards the centre.

(b) 4800 N. The centripetal force is supplied by friction acting on the tyres.

(c) $22°$

3 (a) Maximum at the bottom, minimum at the top.

(b) 3.2 rad s^{-2}

4 (a) 7 N

(b) 10 N

(c) The resultant acts at an angle θ (arctan 0.1 or 6°) below the horizontal into the circle.

(d) A body only has an acceleration towards the centre if it is travelling at constant speed around the circle. This ball has both an acceleration towards the centre and an acceleration downwards.

5 A 'gravity' of g at a distance r from the hub can be produced by spinning the space station with an angular velocity of ω, such that $\omega^2 r = 10$ m s^{-2}. If r is 40 m, $\omega = \frac{1}{2}$ rad s^{-1} and the time for one revolution of the space station would have to be 49π s.

A space ship could dock at the centre, attaining a spin to match the space station's spin as it approached.

Topic 5

1 (a) B

(b) C

(c) D

(d) A

2 (a) D, 3

(b) E, 1

(c) B, 5

(d) C, 2

(e) A, 4

3 See reference text and Q5.8.

4 (a) Kinetic energy $= 1.5 \times 10^3$ J

(b) Frictional couple $= 0.50$ N m

(c) Angular acceleration $= -1.66$ rad s^{-2}

(d) Stopping time $= 60$ s

5 Initial angular velocity of wheel $= \omega = 7.0$ rad s^{-1}

force acting on wheel rim $= F$

impulse on wheel rim $= Ft$

force acting on plank $= F$

impulse on plank $= Ft$

mass of wheel $= m_1 = 1.0$ kg

mass of plank $= m_2 = 1.0$ kg

angular velocity of wheel after contact $= \omega_2$

velocity of plank across ice $= v$

radius of wheel $= r$

moment of inertia of wheel $= I = m_1 r^2$

Assuming velocity of plank $=$ tangential velocity of wheel *after contact*

$$v = r\omega_a$$

For linear motion of plank

impulse $=$ change of momentum

$$Ft = m_2 V$$

For rotational motion of wheel

moment of impulse $=$ change of angular momentum

$$Ft \times r = I\omega_1 - I\omega_2$$
$$m_2 v \times r = I\omega_1 - I\omega_2$$
$$m_2 r^2 \omega_2 = m_1 r^2(\omega_1 - \omega_2)$$

$m_1 = m_2$, therefore

$$\omega_2 = 7 \text{ rad s}^{-1} - \omega_2$$
$$\omega_2 = 3.5 \text{ rad s}^{-1}$$

and

$$v = 0.60 \times \omega$$
$$= 2.1 \text{ m s}^{-1}$$

Change in kinetic energy $= \frac{1}{2}I\omega_1^2 - \frac{1}{2}I\omega_2^2$
$$= 4.4 \text{ J}$$

6 (a) Angular momentum is conserved. If M is the mass of the six people and ω the new angular velocity,

$$M \times 2.5^2 \times \frac{4\pi}{60} \text{ kg m s}^{-1}$$

$$= M \times 0.5^2 \times \omega \text{ kg m s}^{-1}$$

$$\omega = 100\pi \text{ rad s}^{-1}$$

$$= 50 \text{ revolutions per minute}$$

(b) $\dfrac{\text{new energy}}{\text{old energy}} = \dfrac{\frac{1}{2}I_2\omega_2^2}{\frac{1}{2}I_1\omega_1^2} = \dfrac{25}{1}$

The movement of the people towards the centre has produced a large increase in energy. They must have had to provide this energy to do work against forces opposing their movement towards the centre.

Topic 6

1 See section 6.2, question 6.10.
2 The graphs are shown in figure 6.4.

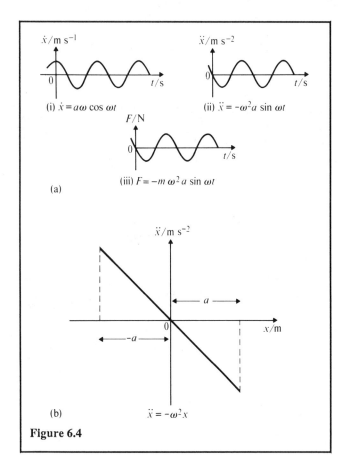

(i) $\dot{x} = a\omega \cos \omega t$

(ii) $\ddot{x} = -\omega^2 a \sin \omega t$

(iii) $F = -m\,\omega^2 a \sin \omega t$

(a)

(b) $\ddot{x} = -\omega^2 x$

Figure 6.4

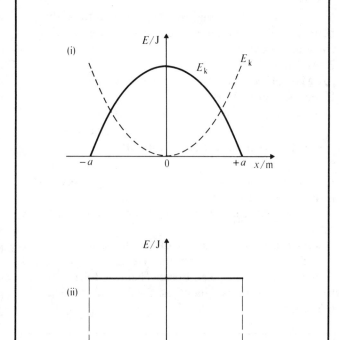

Figure 6.5

3 See section 6.2 (problem solving) and question 6.22, and textbook references.
4 See section 6.2, particularly question 6.6.
5 The graphs are shown in figure 6.5.
6 (a) a is the maximum displacement or amplitude, ϕ is the phase constant.
(b) The required expressions are:
(i) $x = a\omega \cos (wt + \phi)$, and (ii) $+a\omega$, since x is a maximum when $\cos (wt + \phi) = 1$
7 (a) Amplitude $= 0.05$ m.
(b) Frequency $= 4$ Hz.
(c) Period $= 0.25$ s.
(d) (i) $\pm 0.4\pi$ m s^{-1}, (ii) zero.
(e) $+3.2\pi^2$ m s^{-2}.
8 Maximum acceleration $= +0.27$ m s^{-2}
Maximum velocity $= +0.090$ m s^{-1}
Period $= \frac{2}{3}\pi$ s
9 See section 6.4.
10 See section 6.5, particularly question 6.33.

6.3 Unit WV

Topic 1

1 (a) True.
(b) False.
(c) True.
(d) False.
(e) False.
(f) True.
(g) True.
2 See answer to question 1.19.
(a) 0.017 mm.
(b) 0.004 mm wide, if it is to record a sinusoidal variation in a length of 0.017 mm.
(c) 2.5 kHz.
3 (a) See figure 6.6.

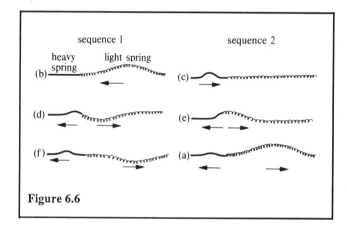

Figure 6.6

(b) (i) In each sequence the amplitudes of the reflected pulse and the pulse transmitted across the junction are less than the amplitude of the incident wave pulse.
(ii) In sequence 2, a short wave pulse in the heavy spring is transmitted through the boundary becoming a long wave pulse in the light spring. The pulse must travel faster in the light spring to produce the longer wavelength. Transmitted and reflected pulses in the heavy spring are all smaller in length than the pulses in the light spring.
(iii) A pulse travelling in a light spring to a boundary with a heavy spring is reflected upside down with a phase change of π (sequence 1). There is no phase change for a wave reflected at a boundary with a ligher spring (sequence 2).
4 See figure 6.7.
5 Velocity, wavelength and amplitude.
6 Only longitudinal waves in the core. The core must be a fluid which cannot transmit transverse waves. Transverse waves require a transmitting medium which has rigidity, but compression waves can travel in solids, liquids and gases.
7 A dispersive medium is one in which the wave speed depends on the frequency (and hence wavelength) of the travelling wave.

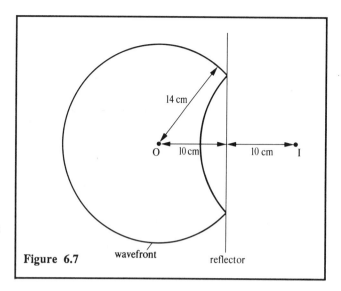

Figure 6.7

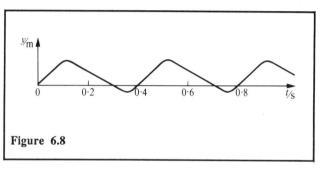

Figure 6.8

8 Figure 6.8 shows the graph of y against t for P:
$v = 0.5 \text{ m s}^{-1}$, $\lambda = 0.2$ m, $f = 5/2 \text{ s}^{-1}$, $T = 0.4$ s.
9 The principle of superposition states that when a number of waves pass through a particular point in a medium, the net disturbance at any instant is the vector sum of the disturbances which each wave would have produced separately at that instant.
(a) The radio waves transmitted from the two stations are *in phase*.
(b) The signal strength at the new position will be the *sum* of the signal strengths from each station alone (a maximum signal strength). The path length from A has increased by $\lambda/2$ and the path length from B has decreased by $\lambda/2$, giving a resulting path difference of λ. The two signals arrive in phase at the new position.
(c) Y has travelled more than 100 m. The path difference is again λ, and ship Y is on an antinodal line. The distance of this antinodal line from the central line XY increases with distance from the sources.

Topic 2

1 (a) A (b) E

2 See section 2.4.

Figure 6.9 shows the position of the string at various time intervals.

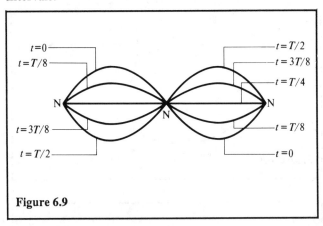

Figure 6.9

3 (a) When the path difference is $\lambda/2$ (a distance equal to $2x$, where x is the distance moved by the tube) the waves arrive $180°$ out of phase (in antiphase), giving a point of minimum intensity. As the tube is pulled out the intensity increases: a point of maximum intensity occurs when the path difference is λ (the waves are now in phase). The path difference between two successive minima or maxima is equal to the wavelength λ.

(b) 340 m s^{-1}.

Extra path difference $= 2 \times 68 \text{ mm} = 136 \text{ mm} = \lambda$

Using

$$c = f\lambda$$
$$c = 2500 \text{ s}^{-1} \times 136 \times 10^{-3} \text{ m}$$
$$= 340 \text{ m s}^{-1}$$

4 (a) 0.30 m

P is a point of minimum intensity, so $(PX - PY) = \lambda/2$.

$$\lambda = 2(0.50 - 0.35) \text{ m}$$
$$= 0.30 \text{ m}$$

(b) 342 m s^{-1}

5 The phenomenon of beats is dealt with in section 2.2.

6 318 Hz or 322 Hz

7
Apparent change in frequency $= 91$ Hz.
Observed frequency (source approaching) $= 500$ Hz.
Observed frequency (source receding) $= 409$ Hz.

8 See section 2.6, particularly Q2.38.

9 See section 2.4, particularly Q2.21.

10 See section 2.4, particularly Q2.23.

11 See section 2.6, in particular experiment WV7 and Q2.42.

12 (a) Sound waves will be reflected normally.

(b) A stationary wave pattern is set up, due to the superposition of the incident and reflected waves, with a wavelength of approximately 0.5 m (assume $c = 300 \text{ m s}^{-1}$). There is no movement of air particles at the wall or at the nodes, which are about 0.25 m apart. All other particles have an imposed vibration, which has a maximum amplitude at the antinodes (about 0.125 m from the nodes).

13 635 Hz

Topic 3

1 (a) See section 3.3.

(b) The critical angle c depends upon the refractive indices of perspex and of the liquid. For water,

$$1.5 \sin c = 1.33 \sin 90°$$
$$c = 71.4°.$$

The angle of incidence ($45°$) is now less than the critical angle for the perspex to liquid interface, and the beam will be refracted away from the normal.

(c) $41.8°$.

$$1.5 \sin c = n_a \sin 90°, \quad \text{where } n_a = 1$$
$$\sin c = 1/1.5$$
$$c = 41.8°$$

(d) No internal reflection can take place. Light is refracted towards the normal (it is travelling from a less dense to a denser medium).

2 (a) See figure 6.10.

(b) The image is 88 mm below the upper surface of the oil. Considering refraction at the water–oil surface,

$$1.33 \sin i_1 = 1.45 \sin i_2$$

For small angles, $\sin A = \tan A$, so

$$1.33 \times \frac{x}{80 \text{ mm}} = 1.45 \times \frac{x}{a_1}$$

and

$$a_1 = 87 \text{ mm}$$

Considering refraction at the oil–air surface,

$$1.45 \sin i_2 = 1 \times \sin i_3$$
$$1.45 = \frac{127 \text{ mm}}{a_2}$$

so $\quad a_2 = 88 \text{ mm}$

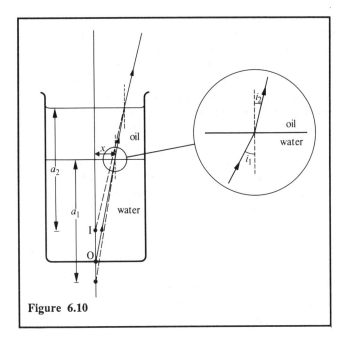

Figure 6.10

3 An expression for the focal length f in terms of the distance d between the object and the image and the magnification m is

$$f = \frac{md}{(1 + m)^2}$$

$d = u + v$ and $m = v/u$,

therefore $d = u + mu = u(1 + m)$,

so $u = d/(1 + m)$ and $v = md/(1 + m)$

$$\frac{1}{f} = \frac{1}{u} + \frac{1}{v} = \frac{u + v}{uv} = \frac{d}{uv}$$

substituting for u and v gives

$$\frac{1}{f} = \frac{(1 + m)^2}{md}$$

4 See section 3.4.

5 See section 3.6.

6 A

7 See section 3.6.

Topic 4

1 (a) Interference and diffraction effects for light waves (for example, Young's slits, diffraction grating). Diffraction of X-rays by crystals (Laue patterns, etc.).
(b) Both light and X-rays have speeds, measured in vacuum, which are found to be identical. They have some common properties: both affect a photographic plate and both produce fluorescence. Both X-ray and light spectra from certain sources can have characteristic lines.
(c) A grating for light has slit separations of the order of 10^{-6} m; a crystal grating has separations of 10^{-9} m.

2 (a) Light passing through the atmosphere is scattered by air molecules; the amount of scattering is much greater for the shorter blue wavelengths than for the red wavelengths. So the scattered light reaching us in all directions contains a relatively stronger component of blue light than the original sunlight.
(b) The unscattered light travelling directly from the sun becomes white minus blue and the sun appears red.
(c) When the scattering particles become much larger than the wavelength of the light the amount of scattering does not depend on wavelength. All colours are scattered about equally, so the cloud appears white. Since little or no light can pass through the cloud without scattering, the cloud is opaque.

3 In a fine mist the particle size is of the order of the wavelength of light. This means that light waves will be scattered by these particles. But the infra-red waves have a wavelength much larger than the size of the water particles and are therefore diffracted around the obstacles and penetrate the mist. So infra-red waves can 'see through' the mist. A thicker fog is produced by larger water particles and, in this case, both light and infra-red waves will be scattered.

4 See text (section 4.4). Sound is a longitudinal vibration and cannot be polarised.

5 Rotate the analyser through 180° about the direction of the light. No change shows that the light is unpolarised. Maximum to *zero* to maximum, in 180°, shows that the light is plane-polarised.

Maximum to *minimum* (not zero) to maximum, in 180°, shows that the light is partially plane-polarised.

6 (a) See figure 4.15 and the answer to question 4.20. Light reflected from the water is nearly plane-polarised and the sunglasses block light polarised in this plane. The glare due to reflection is removed. Light from inside the water is unpolarised (two components, nearly equal) and nearly 50% of the light can pass through the sunglasses to show the 'inside' of the river.
(b) See figure 6.11. Glare is produced by light scattered in the atmosphere. This light is partially or completely plane-polarised and the sunglasses can be used to absorb this 'polarised glare'.

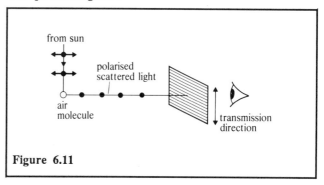

Figure 6.11

Topic 5

1 See section 5.1.

2 (a) Fringes of separation 2.0 mm.
(b) Fringes of separation 1.5 mm.
(c) Fringes of separation 1.0 mm, but with a smaller variation in intensity between maximum and minimum. The minimum intensity is not zero.
(d) A few coloured fringes. The central fringe is white with red edges. Other fringes have a white central band with blue edges towards the centre of the pattern and red edges away from the centre.
(e) Fringes with a separation greater than that for green light.
(f) The pattern will move across the screen in a direction opposite to the direction shown by the arrow, and then disappear.

3 See experiment WV14 and figure 5.11 in section 5.2.

4 The lines will be less intense and the angular separation between the lines will decrease.

5 The pure spectrum is a series of non-overlapping images of the line or point source, each image being formed by the light of a particular wavelength. The requirements for producing a pure spectrum are:
(a) a fine slit illuminated by the radiation,
(b) a collimating lens to produce a plane wave incident at a grating or prism,
(c) a grating or prism which disperses the light,
(d) either a projecting lens to produce a real image on a screen or a telescope to give a virtual image for viewing by eye.

6 See text, section 5.3. The smallest resolvable angular separation θ is 2.5×10^{-14} rad for the eye and 2.7×10^{-3} rad for the radio telescope. The eye has greater resolving power.

6.4 Unit FF

Topic 1

1 C

2 The maximum gravitational force is when the two identical spheres are in contact, that is, when the distance between their centres is $2r$, where r is the radius of the sphere. The mass of a sphere is proportional to r^3. From Newton's law of gravitation we have:

$$F \propto \frac{m_1 m_2}{r^2}$$

therefore

$$F \propto \frac{r^3 r^3}{(2r)^2} \propto \frac{r^6}{r^2}$$

thus

$$F \propto r^4$$

Assumption: a sphere behaves as if its mass is concentrated at the centre.

3 Estimates: charge on each person 2.0×10^{-6} C; distance apart 0.5 m.
From Coulomb's law

$$F = \frac{1}{4\pi\varepsilon_0} \frac{Q_1 Q_2}{r^2}$$

$$F = (9 \times 10^9) \times \frac{(2 \times 10^{-6}) \times (2 \times 10^{-6})}{(0.5)^2}$$

$$\approx 0.1 \text{ N}$$

4 (a) 12 N (b) 12 N

5 (a) $c\theta$

(b) $\dfrac{2GMma}{d^2}$

(c) $G = \dfrac{c\theta d^2}{2Mma}$

(d) The cross attraction between the spheres has been neglected in part (c). The cross attraction has the effect of producing a couple in a counter-clockwise direction and consequently the value used for the deflecting couple was too high. This means that the value for G was too small.

Topic 2

1 4 N kg^{-1}

2 Consider a mass m at the Earth's surface. The gravitational force exerted on the mass is gMm/r^2. (Earth behaves as a point mass M at its centre.) We also know that the force is given by mg.
Thus

$$mg = gMm/r^2$$

Also

$$M = \tfrac{4}{3}\pi r^2 \rho$$

(Assume that the earth is a sphere.)

3 (a) Gravitational field strength $g \propto 1/r$

(b) Gravitational potential $V \propto 1/r$

4 Diagrams of electric field patterns.

5 See text, section 2.3.

6 Two graphs showing the potential varying inversely with distance are added together to form a symmetrical graph with a minimum at the midpoint.

7 (a) 1.094×10^{11} J

(b) $10\,459$ m s^{-1}

8 (a) 4.0×10^4 V m^{-1}

(b) 1.6×10^{-5} N

9 See text, section 2.5, particularly Q2.55.

Topic 3

1 (a) Field in a region between the poles of a magnet (left-hand pole is N pole) in which a current is flowing into the paper. A neutral point is located below the position of the wire.
A force will act *downwards* on the current carrying conductor.

(b) Solenoid lies with its axis in the direction of the Earth's field. The current must flow around the solenoid in the direction A to B. Magnetic field lines leave end A; the equally-spaced lines inside the solenoid indicate a uniform field in the region. Neutral points are located east and west of the magnet and equidistant from it.

2 (a) Force between parallel currents is proportional to product $I_1 I_2$. Therefore wire B will be acted on by a resultant force to the right and will move this way if free.

(b) A force will act radially outwards on each turn due to the field inside the solenoid tending to make the loop turns expand outwards. The force between adjacent turns will be attractive (between parallel currents) and so the coil will tend to shrink longitudinally.

3 See section 3.6.

4 See section 3.5 and experiment FF6.

5 (i) 0.024 N (ii) 0.012 N

6 (b) Attractive force between wires

$$= \frac{\mu_0 I_1 I_2}{2a} \text{ per metre}$$

$$= 2.8 \times 10^{-4} \text{ N m}^{-1} \text{ acting horizontally}$$

Force due to the Earth's magnetic field per metre length is BI. $\therefore F = 1.5 \times 10^{-3}$ N m^{-1} acting 30° above the horizontal.

(c) The pull of the Earth and the pull of the cable element on either side. Only the tension will change in magnitude and direction when the current is switched on.

7 See section 3.4 for derivation of Hall p.d. V_H.

$$V_H = \frac{BI}{net}$$

where t is the thickness

$$B = 1.9 \times 10^{-2} \text{ T}$$

8 (a) 3π mT

(b) 1.5 mT

9 See section 3.6 and in particular question 3.31.

10 6 mT

Note. Mirror deflection is an angle of 0.015 rad.

Topic 4

1 6.7 km s^{-1}

$$v = \sqrt{\left(\frac{GM}{r}\right)}$$

Therefore

$$v = \sqrt{\left(\frac{6.7 \times 10^{11} \times 6 \times 10^{24} \text{ m}^2}{9.0 \times 10^6 \text{ s}^2}\right)}$$

2 3.5×10^7 m s^{-1}

$$eV = \tfrac{1}{2}mv^2$$

$$v = \sqrt{\left(\frac{2eV}{m}\right)}$$

$$v = \sqrt{\left(\frac{2 \times 1.6 \times 10^{-19} \times 3.5 \times 10^3 \text{ m}^2}{9 \times 10^{-31} \text{ s}^2}\right)}$$

3 (a) The force is directed towards the centre of the circular path (see figure 4.7)
(b) 1.6×10^6 m s^{-1}

$$Bev = \frac{mv^2}{r}$$

$$v = \frac{Ber}{m}$$

$$v = (0.5 \times 6.5 \times 10^7 \times 5 \times 10^{-2}) \text{ m s}^{-1}$$

4 See section 4.2 and Q4.13.
5 See section 4.2 and Q4.11.

6.5 Unit TP

Topic 1

1 See section 1.2.
2 (a) Correct, by the definition of the thermodynamic scale.
(b) Incorrect. The n.b.p. of water is 100 °C or 373.15 K to the accuracy of the best available measurements, not by definition.
3 550 K is within the ranges of the two thermometers. The mercury-in-glass thermometer would be the least suitable, since it imposes restrictions on oven design if the bulb is to be inside the oven and the scale outside. The thermocouple has the advantage of being able to be placed wholly inside the oven, with the temperature being read on a remote meter. The thermocouple is also more appropriate for this purpose, since it is cheaper and can give direct readings.
4 A method using a resistance thermometer or thermocouple is appropriate. The following discussion considers the example of a resistance thermometer.
By measuring R at different known Celsius temperatures a calibration curve can be drawn. Measuring the resistance at any unknown temperature and using the calibration curve will give the unknown Celsius temperature. Temperature in kelvins can be measured on the resistance scale by finding R_T at the unknown temperature and R_{tr} at the triple point of water and using $T_R = 273.16 \text{ K} \times R_T/R_{tr}$.
Alternatively, the resistance thermometer can be calibrated to read temperature on a resistance scale by finding the values of the resistance at two appropriate fixed points. For example, using the ice point and the melting point of zinc ($\theta_z = 419.58$ °C),

$$\theta_R = \frac{R_\theta - R_0}{R_2 - R_0} \times 419.58 \text{ °C}$$

This scale will be in agreement with the I.P.T.S. at the two fixed points and will give closer agreement over the whole range (0–300 °C) than would be obtained using the steam point as the upper calibration point.
Even closer agreement between the I.P.T.S. and the calibrations of the resistance thermometer could be obtained by measuring the resistance at three fixed points and using this information to obtain values of α, β and θ in the equation $R_\theta = R_0(1 + \alpha)\theta + \beta\theta^2)$.
The ratio β/α in the above equation is of the order of 10^{-4}. If two fixed points are used and a straight line graph drawn to define temperatures on the resistance scale, then extrapolating beyond the upper fixed point (419.58 °C) would produce an inaccuracy of about 1 K at a temperature of around 500 °C and about 4 K at a temperature of 600 °C.

5 $pV = \dfrac{m}{M}RT$

$$T = \frac{pVM}{mR} = \frac{1.01 \times 10^5 \times 10^{-3} \times 4}{0.166 \times 8.31}$$

$$= 293 \text{ K}$$

6 (a) $37\,^\circ$C. The temperature in kelvins can be read directly from the graph of R against T (ideal gas scale). Subtract 273 to obtain the temperature in $^\circ$C.

(b) For a platinum resistance scale using $0\,^\circ$C and $100\,^\circ$C,

$$\frac{\theta}{100} = \frac{R_\theta - R_0}{R_{100} - R0} = \frac{17 - 16}{18 - 16} = \frac{1}{2}$$

so

$$\theta = 50\,^\circ\text{C}$$

Alternatively, if $R_\text{T} = 17\,\Omega$, T on the platinum resistance scale is given by

$$T = 273.16\,\text{K} \times \frac{R_\text{T}}{R_\text{tr}} = \frac{273.16 \times 17}{16}\,\text{K} = 290\,\text{K}$$

so

$$\theta = 17\,^\circ\text{C}$$

7 See section 1.3 and experiment TP3.

Topic 2

1 Specific heat capacity is associated with change in temperature, whereas specific latent heat is concerned with change of phase from solid to liquid or liquid to vapour.

2 (a) E (b) A (c) C (d) D

3 Temperature is sometimes referred to as the degree of hotness. It is the quality which determines the *direction* of heat flow when two bodies are placed in contact: heat flows from the body at a higher temperature to the one at the lower temperature (zeroth law of thermodynamics); it is measured in degrees celsius or kelvin.

Heat is defined as the energy that is transferred from a body at a higher temperature to one at a lower temperature. It is measured in joules.

The internal energy of a system is the sum total of the kinetic and mutual potential energies of the particles that make up the system.

4 See section 2.3 and experiment TP4.

5 See section 2.3 and experiment TP5.

6 $380\,\text{m s}^{-1}$

Increase in internal energy of the lead pellet is

$m(1.3 \times 10^2\,\text{J kg}^{-1}\,\text{K}^{-1})(312\,\text{K}) + m(2.1 \times 10^4\,\text{J kg}^{-1})$

where m is the mass of the pellet.

Kinetic energy of lead pellet is $\frac{1}{2}mv^2$, where v is the speed of the pellet. 85% of this energy is transformed into internal energy, therefore

$\frac{85}{100} \times \frac{1}{2}mv^2 = m(1.3 \times 10^2 \times 312 + 2.1 \times 10^4)\,\text{J kg}^{-1}$

7 $1.69 \times 10^3\,\text{J kg}^{-1}\,\text{K}^{-1}$

Let V be the volume of nitrogen at s.t.p., then

$$\frac{(8.00 \times 10^{-4}\,\text{m}^3)}{294\,\text{K}} = \frac{V}{273\,\text{K}}$$

$$V = 7.43 \times 10^{-4}\,\text{m}^3$$

$$\text{Mass of nitrogen} = (7.43 \times 10^{-4}\,\text{m}^3)(1.25\,\text{kg m}^{-3})$$
$$= 9.29 \times 10^{-4}\,\text{kg}$$

Energy lost by ice when cooling from $-1\,^\circ$C to $-196\,^\circ$C
$$= (6.00 \times 10^{-4}\,\text{kg})c(195\,\text{K})$$

where c is the mean specific heat capacity of ice.

Energy needed to change phase of nitrogen
$$= (9.29 \times 10^{-4}\,\text{kg})$$
$$\times (2.13 \times 10^5\,\text{J kg}^{-1})$$

Topic 3

1 C

2 See section 3.1.

3 See sections 3.1 and 3.2.

4 See section 3.2, particularly question 3.3.

5 360 K

Consider a cross-sectional area A, and let T be the temperature of the junction.

For steady state, we have

$$\frac{(80\,\text{W m}^{-1}\,\text{K}^{-1})A(373\,\text{K} - T)}{0.4\,\text{m}}$$

$$= \frac{(25\,\text{W m}^{-1}\,\text{K}^{-1})A(T - 293\,\text{K})}{0.5\,\text{m}}$$

6 (a) $\dfrac{\text{d}Q}{\text{d}t} = -\lambda A \dfrac{\text{d}\theta}{\text{d}x}$

(b) The flow of heat is vertical, and, since at a given level a selection of rock is surrounded by rock at the same temperature, no heat flow 'sideways' will occur. So a steady one-dimensional flow of heat is expected.

(c) For stratum 1, $T = -1.2\,\text{K}$, $x = 45\,\text{m}$, so

$$\frac{\text{d}Q}{\text{d}t} = \frac{2.7 \times 1 \times 1.2}{45}\,\text{W m}^{-2}$$

$$= 0.072\,\text{W m}^{-2} = 72\,\text{mW m}^{-2}$$

For stratum 2, $T = -2.9\,\text{K}$, $x = 140\,\text{m}$, so

$$\frac{\text{d}Q}{\text{d}t} = \frac{3.5 \times 1 \times 2.9}{140}\,\text{W m}^{-2}$$

$$= 72.5\,\text{mW m}^{-2}$$

So $\text{d}Q/\text{d}t$ is the same, within experimental error.

(d) Temperature gradient in stratum 2 $= -\dfrac{2.9}{140}\,\text{K m}^{-1}$

so temperature rise in 375 m is

$$\frac{375 \times 2.9}{140}\,\text{K} = 7.77\,\text{K}$$

Temperature gradient in stratum 3 is $-\dfrac{2.9}{140} \times \dfrac{3.5}{1.9}\,\text{K m}^{-1}$

so temperature rise in 3400 m is

$$\frac{3400 \times 2.9 \times 3.5}{140 \times 1.9}\,\text{K} = 129.7\,\text{K}$$

Total temperature rise $= (7.77 + 129.7)\,\text{K}$
Temperature at 4.0 km $= (302.6 + 7.77 + 129.7)\,\text{K}$
$= 440\,\text{K}$

(e) High rate of heat flow or low thermal conductivity, or both, will lead to high temperature at moderate depth.

(f) Daily and yearly temperature variations affect the top few metres. Surface water flow will distort heat flow.

7 (a) The data show that the law is approximately true.

Metal	$(\lambda/\sigma)/10^{-6}\,\text{W}\,\Omega\,\text{K}^{-1}$
aluminium	5.8
copper	6.2
iron	7.6
lead	6.9
silver	6.3

(b) and (c) see section 3.4

8 See section 3.2.

9 See section 3.5.

Topic 4

1 The collision process is random and molecules may be speeded up or slowed down by collision. The result of these random collisions is a distribution of speeds which is determined by the temperature of the gas (see section 4.1).

$c_{\text{r.m.s.}}$ is defined in question 4.5.

2 This is derived in question 4.6.

3 Temperature is proportional to mean molecular translational kinetic energy, defined by $\frac{1}{2}m\overline{c^2} = \frac{3}{2}kT$. The energy of each degree of freedom of a molecule is $\frac{1}{2}kT$. $p = \frac{1}{3}\rho\overline{c^2}$, and if N molecules of mass m occupy volume V, then

$$pV = \tfrac{1}{3}NM\overline{c^2} = \tfrac{2}{3}N(\tfrac{1}{2}m\overline{c^2}) = NkT$$

For one mole of gas

$$pV_m = N_A kT = RT$$

Unit of R ia $\text{J K}^{-1} \text{mol}^{-1}$.

4 Qualitatively we can say that at constant temperature the average speed of the molecules remains constant so the pressure of the gas will only depend on the number of collisions on unit area of the surface in unit time. It is reasonable to assume that this will be proportional to the density of molecules in the gas. If the volume is halved, the number of molecules colliding on unit area in unit time will be doubled, thus doubling the pressure. Hence, pV is unchanged.

Quantitatively, since we have shown that $p = \frac{1}{3}\rho\overline{c^2}$, then $pV = \frac{1}{3}mN\overline{c^2}$.

Assuming that constant temperature implies no change in the internal energy of the gas, the total kinetic energy of the N molecules ($\frac{1}{2}mN\overline{c^2}$) is unchanged. Hence pV is constant at constant temperature for a fixed amount of gas.

5 Total transitional kinetic energy per mole of gas $= \frac{3}{2}RT$
Therefore

$$\tfrac{1}{2}M_m c^2 = \tfrac{3}{2}RT$$

$$c_{\text{r.m.s.}} = \sqrt{\overline{c^2}} = \sqrt{\frac{3RT}{M_m}}$$

$$\frac{c_{\text{r.m.s.}} \text{ of } O_2 \text{ at } 27\,^{\circ}\text{C}}{c_{\text{r.m.s.}} \text{ of } H_2 \text{ at } 0\,^{\circ}\text{C}} = \sqrt{\left(\frac{300 \times 2}{273 \times 32}\right)}$$

$$= 0.262$$

$$c_{\text{r.m.s.}} \text{ of } O_2 = 0.26 \times 1.84 \times 10^3 \text{ m s}^{-1}$$
$$= 4.8 \times 10^2 \text{ m s}^{-1}$$

6 (a) $pV = nRT$ for n moles of a gas

$$n = \frac{\text{mass of gas}}{\text{molar mass}} = \frac{M}{M_m}$$

$$M = \frac{M_m pV}{RT}$$

$$= \frac{0.0040 \text{ kg mol}^{-1} \times 1.0 \times 10^5 \text{ Pa} \times 0.050 \text{ m}^3}{8.3 \text{ J mol}^{-1} \text{ K}^{-1} \times 300 \text{ K}}$$

$$= 0.0080 \text{ kg}$$

(b) $c_{\text{r.m.s.}} = \sqrt{\dfrac{3RT}{M_m}}$

$$= \sqrt{\left(\frac{3 \times 8.3 \text{ J mol}^{-1} \text{ K}^{-1} \times 300 \text{ K}}{0.0040 \text{ kg mol}^{-1}}\right)}$$

7 See section 4.5. For an ideal gas $(C_p - C_v) = R$, and for an ideal monatomic gas $C_v = 3R/2$, therefore $C_p = 5R/2$ and $\gamma = 5/3$.

8 (a) If V is the initial volume,

$$p_1, V, T_1 \xrightarrow[\text{compression}]{\text{isothermal}} 2p_1, \frac{V}{2}, \quad T_1$$

$$\xrightarrow[\text{expansion}]{\text{adiabatic}} p_2, V, T_2$$

For adiabatic change

$$p_2 V^{1.4} = 2p_1\left(\frac{V}{2}\right)^{1.4}$$

therefore

$$p_2 = \frac{2p_1}{2^{1.4}} = 0.76p_1$$

pV/T is constant throughout, so

$$\frac{p_1 V}{T_1} = \frac{0.76p_1 V}{T_2}$$

$$T_2 = 0.76T_1$$

(b) $5.0T_1$ J

The energy required equals $C_V \times 0.24T_1$, and since $\gamma = 1.4, C_V = 5R/2$.

9 See section 4.4.

10 See section 4.6.

11 See section 4.5.

12 See figure 6.12.

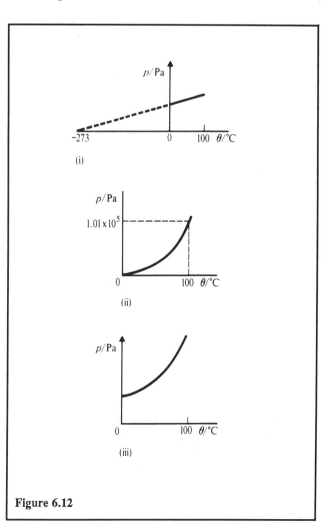

(i)

(ii)

(iii)

Figure 6.12

13 (a) If mercury is poured into the open tube the vapour will be compressed. The vapour pressure will temporarily exceed the equilibrium s.v.p. and the vapour will temporarily be supersaturated. The rate of condensation will exceed the rate of evaporation until dynamic equilibrium is again established, with meniscus B still 50 mm below meniscus A. The normal boiling

point is below 50 °C, since at 50 °C the s.v.p. is greater than atmospheric pressure.
(b) If the temperature is raised, the rate of evaporation will exceed the rate of condensation until a new dynamic equilibrium is established at a higher s.v.p. Mercury meniscus B will fall and A will rise.
14 See section 4.7.

6.6 Unit EM

Topic 1

1 Faraday's law. The magnitude of the induced e.m.f. is directly proportional to the rate of change of flux linkage or rate of flux cutting.
Lenz's law. The direction of the induced current is always such as to oppose the change causing it.
2 When the disc rotates, there is a force towards the centre of $Be\omega r$ on an electron distance r from the centre. Electrons will move towards the centre and establish a p.d. in the electric field between rim and centre until the forces on an electron due to the electric and magnetic fields balance.

Then $Be\omega r = \dfrac{Ve}{r}$ at any point a distance r from the centre.

The p.d. between rim and centre is $B\omega a^2$ (a = disc radius) with the point A positive with respect to B. A will act like the positive terminal of a cell and, if a resistor is connected between A and B, an induced current will flow in the circuit in the direction $A \rightarrow R \rightarrow B \rightarrow A$ (electrons will flow in the opposite sense).
A flow of electrons from A to B in the disc will produce a force to the left on each electron and a resulting *anticlockwise* torque. The size of this retarding torque will be proportional to the electron drift velocity and the induced current in the disc; thus, the torque required to keep the disc rotating will increase as the current in the resistor increases.
3 (a) Anticlockwise current in the coil (viewed from the magnet). The induced current will establish flux opposed to the flux of the approaching magnet and the coil will have a N pole facing the magnet producing repulsion. Energy will have to be supplied to keep the magnet moving towards the coil and this will then be transformed into internal energy in the resistor when a current flows through the resistance (consistent with energy conservation).
(b) If ξ is the induced e.m.f. in a coil of resistance R

    rate of thermal dissipation of energy is ξ^2/R
    rate of doing work in moving the magnet
$$= F \times \text{distance moved per second}$$
$$= \text{force on magnet} \times \text{velocity}$$

  force on magnet $\propto \dfrac{1}{R}$ for a given velocity

       and induced e.m.f.

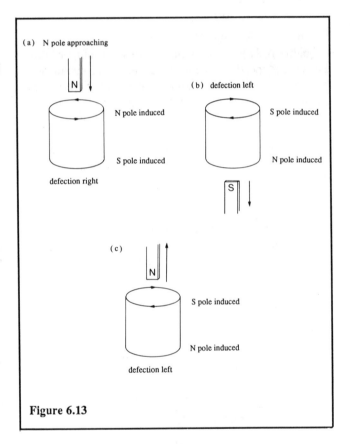

Figure 6.13

4 Suppose that a N pole enters the coil, figure 6.13. The induced current makes the top end of the coil a N pole (to oppose the approaching magnet). This anticlockwise current causes a deflection to the right.
(a) As the magnet passes through the coil the deflection decreases and is momentarily *zero* as the magnet passes through the centre of the coil.
(b) A S pole is now leaving (the other end of the coil) and this end of the coil now becomes a N pole (to attract the receding magnet). The current flows in the opposite direction i.e. there is a deflection to the *left*.
When the magnet is at the centre of the coil there is no relative movement between the coil and the magnet therefore the current is zero.

(c) When the magnet is projected upwards a S pole will be induced at the top end (to attract the receding magnet) and hence the deflection will be to the left.

5 When a conductor moves in a magnetic field an e.m.f. is induced in it.

The resistance of the disc is low and thus a large current may be induced in the disc (an eddy current).

The current flows in such a direction (sense) as to oppose the movement.

A current carrying conductors moving in a magnetic field will experience a force. The direction of this force is such as to oppose the movement of the pendulum and bring it to rest.

Pendulum B will continue to oscillate and very little braking effect will be observed.

The eddy currents have been reduced because the air gaps have reduced the size of the internal loops in which the eddy currents can flow.

Topic 2

1 The *rotor* is the name given to the field coils (which rotate) of a generator whereas the *stator* is the name given to the armature coils (which are stationary).

2 (a) $\xi = Blv$

(b) See figure 6.14.

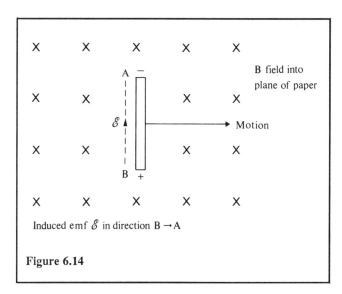

Induced emf $\mathscr{E}$ in direction B → A

Figure 6.14

3 (a) Induced e.m.f. is a maximum when $\sin wt$ is 1 i.e. wt is 90°, see figure 6.15.

Maximum e.m.f. depends upon
(i)   Magnetic flux density B
(ii) Area of coil A
(iii) Number of turns N
(iv) Angular velocity ω

(b) $\xi = BAN\omega \sin \omega t$

(c) See figure 6.18.

(d) $2\pi \times 10^{-2}$ V (6.3×10^{-2} V)

Using $\xi_0 = BAN\omega$

$$\xi_0 = 2.0 \times 10^{-2} \times 10 \times 10^{-4} \times 50 \times 2\pi \times 10$$
$$\xi_0 = 2\pi \times 10^{-2} \text{ V}$$

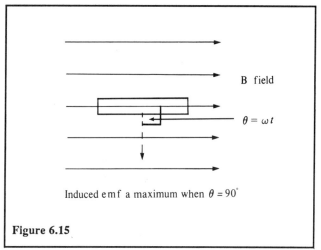

Induced emf a maximum when $\theta = 90°$

Figure 6.15

4 Induced p.d. $= Blv$
$$= 3.0 \times 10^{-5} \text{ T} \times 50 \text{ m} \times 200 \text{ m s}^{-1}$$
$$= 0.30 \text{ V}$$

The induced p.d. between wing tips will vary through two maxima and two zero points during one loop. The induced e.m.f. will be zero when the plane is flying in the direction of the Earth's total field or in the opposite direction (i.e. 60° to the horizontal) and maximum when the plane is flying perpendicular to the total field (30° to the horizontal).

5 (a) See figure 6.16.

(b) The field coils are in parallel with the rotor and hence the applied p.d. V across the coil will remain constant. The resultant p.d. across the rotor however changes due to the back e.m.f. ξ which is induced as the coil in the motor rotates. If the rotor has resistance R and carries a current I we have

$$V - \xi = IR$$

The back e.m.f. does not affect the p.d. across the field coil.

(c) $240 - \xi = 5 \times 1.5$

Hence

$$\xi = 232.5 \text{ V}$$

(d) The rate of rotation must fall and the motor slows down. The induced e.m.f. in the rotor will fall. The applied p.d. can now drive a larger current through the rotor, so the current rises.

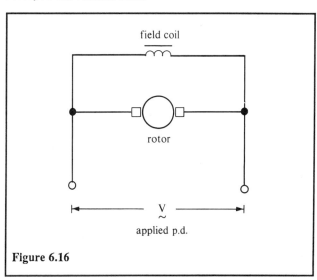

Figure 6.16

Topic 3

1 The e.m.f. inductance L of a coil is defined by the equation

$$L = \frac{\xi}{dI/dt}$$

where ξ is the e.m.f. induced in the coil when the rate of change of current is dI/dt.

The unit of self inductance is the henry, H.

Factors that determine the inductance of a long solenoid

$$\xi = N\frac{d\phi}{dt} \quad \phi = BA \quad B = \mu_0\frac{NI}{l}$$

Hence $\xi = N\mu_0\dfrac{N}{l}\dfrac{dI}{dt}\cdot A$

Thus $L = \dfrac{\mu_0 A N^2}{l}$

L depends upon area of cross section A
number of turns squared N^2
length of solenoid l

2 $\xi_s = -M\dfrac{dI_p}{dt}$

$E = 1.0 \times 10^{-6}\,\text{H} \times 200\,\text{A s}^{-1} = 2.0 \times 10^{-4}\,\text{V}$

3 (a) See figure 6.17, curve A.

$$\text{Steady current} = \frac{\text{applied e.m.f.}}{\text{resistance}}$$

(b) See figure 6.17 curves B and C.

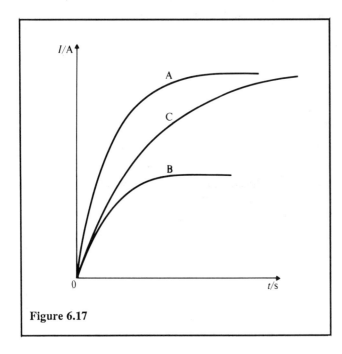

Figure 6.17

4 See figure 6.18.

$$\text{Ratio } \frac{N_p}{N_s} = \frac{240}{12} = \frac{20}{1}$$

When a current is drawn from the secondary circuit it causes the flux in the core to decrease. The induced e.m.f. in the primary will also drop and so the primary current will increase.

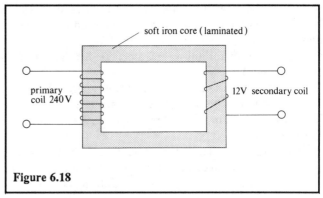

Figure 6.18

5 When a magnetic material is taken through a complete magnetic cycle the magnetization of the material B lags behind the magnetizing field B_0, figure 6.19.

The energy required to take the material through a cycle (proportional to the area of the loop) increases the internal energy of the specimen. This is known as *hysteresis loss*.

It is of importance in the design of a transformer because the core is subjected to an alternating magnetic field which takes the material through many magnetization cycles every second.

This effect can be minimised by having a material which has a narrow hysteresis loop (figure 6.22).

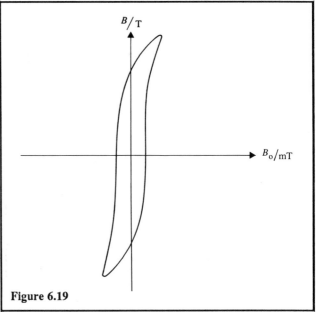

Figure 6.19

6 The following results are obtained from the graph.

(a) Current at $t = 5$ s is 1.9 A.

The p.d. required to maintain this current through 4 Ω is 7.6 V.

(b) Back e.m.f. is 4.4 V at $t = 5$ s.

(c) Gradient of tangent = 0.23 A s^{-1} = dI/dt

(d) $L = \dfrac{4.4\,\text{V}}{0.23\,\text{A s}^{-1}} = 19\,\text{H}$

7 (a) $\dfrac{V_p}{V_s} = \dfrac{N_p}{N_s}$ for an ideal transformer

Assumptions (i) Primary coil has negligible resistance.
(ii) All the flux in the core links both the primary and secondary.
(iii) Secondary is on open circuit.

(b) Secondary p.d. = 60 V, output current = 2 A
output power = input power = 120 W

8 Unit of $L = $ V A^{-1} s   Unit of $I_0^2 = A^2$

Unit of $\frac{1}{2}LI_0^2$ has the dimensions of energy.
The energy $\frac{1}{2}LI_0^2$ stored in the magnetic field is transferred to internal energy in the resistor when the circuit is opened.

(i)
$$I = 0.15(1 - e^{-2.5/10}) \text{ A}$$
$$I = 0.15(1 - 0.78) \text{ A} = 33 \text{ mA}$$
(ii)
$$\frac{1}{2}LI_0^2 = \frac{1}{2} \times 10 \text{ H} \times (1.5 \times 10^{-1})^2 \text{ A}^2$$
$$= 5 \times 2.25 \times 10^{-2} \text{ J}$$
Energy stored = 0.11 J
Supply p.d. = I_0R = 38 V

Topic 4

1 (a) The r.m.s. value of an a.c. is defined as the value of the steady current which would give the same average power dissipation in a resistor.
(b) $I_{\text{r.m.s.}} = I_0/\sqrt{2}$

2 A moving coil meter can be adapted to measure alternating current by using a rectifier to convert the a.c. to d.c. This may be either a single semiconducting diode giving half wave rectification, figure 6.20a, or four diodes connected to form a full wave bridge rectifier, figure 6.20b. The scale of the rectified meter is calibrated to read r.m.s. values of current on the assumption that the waveform is sinusoidal.

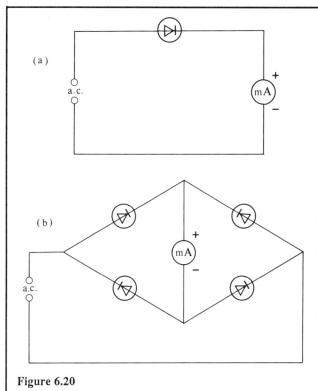

Figure 6.20

3 Use $E = E_0 \sin wt$
(a) $E_0 = 10$ V

(b) $E_{\text{r.m.s.}} = \dfrac{10}{\sqrt{2}} \text{ V} = 7.1 \text{ V}$

(c) $\omega = 500\pi$ $\omega = 2\pi f$ $\therefore f = 250 \text{ Hz}$
4 See figure 6.21.

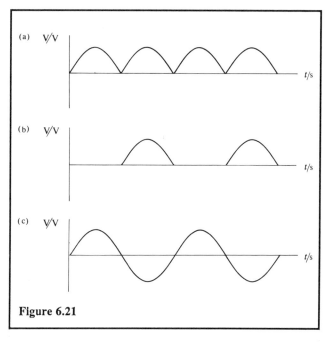

Figure 6.21

5 (a) The p.d. across the capacitor *lags* the current by 90° or $\pi/2$.
(b) See figure 6.22.
6 (i) The supply.
(ii) The capacitor.

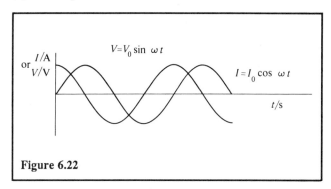

Figure 6.22

Topic 5

1 The opposition of a capacitor to a.c. is called the capacitive reactance X_C, where X_C equals $1/2\pi fC$. The opposition of an inductor to a.c. is called the inductive reactance X_L, where X_L equals $2\pi fL$.

2 When a capacitor is connected to an alternating supply the capacitor is being charged, discharged, charged in the opposite direction and discharged again. This occurs fifty times per second (the frequency of the a.c. supply) and the charging and discharging currents pass through the circuit although they do not pass through the capacitor. When the frequency of the alternating supply is increased the charge time flows on and off the plates of the capacitor in a shorter time, hence, since current is rate of flow of charge it will increase.

3 The current and the applied p.d. are out of phase. The current reaches a maximum value 90° (π/rad) or a quarter of a period $T/4$ after a maximum value of p.d. This can be represented on a vector diagram as shown in figure 6.23.

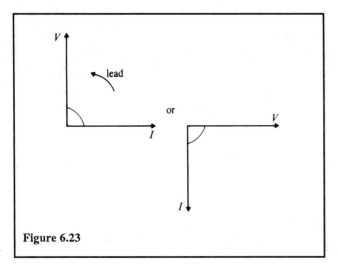

Figure 6.23

4 (a) See figure 6.24.
(b) (i) Current increases, (ii) current increases.
$$V_0/I_0 = X_C$$
where
$$X_C = \frac{1}{2\pi fC}$$
Thus
$$I_0 = 2\pi fCV_0$$

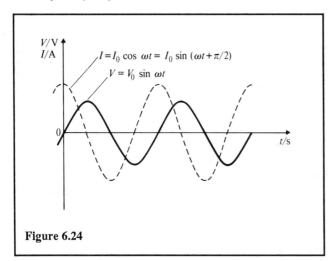

Figure 6.24

5 See figure 6.25.
V_L leads the current by 90°
V_C lags the current by 90°
V_R is in phase with the current
(a) (i) The vector sum of $(V_L - V_C)$ and V_R is equal to the applied p.d. V.
$$V = \sqrt{[(6-2)^2 + 3^2]}$$
$$V = 5 \text{ V}$$

(ii) The phase angle ϕ between the applied p.d. and the current is given by
$$\tan \phi = 4/3$$
$$\phi = 53.1°$$

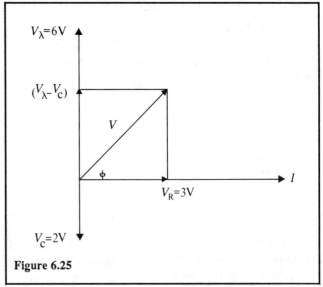

Figure 6.25

(b) The current in the circuit is a maximum because the impedance, Z, of the circuit has a minimum value. Changing the value of the capacitance alters the capacitive reactance X_C. When X_C is equal to the inductive reactance X_L the impedance takes a minimum value being equal to the resistance R.
$$Z = \sqrt{[(X_L - X_C)^2 + R^2]}$$
when
$$X_L = X_C$$
$$Z = R$$

6 In a pure capacitor or an inductor the average power dissipated during a complete cycle is zero on account of a phase difference of 90° between the applied p.d. and the current. For part of the cycle, power is drawn from the source and energy is stored in the electric/magnetic field of the capacitor/inductor. In another part of the cycle, when the capacitor discharges/magnetic field decreases, the energy which was stored in the field is returned to the source (see figure 6.26).
Although the mean power during a cycle is zero, a large amount of energy flows in and out of the capacitor/inductor every quarter cycle. In practice the capacitor/inductor has some resistance and some energy is dissipated as internal energy.

7 (a) (i) 900π ohm
$$X_L = \omega L = 2\pi fL$$
$$X_L = 2\pi \times 600 \times 0.75 \text{ ohm}$$
(ii) 900π ohm. At resonance the inductive reactance is equal to the capacitive reactance.
(iii) 9×10^{-8} F
$$X_C = \frac{1}{\omega C} = \frac{1}{2\pi fC}$$
$$C = \frac{1}{2\pi \times 600 \times 900\pi} \text{ F}$$
(iv) 1.25 A
$$I_{\text{r.m.s.}} = \frac{V_{\text{r.m.s.}}}{R}$$
$$I_{\text{r.m.s.}} = \frac{250}{200} \text{ A}$$

(b) At resonance the p.d. across the inductor is in antiphase with the p.d. across the capacitor. V_L leads by 90°, V_C lags by 90° and V_R is in phase with the supply p.d.

(c) 1125π V

$$V_C = I_{\text{r.m.s.}} \times X_C$$
$$V_C = 1.25 \times 900\pi \text{ V}$$

The p.d. lags the current by 90°.

(d) In a practical tuned circuit, a low series resistance means that the resonant current is a maximum for a given supply voltage. This means a narrow resonance curve and this increases the selectivity of the circuit.

(e) 900%

$$I_{\text{r.m.s.}} = \frac{250}{20} = \frac{25}{2} \text{ A}$$

$$V_C = \frac{25}{2} \times 900\pi \text{ V}$$

$$\% \text{ increase} = \frac{\frac{25}{2} \times 900\pi - \frac{5}{4} \times 900\pi}{\frac{5}{4} \times 900\pi} \times 100\%$$

8 (a) See figure 6.27.

(b) (i) 159 Hz

At resonance $X_L = X_C$

$$\omega L = \frac{1}{\omega C}$$

$$\omega^2 = \frac{1}{LC}$$

$$f_0 = \frac{1}{2\pi\sqrt{(LC)}}$$

$$f_0 = \frac{1}{2\pi\sqrt{100 \times 10^{-3} \times 10 \times 10^{-6}}} \text{ Hz}$$

(ii) $I_{\text{r.m.s.}} = 0.03$ A

$$I_{\text{r.m.s.}} = \frac{1.50}{50} \text{ A}$$

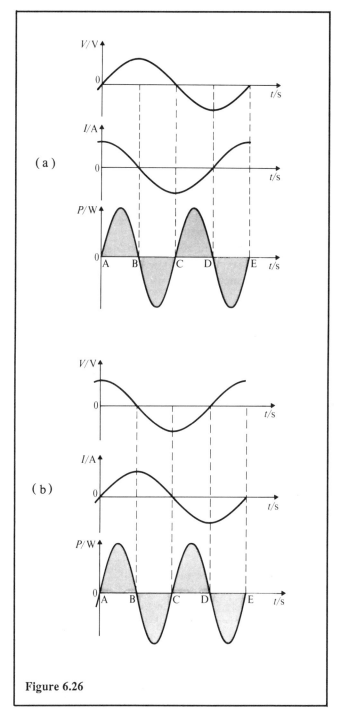

(a)

(b)

Figure 6.26

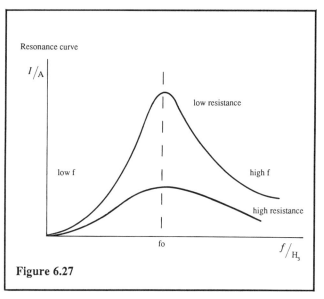

Resonance curve

low resistance

low f

high f

high resistance

f_0

Figure 6.27

6.7 Unit EN

Topic 1

1 See section 1.2, in particular Q1.1.
2 The work function ϕ is the energy that is required to remove an electron from the surface of a metal.
3 See section 1.3.
4 750 V
When the drop is stationary the force exerted on the charged oil drop by the electric field is equal to its weight.

Force exerted by electric field

$$= 6.4 \times 10^{-19}\,\text{C} \times \frac{V}{20 \times 10^{-3}\,\text{m}}$$

where V is the p.d. across the plates.

Weight of the oil drop $= 2.4 \times 10^{-14}$ N

Thus

$$\frac{(6.4 \times 10^{-19}\,\text{C})V}{20 \times 10^{-3}\,\text{m}} = 2.4 \times 10^{-14}\,\text{N}$$

$$V = 750\,\text{V}$$

5 (a) 3.6×10^7 m s^{-1}
The kinetic energy W acquired by an electron is given by

$$W = eV$$

Hence

$$\tfrac{1}{2}mv^2 = eV$$

$$v = \left(\frac{2eV}{m}\right)^{1/2}$$

$$v = [2 \times (1.8 \times 10^{11}\,\text{C kg}^{-1}) \times (3.6 \times 10^3\,\text{V})]^{1/2}$$

$$v = 3.6 \times 10^7\,\text{m s}^{-1}$$

(b) 2.0×10^{-3} tesla
The force exerted on the electron by the magnetic field provides the necessary centripetal force.
Thus

$$BeV = \frac{mv^2}{r}$$

$$B = \frac{mv}{er}$$

$$B = \frac{3.6 \times 10^7\,\text{m s}^{-1}}{(1.8 \times 10^{11}\,\text{C kg}^{-1})(0.1\,\text{m})}$$

$$B = 2.0 \times 10^{-3}\,\text{tesla}$$

6 (a) (i) $F_{\text{E}} = EQ$ (parallel to E for positive charge, oppositely directed for negative charge) (ii) $F_{\text{B}} = BQv$ (perpendicular to the plane of B and v)
(b) This is considered in section 1.5.
(c) 1.35×10^{-2} tesla
Speed of electrons is 5.9×10^6 m s^{-1}
7 (a) This is covered in section 1.5 and experiment ES1.
(b) 1.6×10^{-19} C
Suppose the drop has a negative charge of magnitude Q.
Vector diagrams are shown in figure 6.28.

$$\tan 21°48' = \frac{(5.0 \times 10^4\,\text{V m}^{-1})Q}{2.0 \times 10^{-14}\,\text{N}}$$

$$Q = 1.6 \times 10^{-19}\,\text{C}$$

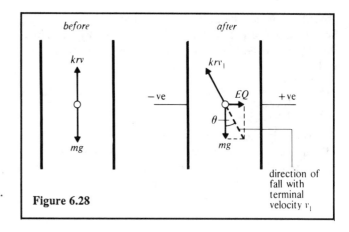

Figure 6.28

Topic 2

1 (a) γ
(b) β
(c) α and β
(d) α
(e) γ
(f) β
(g) α
(h) γ
(i) β
(j) α
2 (a) See section 2.3; but the end window must be made of mica to allow alpha particles to enter.
(b) The quenching agent gives a short 'dead' time, when the tube will not respond to a new ionisation radiation.
3 Refer to experiment EN3.
4 (a) Alpha particles.
(b) α-particles were emitted with different energies.
5 The answer should include reference to the high ionisation produced by α-particles and their short range.
6 Yes. The intensity of γ radiation varies inversely as the square of the distance from a source, so distance gives some protection. Lead shielding is another form of protection.

Topic 3

1 (a) Proton.
(b) Electron.
(c) Neutron.
2 C (protons and neutrons).
3 (a) 53 protons $(10^{-15})^3$
(b) 78 neutrons
4 D $(10^{-15})^3/(10^{-10})^3 = (10^{-5})^3 = 10^{-15}$
5 A large charge concentrated in a small volume is required to produce a large deflection. This only occurs at the nucleus. The cross-section of the nucleus is 10^{-10} times the cross-section of the atom.
6 See section 3.1 and in particular Q3.3.
7 (a) The position of the nucleus is found by drawing a line through the point of closest approach which bisects the angle between the paths before and after scattering. All these lines, for various tracks, should meet at the nucleus.

(b) Original k.e. of α-particle = p.e. of the system when the α-particle has reached its position of closest approach (and is stationary).

$$\frac{1}{4\pi\varepsilon_0} \cdot \frac{2Ze^2}{d} = eV$$

Substituting values and rearranging we have

$$d = \frac{(9 \times 10^9 \text{ N m}^2 \text{ C}^{-2}) \times 158(1.6 \times 10^{-19} \text{ C})}{5 \times 10^6 \text{ V}}$$

$$= 4.6 \times 10^{-14} \text{ m}$$

(c) On the scale of the diagram in the text the distance of closest approach is 10 mm.
If x is the distance from the nucleus to the 'edge of the atom' on the diagram then

$$\frac{x}{3 \times 10^{-10} \text{ m}} = \frac{1.0 \times 10^{-2}}{4.6 \times 10^{-14}}$$

x is approximately 65 m.

8 (a) $^{30}_{14}\text{Si}$ (b) $^{1}_{0}\text{n}$ (c) $^{1}_{0}\text{n}$ (d) γ-radiation – energy.

9 24.3

10 (a) $EQ = BQv$ for ions which travel along XY

$$B = \frac{E}{v} = 0.21 \text{ T}$$

(b) $mv^2/r = BQv$

$$r = \frac{10^4}{6 \times 10^{-2} \times 1.4 \times 10^6} \text{ m}$$

$$= 0.15 \text{ m}$$

(c) For $^{15}\text{N}^{+}$ $Q/m = 1.06 \times 10^6 \text{ C kg}^{-1}$; $r = 0.16$ m
For $^{14}\text{N}^{++}$ $Q/m = 2.28 \times 10^6 \text{ C kg}^{-1}$; $r = 0.075$ m

Topic 4

1 Refer to sections 4.1 and 4.2.

2 (a) α particles. The nucleon number has decreased by 4, the proton number by 2. (γ rays are also emitted.)
(b) β particles. The nucleon number has remained the same, the proton number has increased by 1. (γ rays are also emitted.)

3 (a) $^{4}_{2}\text{He}$
(b) $^{228}_{90}\text{Th}$

4 An uncharged neutron changes into a positively charged proton, and emits a particle with an equal and opposite charge.

5 $\frac{1}{4}$

6 (a) 1 mg of the isotope contains 4.0×10^{19} atoms.
In 2 minutes, $\frac{1}{2} \times 4.0 \times 10^{19}$ atoms decay.
In 6 minutes, $(\frac{1}{2} + \frac{1}{4} + \frac{1}{8})(4.0 \times 10^{19}) = 3.5 \times 10^{19}$ atoms decay.
(b) The random nature of the disintegration produces statistical variations from the expected number.

7 See section 4.4 and particularly Q4.9.

8 Refer to the mathematics extension on radioactive decay in section 4.3.

9 (a) 0.0125 s^{-1}
(b) 1.42×10^{17} s or 4.51×10^9 years

10 12.3 s^{-1}

11 For the same number of atoms of each substance

$$\frac{\text{rate of decay of radium}}{\text{rate of decay of uranium}} \approx 2.5 \times 10^6$$

12 See section 2.4 for details of the nature and properties of radiation.
α particles are very damaging because they ionise very heavily, depositing all their energy in a small amount of tissue. Shielding is very easy, a few centimetres of air or thin paper will protect completely.
β particles ionise less strongly and so are more penetrating. The energy of the emission is characteristic of the decay.
γ is least ionising and most penetrating. Intensity falls according to the inverse square law in air and vacuum, and exponentially in matter. Complete protection is impossible, but absorbers such as lead and concrete are used when levels are high. 1 centimetre of lead reduces the intensity of γ radiation by approximately 50%. It is called the half thickness.

13 γ radiography shows up internal contrast between the iron, rust and stone. (This and another examples are given in *Radioactivity, how it can be used*, UKAEA.)

Topic 5

1 See section 5.1.

2 $A = 216$, $Z = 90$
For α-particle,

$$10^{-12} \text{ J} = \tfrac{1}{2}(6.7 \times 10^{-27} \text{ kg})v^2$$
$$v = 1.7 \times 10^7 \text{ m s}^{-1}$$

Applying the law of conservation of momentum,
velocity of recoil nucleus

$$= \frac{6.7 \times 10^{-27} \times 1.7 \times 10^7}{3.5 \times 10^{-25}} \text{ m s}^{-1}$$

$$= 3.3 \times 10^5 \text{ m s}^{-1} \text{ in opposite direction}$$

Note. Working to two significant figures the difference between the mass of a thoron nucleus and the mass of the product nucleus is here *not* significant.

3 (a) Change in $N = -10$
Change in $Z = -6$
(b) Products $^{222}_{86}\text{Em}$, $^{218}_{84}\text{Po}$, $^{218}_{85}\text{At}$, $^{214}_{83}\text{Bi}$, $^{214}_{84}\text{Po}$, $^{210}_{82}\text{Pb}$
(c) For stable light elements ($Z < 20$) $N/Z = 1$
The ratio increases for greater values of Z; e.g. in the region around $Z = 50$, $N/Z \approx 1.3$, while around $Z = 80$, $N/Z \approx 1.5$
(d) See text following question 5.11.

4 See introduction to section 5.3. Fission produces an increase in binding energy per nucleon as a uranium nucleus with relatively low binding energy per nucleon E_B/A splits into two stable nuclides with high binding energy per nucleon located nearer the peak of the curve. The increase in binding energy per nucleon results in an increase in mass defect and the release of energy. This is also true when light elements having a low value of E_B/A undergo fusion to produce a nuclide with a higher value of E_B/A.

Topic 6

1 D. The unit of the Planck constant is the joule second.

2 (a) The photoelectric effect.

(b) By assuming that electromagnetic radiation consists of packets of energy or photons. The energy E of a photon is given by

$$E = hf$$

where f is the frequency of the radiation and h is the Planck constant. An electron will be emitted from the surface of a metal if the energy of the incident photon is greater than the energy that is required to liberate an electron from the surface.

That is, if $hf > \phi$ where ϕ is the work function of the metal.

3 If the frequency of the incident radiation is less than 6.0×10^{14} Hz then no photoelectric emission is possible.

4 3.3×10^{-19} J

$$\text{Frequency} = \frac{3 \times 10^8 \text{ m s}^{-1}}{6 \times 10^{-7} \text{ m}}$$

$$E = 6.6 \times 10^{-34} \text{ J s} \times 5 \times 10^{14} \text{ s}^{-1}$$

5 (a) ϕ is the work function of the metal (see topic 1, section 1.2).

(b) The expression $\frac{1}{2}mv_{max}^2$ is the kinetic energy of the fastest electrons, i.e. those which are released from the surface of the metal. A range of speeds is possible because an electron may be released from below the surface and may need more than the minimum value to escape.

(c) This occurs because the energy of the incident photons is less than the least energy that is required to release an electron from the surface.

That is

$$hf < \phi$$

6 Cannot explain (i) threshold frequency, (ii) maximum speed dependent upon frequency, (iii) maximum speed is independent of intensity.

7 (a) The minimum positive potential difference that has to be applied between the cathode and anode to prevent the most energetic electrons reaching the anode, that is

$$eV_s = \frac{1}{2}mv_{max}^2$$

(b) Einstein's photoelectric equation can be rewritten as

$$hf = eV_s + \phi$$

rearranging

$$V_s = (h/e)v - \phi/e$$

gradient of graph $= h/e$

When V_s is zero

$$\phi = hf_0$$

Topic 7

1 (a) An excitation potential is the potential through which an electron must be accelerated so that an inelastic collision occurs between the electron and gas atom in which the atom receives energy to raise one of its electrons into an excited energy state.

(b) The ionisation potential of an atom is the potential through which an electron must be accelerated so that an inelastic collision occurs with the gas atom in which all the electron's energy is transferred to the gas atom to produce ionisation (the atom receives energy which removes one electron).

(c) Electrons within the atom can only exist in certain energy levels and therefore the atom as a whole can only receive or give out energy in discrete amounts as an electron moves between energy levels.

(d) Line spectra contain a limited number of discrete frequencies emitted as a result of transitions by electrons in the atom from an excited energy state E_2 to a lower energy state E_1, where each emitted frequency is given by the equation, $E_2 - E_1 = hf$.

2 See section 7.2.

3 C

4 The experiment must show the existence of more than one energy level, e.g. the existence of an ionisation level and excitation level can be shown by describing experiments EN14 and EN15 or several excitation levels can be shown by a description of the Franck–Hertz experiment. Describing EN14 only is not adequate.

5 See text section 7.2 and figure 7.6.

Each series groups together all transitions to a common lower energy level. Longer wavelength series are possible (e.g. a series in the infra-red due to transitions between levels with higher n values and the level $n = 4$).

6 See the introduction to section 7.3 including figure 7.9 and the answer to Q7.7.

7 (a) Both these intensity distributions show (i) a continuous X-ray spectrum, (ii) a sharp cut off at a minimum wavelength (λ_{min}), (iii) characteristic line spectra.

(b) See explanation of X-ray spectra in section 7.3.

(c) (i) Different accelerating p.d.; as V increases λ_{min} decreases. (ii) Different target material.

8 (a) 4.0×10^{-15} J

(b) 6.25×10^{18} Hz

(c) 6.4×10^{-34} J s

6.8   Unit ES

Topic 1

1 (a) A 0.005 Ω resistor should be connected in parallel. If the shunt resistance is R_s,

$$0.002\ \text{A} \times 5.0\ \Omega = 19.998\ \text{A} \times R$$

(b) A 74 950 Ω resistor should be connected in series. If the series resistance is R

$$(R + 50\ \Omega) \times 0.002\ \text{A} = 150\ \text{V}$$

2 (a) A vertical line of length 3 cm will show the peak-to-peak p.d.
(b) The trace will show one complete wave per centimetre, since at a frequency of 200 Hz, the time for one cycle is 5 ms.
3 100 Hz.
The spot takes 5 ms to travel a distance of 1 cm, so the time for 1 complete cycle is 10 ms.
4 The potentiometer method is a null deflection method, so it measures the p.d. across the terminals of a cell on open circuit, and no current is supplied by the cell.
5 The percentage error in the reading is less, since the balance length is longer.
6 (a) If the deflection is always in the same direction, then either the p.d. across the wire is less than the unknown p.d., or the unknown p.d. is connected the wrong way round.
(b) If the deflection always has the same value (not zero) the galvanometer has been placed in series with the driver cell.

Topic 2

1 See section 2.2.
2 1.20×10^{-4} C on each capacitor.
60 V, 20 V and 40 V across 2 μF, 6 μF and 3 μF capacitors respectively.
3 See section 2.3.
4 $C = \dfrac{\varepsilon_0 A}{d}$ C farad ε_0 farad metre^{-1}
A metre^2
d metre
ε_0 is the permittivity constant
5 See section 2.5, particularly Q2.20.
6 1.2×10^{-3} J
7 0.34 mm
8 See section 2.3, and particularly experiment ES4.
9 $\dfrac{C_1 C_2}{C_1 + C_2} + C_3$
10 See section 2.3, particularly Q2.10.

Topic 3

1 See section 3.1.
2 See section 3.2, and experiment ES8.

3 Comment should include reference to the functions of:
R_1 and R_3 (bias resistors)
R_2 (load resistor)
C_1 (isolating capacitor)
C_2 (decoupling capacitor)
T_1 and T_2 (transistors)
4 $I_b = 25\ \mu\text{A}$, $R = 2.4 \times 10^5\ \Omega$ or 0.24 MΩ

$$I_e = \frac{3}{2 \times 10^3} = 1.5\ \text{mA}$$

$$I_b = \frac{1.5}{60} = 0.025\ \text{mA}$$

Using $V = IR$

$$R = \frac{6}{2.5 \times 10^{-6}}\ \Omega$$

5 $I_b = \dfrac{(2.7 - 0.7)\ \text{V}}{10^3\ \Omega} = 2\ \text{mA}$

$$I_c = \frac{(12 - 2)\ \text{V}}{100\ \Omega} = 0.1\ \text{A} = 100\ \text{mA}$$

$$\text{Gain} = \frac{I_c}{I_b} = \frac{100}{2} = 50$$

Topic 4

1 (a)

A	B	Output
0	0	0
0	1	1
1	0	1
1	1	0

(b)

A	B	Output
0	0	0
0	1	0
1	0	1
1	1	1

2 (a) In the light the input p.d. to the NOT gate is low, so the output is high and the LED is on.
(b) When the water reaches the contacts the resistance falls to a low value making the input p.d. to the gate low and the output high.
3 (a) See figure 6.29.
(b) Truth table (No = 0; Yes = 1)

Foot switch pushed	Button pushed	Safety guard down	Machine working
0	0	0	0
0	0	1	0
0	1	0	0
0	1	1	1
1	0	0	0
1	0	1	1
1	1	0	0
1	1	1	1

4 Analogue signals are susceptible to interference and corruption due to the mains, radio broadcasts, changes in cable resistance and faulty calibration of the receiving equipment.
Digital signals can be sent and received with a very high degree of accuracy and with added error correction codes.

The received signal, after processing, could be expected to be exactly the same as the transmitted signal.
If a high degree of accuracy is important the digital solutions offers great advantages. However, it would be more complicated and costly than the analogue solution in most cases.

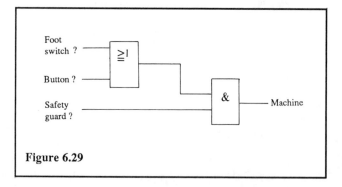

Figure 6.29

5 (a) It would be equivalent to an AND gate.
(b) It would be equivalent to an OR gate.
6 40p. There are two ways to tackle this type of problem. Either find an equivalent for each gate in terms of NAND (or NOR) gates (80p), or construct the truth table and try to recognise the function of the whole circuit and see if it can be simply implemented. (Try three NOTs and a NAND.)

Topic 5

1 (a) The gain of the circuit is controlled by the value of the resistance of the LDR. In bright light the gain will fall to 10^{-4} and rise to 10 in total darkness. In effect it will produce an audible warning of darkness.
(b)

$$A_{CL} = \frac{R_2}{R_1}$$

$$-5 = -\frac{R_{LDR}}{1\ m\Omega}$$

Hence

$$R_{LDR} = 5\ m\Omega$$

(c) Exchange the 1 MΩ resistor for a thermistor (negative temperature coefficient) and replace the LDR with a fixed value resistor.
2 (a) Trace (i) is the inverting amplifier.
(b) (i) −26 (ii) 6.7
(c) (i) 3.84 kΩ (ii) 17.5 kΩ
(d) Gain too large, input signal too large.
3 (a) $A_{CL} = 25$ $\beta = \frac{1}{25} = 0.04$
(b) See figure 6.30.
(c) See figure 6.31.
(0.8 V × 25 = 20 V which is greater than the supply voltage)

4 (a) −0 V
(b) −8.2 V
(c) Inverting input at higher negative voltage so output goes to positive maximum.
(d) 100 kΩ
(e) LED goes off as output swings to negative maximum.
(f) Make 100 kΩ a variable resistor.
(g) Exchange positions of LDR and 100 kΩ resistor.
5 (a) 4 V (b) Frequency decreases because C charges up more slowly as R is now larger.

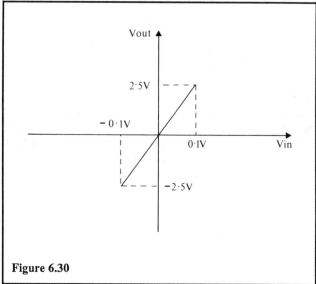

Figure 6.30

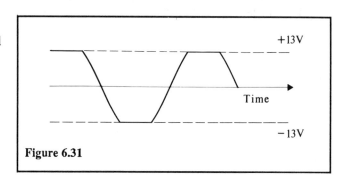

Figure 6.31

Answers to Parts 1, 2 and 3

Part 1

1.1 (a) FALSE. It is desirable but not essential to have a good grade at GCSE level in physics (see section 1.1).
(b) About 5 hours timetabled and 5 hours for homework. Total about 10 hours per week.
1.2 (a) See 'Why independent study?' If you remembered all six points you can congratulate yourself!
(b) See 'Limitations'. Eight points here: even more of a strain on your memory! But they are things which become easier to recall when you are actually using APPIL.
1.3 (a) Objectives and questions on objectives; self-assessment questions.
(b) Study questions; objectives.
(c) Study questions, discussion questions.
1.4 Consult your teacher about your rate of progress, and use the unit 'Progress Monitor' to plan your work in advance.
1.5 (a) Facts, concepts, skills, attitudes.
(b) Facts.
(c) Concepts.
(d) 16 to 17 years.
1.6 Answers to Development questions are not usually given, although occasionally they are.
1.7 Answers to Study questions are not usually given.
1.9 (a) To assist learning, any method which makes you *think* about the subject matter is better than copying, which can be (and often is) done in an unthinking way.
(b) To identify important ideas, make a list.
(c) To give structure to the subject matter, construct an 'ideas diagram', or devise headings and sub-headings.
(d) For revision purposes, notes related to the objectives are very useful.
1.11 Repetition in a different form helps you to understand and remember.

Part 2

2.1 (a) 2.0% (in x) + 0.5% (in I) + 5.0% (in A) = 7.5%
(b) 9.8×10^{10} Pa
(c) 0.7×10^{10} Pa
(d) $E = (9.8 \pm 0.7) \times 10^{10}$ Pa
2.2 Newcomb

Part 3

3.1 (a) Acceleration is defined as the rate of change of velocity.
So

$$[\text{acceleration}] = \frac{[\text{change of velocity}]}{[\text{time taken}]}$$
$$= \frac{[\text{L T}^{-1}]}{[\text{T}]} = [\text{L T}^{-2}]$$

The unit is, therefore, metre per second squared, m s^{-2}.
(b) Defining equation: work = force × distance
So

$$[\text{energy}] = [\text{force}] \times [\text{distance}]$$
$$= [\text{M L T}^{-2}] \times [\text{L}]$$
$$= [\text{M L}^2 \text{ T}^{-2}]$$

The joule is equivalent to kg m^2 s^{-2}.
3.3 (a) 2, 125, 0.001, $\frac{4}{3}$
(b) Largest is $1/10^{-2} = 100$
Smallest is $\sqrt[3]{1000} = 10$
3.4 6.32, 1.58
$10^{0.8} = 10^{0.5} \times 10^{0.3} \approx 3.16 \times 2$
$10^{0.2} = 10^{0.5}/10^{0.3} \approx 3.16/2$
3.5 $\log_{11} 121 = 2$, $\log_4 32 = 5/2$
3.6 (a) $4^3 = 64$, $\log_4 64 = 3$, $10^{-2} = 0.01$, $\log_{10} 0.01 = -2$
(b) Taking logarithms:
$\lg 7.27 = 0.8615$
$\lg 0.277 = \bar{1}.4425 = -0.5575$
$-\frac{1}{3}(-0.5575) = 0.1858$
$0.8615 + 0.1858 = 1.0473$
Using 10^x key: antilog $1.0473 = 11.15$
3.7 (a) $y = x/2 + 3$
(b) $v = \sqrt{\dfrac{Fr}{m}}$
3.8 (a) $r = \dfrac{R(E-V)}{V}$
(b) 0.5 Ω
3.9 (a) $x = 2.5$
(b) $y = 3.5$
3.10 $r = 0.40$ Ω $E = 3.0$ V

$$2.5 = \frac{2E}{2+r}, \therefore 5 + 2.5r = 2E \ldots \tag{1}$$

$$2.8 = \frac{5.6E}{5.6 + r}$$

Dividing both sides by 2.8 gives

$$1 = \frac{2E}{5.6 + r} 5.6 + r = 2E \ldots \tag{2}$$

Thus $5 + 2.5r = 5.6 + r$ gives $r = 0.4$
Substituting this value of r in (1) gives $E = 3$ V
3.11 (a) Complete table:

x	12	10	8	6	4	2	0	−2
y	30	25	20	15	10	5	0	−5

(b) $y = 2.5x$
(c) $x = 0.4y$
3.12 (a) Yes
(b) $V/I = $ a constant = 1.095 Ω
(c) Straight line through origin.
3.13 (a) 400 mm, 333.3 mm
(b) $I = k/f$ or $f = k/I$ or $fI = k$; unit of k is Hz mm (figure A1).

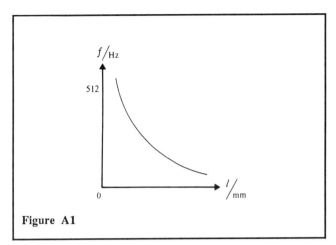

Figure A1

3.14 (a) $T = \dfrac{k}{\sqrt{g}}$ (b) $T_M = \sqrt{24}$ s

$T\sqrt{g} = k$ therefore $T^2 g = k^2$
$T_E^2 G_E = T_M^2 G_M$
$T_M^2 = 24$ s^2
where T_M is the period on the Moon.

3.15 (a) $F \propto 1/d^2$ (b) $F \propto m_1$
(c) $F \propto m_2$ (d) $F \propto m_1 m_2/d^2$

3.16 $\dfrac{pV}{T} = k$ or $p \propto \dfrac{T}{V}$

The results support the relationship
$pV/T = 0.24$ J k^{-1}

3.19 $R_\theta = R_0 \alpha \theta + R_0$
A graph of R_θ/Ω against $\theta/°C$ will have gradient $R_0\alpha$ and intercept R_0
therefore

$$\alpha = \frac{\text{gradient}}{\text{intercept}}$$

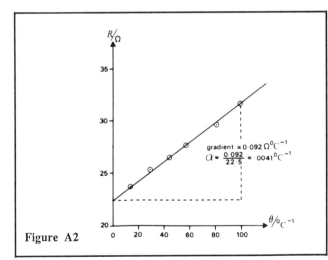

Figure A2

3.20 From the graph (figure A2) $R_{100} - R_0 = 9.2$ Ω
By extrapolation
$R_{100} = R_0 - 9.2$ $\Omega = 13.3$ Ω
    $= 13.3$ Ω

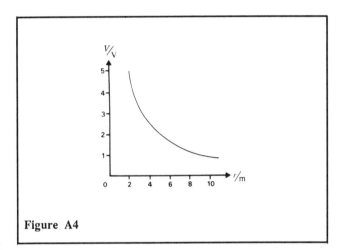

Figure A3

3.21 (a) Figure A3 shows graph of P against I.
(b) Figure A4 shows graph of V against r.
When $V = r$, $r = 3.16$ m

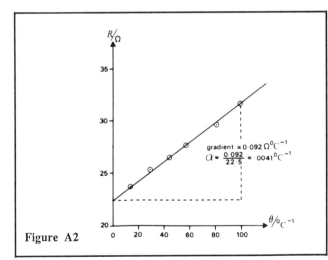

Figure A4

3.22 The graph of s against t^2 is a straight line and the uniform acceleration is 0.44 m s^{-2}.

3.23 Draw graphs of:
(a) F against $1/r^2$
(b) E against v^2
(c) T against $\sqrt{l}$ or T^2 against l.
All these graphs should be straight lines through the origin.

(d) $E = \dfrac{R + r}{R} = 1 + \dfrac{r}{R}$

$$\frac{1}{V} = \frac{r}{R} \cdot \frac{1}{R} + \frac{1}{E}$$

Plot a graph of $\dfrac{1}{V}$ against $\dfrac{1}{R}$ to obtain a straight line of gradient r/E, intercept $1/E$.

3.24 $pV^\gamma = k$
therefore

$\log p + \gamma \log V = \log k$
    $\log p = -\gamma \log V + \log k$

A graph of $\log p$ against $\log V$ has a gradient $-\gamma$ and intercept $\log k$.

3.25 The area of all the strips represents the total number of cars passing in the fixed time interval with speeds between 60 m s^{-1} and 70 m s^{-1}. Figure 3.10 gives this number as 64 cars, which agrees with figure 3.9.

3.26 The unit of N_c is s m^{-1}. The shaded area represents the number of molecules with speeds between 200 m s^{-1} and 202 m s^{-1}. The area represents a number, without a unit.

3.27 (a) $w = \dfrac{v}{r} = 40 \text{ rad s}^{-1}$

(b) Record diameter = 30 cm

$$v = \frac{33\pi \times 0.3 \text{ m s}^{-1}}{60} = \frac{3.3\pi}{20} \text{ m s}^{-1}$$

3.28 $a = \dfrac{dv}{dt}$

The gradient of the curve at a point gives the instantaneous value of the acceleration.

3.29a (a) (i) The acceleration is 0.5 m s^{-2} (gradient of graph). (ii) The distance travelled is 125 m (area underneath curve).

(b) Area underneath the curve represents the quantity of electricity which flows through the torch bulb in two hours.

$$Q = (3 + 1.5) \times 10^{-3} \times 60 \times 60 \text{ C} = 162 \text{ C}$$

(c) (i) The acceleration is -10 m s^{-2}

(ii) The area underneath the curve is the total distance travelled.

$$s = 20 \text{ m} + 20 \text{ m} = 40 \text{ m}$$

Note. This is 20 m in one direction and 20 m in the opposite direction; e.g. a ball thrown upwards and returning to its starting point.

3.29b The work done is represented by the area between the curve and the x-axis (extension).

In the graph shown in figure A5 the work done is represented by the area of trapezium ABCD.

$$W = \frac{(3.0 + 1.5)}{2} \text{N} \times 3.0 \times 10^{-3} \text{ m}$$
$$= 6.75 \times 10^{-3} \text{ J}$$

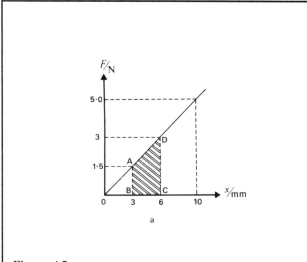

Figure A5

In the graph shown in figure A6 the axes are reversed (did that catch you out?) and the work done is represented by area ABCDE.

Work done in stretching from 3.0 mm to 4.0 mm

$$= \frac{(7.5 + 10)}{2} \text{N} \times 10^{-3} \text{ m}$$

Work done stretching from 4.0 mm to 6.0 mm

$$= \frac{(10 + 12)}{2} \text{N} \times 2 \times 10^{-3} \text{ m}$$

Total work done $= (8.75 + 22) \times 10^{-3} \text{ J}$
$$= 30.75 \times 10^{-3} \text{ J}$$

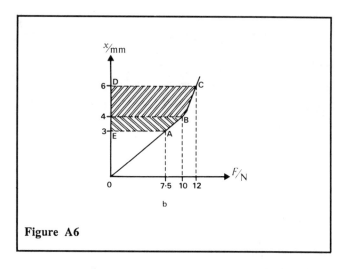

Figure A6

3.30 The order of adding displacements makes no difference to the final answer.

3.31 Displacements in three dimensions can be added by taking them in turn and adding to the total (resultant) so far. Any *two* displacements placed head to tail *must* lie in a plane, so you just add the first two, add the third to that result and so on.

An alternative answer is to resolve (separate) each displacement into its 3D components (see later) and add all the components in each direction. These can then be combined to give the final result.

3.32 (a) East 4.4 km, north 2.4 km.

(b) $x = r \cos\theta$, $y = r \sin\theta$

3.33 Figure A7 shows the vector diagram.

Ground speed $= (50^2 + 350^2)$ knots
$$= 354 \text{ knots}$$

Direction θ N of W where $\theta = \arctan 5/35$
$$= 8°8'$$

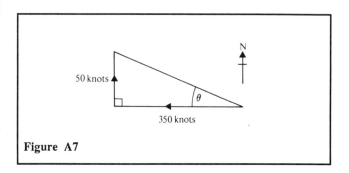

Figure A7

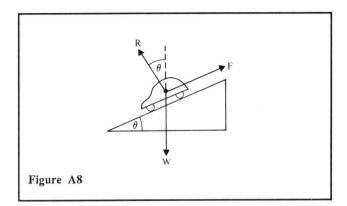

Figure A8

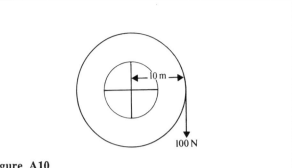

Figure A10

3.34

$\sin \theta = 1/4$
$\theta = 14°29'$

Figure A8 shows the forces acting on the car.
Resolving W along and normal to the road:
(a) $R = W \cos \theta$
   $= 1000 \, \text{kg} \times g \times 0.97$
   $= 970 \, \text{N}$ (taking g as $10 \, \text{N kg}^{-1}$)
(b) $F = W \sin \theta$
   $= 1000 \, \text{kg} \times g \times 0.25$
   $= 2500 \, \text{N}$

Note. Resolving vertically and horizontally will give the same answers, but only by solving two simultaneous equations.

3.35 Figure A9 shows the forces actings on the aeroplane.

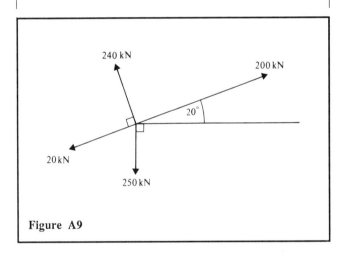

Figure A9

Net force horizontally
   $= [(200 - 20) \cos 20° - 240 \cos 70°] \, \text{kN}$
   $= (169.1 - 82.1) \, \text{kN}$
   $= 87.0 \, \text{kN}$
Net force vertically
   $= [240 \cos 20° + (200 - 20) \cos 70°$
   $\quad - 250] \, \text{kN}$
   $= (225.5 + 61.6 - 250) \, \text{kN}$
   $= 37.1 \, \text{kN}$
Resultant $= \sqrt{(87^2 + 37.1^2)} \, \text{kN}$
   $= 94.5 \, \text{kN}$
   $\theta = \arctan (37.1/87)$
   $= 23.1°$

3.36 $F = W \sin \theta = 5 \, \text{N}$

3.37 The situation is illustrated in figure A10.
$$a = \frac{F}{m} = \frac{100 \, \text{m s}^{-2}}{3.0 \times 10^4} = 3.3 \times 10^3 \, \text{m s}^{-2}$$
$$W = \frac{\tau}{I} = \frac{100 \times 10}{3.0 \times 10^5} = 3.3 \times 10^{-3} \, \text{rad s}^{-2}$$

3.38 The unit of R is $\Omega = \dfrac{\text{V}}{\text{A}} = \dfrac{\text{V}}{\text{C s}^{-1}}$ and of c is $\text{F} = \dfrac{\text{C}}{\text{V}}$

Thus the units of τ_c are $\dfrac{\text{V}}{\text{C s}^{-1}} \cdot \dfrac{\text{C}}{\text{V}} = \text{s}$.

3.39 (a) Yes, because in equal intervals of 10 s the leakage rate changes by a constant factor of 1.3 or 0.77, i.e. $78/60 = 1.3$, $60/47 = 1.3$, etc.
(b) Leakage rate at 60 s = 22/1.3 or $22 \times 0.77 = 17 \, \text{cm}^3 \, \text{s}^{-1}$. Rates at 70 s and 80 s are 13 and $10 \, \text{cm}^3 \, \text{s}^{-1}$
(c) Rate of leakage is proportional to volume remaining.
$$\frac{\text{Leakage rate at 0 s}}{\text{Leakage rate at 80 s}} = \frac{\text{Volume at 0 s}}{\text{Volume at 80 s}}$$
$$\frac{78}{10} = \frac{V_0}{320}$$
$$V_0 = 2500 \, \text{cm}^3$$

3.40 (a) If
$$I = I_0 e^{-\mu t}$$
$$\ln I/I_0 = -\mu t$$
For 30% absorption $I/I_0 = 0.7$
   $\ln 0.7 = -0.356 = -\mu \times 5 \times 10^{-3} \, \text{m}$
   $\mu = 71 \, \text{m}^{-1}$
(b) For 50% absoption $\ln 0.5 = -0.69 = -71x$
   $x = 0.69/71 \, \text{m}$
   $= 9.7 \times 10^{-3} \, \text{m}$ (9.7 mm)

Useful data

Symbols for physical quantities

acceleration	$a, \ddot{x}$	$m\,s^{-2}$
acceleration of free fall	g	$m\,s^{-2}$
acceleration, angular	α	$rad\,s^{-2}$
amount of substance	n	mol (mole)
angle	α, β, γ, etc.	rad, °
angle, Bragg	θ	rad, °
angular frequency	ω	$rad\,s^{-1}$
angular momentum	L	J s
angular velocity	ω	$rad\,s^{-1}$
area	A	m^2
atomic number	Z	
Avogadro constant	N_A	mol^{-1}
Boltzmann constant	k	$J\,K^{-1}$
Bragg angle	θ	°
bulk modulus	K	Pa
capacitance	C	F
charge, electric	Q	C
charge density, surface	σ	$C\,m^{-2}$
charge on electron	e	C
coefficient of friction	μ, f	
common temperature	θ, t	°C
conductance	G	S (siemens)
conductivity, electrical	σ	$S\,m^{-1}$
conductivity, thermal	λ	$W\,m^{-1}\,K^{-1}$
critical angle	c	rad, °
current, electric	I	A
decay constant, radioactive	λ	s^{-1}
density	ρ	$kg\,m^{-3}$
diameter	d	m
displacement	x	m
electric charge	Q	C
electric charge density, surface	σ	$C\,m^{-2}$
electric current	I	A
electric field strength	E	$V\,m^{-1}$ or $N\,C^{-1}$
electric flux	Ψ	C
electric flux density	D	$C\,m^{-2}$
electric potential difference	V	V
electrical conductivity	σ	$S\,m^{-1}$
electromotive force	$E, \mathscr{E}$	V
electron mass	m_e	kg
elementary (electron) charge	e	C
emissivity	ε	
energy	E, W	J
energy, internal (of gas)	U	J
energy, kinetic	E_k	J
energy, potential	E_p	J
energy, radiant	Q	J
entropy	S	$J\,K^{-1}$
expansivity, linear	α	K^{-1}
Faraday constant	F	$C\,mol^{-1}$
field strength, electric	E	$V\,m^{-1}$
field strength, magnetic	H	$A\,m^{-1}$
flux, electric	Ψ	C
flux, magnetic	Φ	Wb
flux density, electric	D	$C\,m^{-2}$
flux density, magnetic	B	T
force	F	N
frequency	f, v	Hz, s^{-1}
frequency, angular	ω	$rad\,s^{-1}$
frequency, rotational	n	s^{-1}
gravitational constant	G	$N\,m^2\,kg^{-2}$
gravitational field strength	g	$N\,kg^{-1}$

heat capacity	C	$J\,K^{-1}$
heat capacity, specific	c	$J\,kg^{-1}\,K^{-1}$
heat flow rate	Φ	W
heat, quantity of	Q	J
impedance	Z	Ω
inductance, mutual	M	H (henry)
inductance, self	L	H
internal energy (of gas)	U	J
kinetic energy	E_k	J
latent heat	L	J
latent heat, specific	l	$J\,kg^{-1}$
length	l	m
linear expansivity	α, λ	K^{-1}
linear strain	ε, e	
magnetic field strength	H	$A\,m^{-1}$
magnetic flux	Φ	Wb
magnetic flux density	B	T (tesla)
mass	m, M	kg
mass, molecular	m	kg
mass number	A	
mass of electron	m_e	kg
mass of neutron	m_n	kg
mass of proton	m_p	kg
mean free path	λ	m
modulus, bulk	K	Pa
modulus, shear	G	Pa
modulus, Young	E	Pa
molar gas constant	R	$J\,mol^{-1}\,K^{-1}$
molar heat capacity at constant pressure	C_p	$J\,mol^{-1}\,K^{-1}$
molar heat capacity at constant volume	C_v	$J\,mol^{-1}\,K^{-1}$
molar mass	m_m	
molar volume	V_m	$m^3\,mol^{-1}$
molecular mass	m	kg
molecular velocity	c	$m\,s^{-1}$
moment of force	M	N m
moment of inertia	$I, \mathcal{J}$	$kg\,m^2$
momentum	p	N s
momentum, angular	L	J s
mutual inductance	M	H
neutron number	N	
nucleon number	A	
number density of molecules	n	m^{-3}
number of molecules	N	
number of turns on coil	N	
period	T	s
permeability	μ	$H\,m^{-1}$
permeability of vacuum	μ_0	$H\,m^{-1}$
permeability, relative	μ_r	
permittivity	ε	$F\,m^{-1}$
permittivity of vacuum	ε_0	$F\,m^{-1}$
permittivity, relative	ε_r	
phase angle	ϕ	rad, °
Planck constant	h	J s
potential energy	E_p	J
potential difference, electric	V, U	V
potential, electric	V	V
power	P	W
pressure	p, P	Pa (pascal)
proton number	Z	
radioactive decay constant	λ	s^{-1}
radioactive half life	$T_{\frac{1}{2}}$	s
radius	r	m
ratio C_p/C_v	γ	
reactance	X	Ω
refractive index	n	
resistance	R, r	Ω

root mean square speed	c_{rms}	$m\,s^{-1}$
self inductance	L	H
shear modulus	G	Pa
specific charge (electron)	e/m_e	$C\,kg^{-1}$
specific heat capacity	c	$J\,kg^{-1}\,K^{-1}$
specific latent heat	l	$J\,kg^{-1}$
speed	u, v	$m\,s^{-1}$
speed, average	$\bar{c}$	$m\,s^{-1}$
speed of light (vacuum)	c	$m\,s^{-1}$
speed of sound	c	$m\,s^{-1}$
strain, linear	ε, e	
strain, shear	γ	
stress, normal	σ	Pa
stress, shear	τ	Pa
surface charge density	σ	$C\,m^{-2}$
surface tension	γ, σ	$N\,m^{-1}$
temperature coefficient of resistance	α	$\Omega\,m$
temperature, common (Celsius)	θ, t	°C
temperature, thermodynamic (absolute)	T	K
thermal capacity	C	$J\,K^{-1}$
thermal conductivity	λ	$W\,m^{-1}\,K^{-1}$
time	t	s
torque	T	$N\,m$
velocity, angular	ω	$rad\,s^{-1}$
viscosity	η	Pa s
volume	V, v	m^3
wavelength	λ	m
weight	W	N
work	W	J
work function	Φ	V
Young modulus	E	Pa

Physical constants and values

Quantity	Magnitude		Unit	Symbol
speed of light	2.997 925	$\times 10^8$	$m\,s^{-1}$	c
Planck constant	6.626 196	$\times 10^{-34}$	J s	h
Boltzmann constant	1.380 622	$\times 10^{-23}$	$J\,K^{-1}$	k
Avogadro constant	6.022 169	$\times 10^{23}$	mol^{-1}	L, N_A
mass of proton	1.672 614	$\times 10^{-27}$	kg	m_p
mass of neutron	1.674 920	$\times 10^{-27}$	kg	m_n
mass of electron	9.109 558	$\times 10^{-31}$	kg	m_e
charge of proton or electron	$\pm$1.602 191 7	$\times 10^{-19}$	C	e
specific charge of electron	$-$1.758 796	$\times 10^{11}$	$C\,kg^{-1}$	e/m_e
molar volume at s.t.p.	2.241 36	$\times 10^{-2}$	$m^3\,mol^{-1}$	V_m
Faraday constant	9.648 670	$\times 10^4$	$C\,mol^{-1}$	F
triple point of water	273.16 exactly		K	
absolute zero	$-$273.15 exactly		°C	
permittivity of vacuum	8.854 185 3	$\times 10^{-12}$	$F\,m^{-1}$	ε_0
or approx.	$1/36\pi$	$\times 10^{-9}$		
permeability of vacuum	4π (exactly)	$\times 10^{-7}$	$H\,m^{-1}$	μ_0
or	1.256 637	$\times 10^{-6}$		
$\lambda_{max}T$ (Wien's Law)	2.8978	$\times 10^{-3}$	m K	$\lambda_{max}T$
molar gas constant	8.314 34		$J\,mol^{-1}\,K^{-1}$	R
gravitational constant	6.6732	$\times 10^{-11}$	$N\,m^2\,kg^{-2}$	G
water specific heat capacity (15 °C)	4.1855	$\times 10^3$	$K\,kg^{-1}\,K^{-1}$	c
velocity of sound, air, s.t.p.	333.46		$m\,s^{-1}$	c